Bill Langley

GRAND CANYON
WILD
FLOWERS

By

W. B. McDOUGALL

Published by

THE MUSEUM OF NORTHERN ARIZONA · FLAGSTAFF

THE GRAND CANYON NATURAL HISTORY ASSOCIATION

The publication of this bulletin was assisted by funds granted by the
Grand Canyon Natural History Association.

EDITOR: DIONY H. SUTHERLAND   DRAWINGS: BARTON A. WRIGHT

Preface

The second edition of the *Checklist of Plants of Grand Canyon National Park,* which was prepared by the undersigned, was published in 1947. At that time it was realized that while the checklist was of considerable scientific value it was practically useless for the average Park visitor who may be without botanical training but is interested in learning something about the plants that are seen in the Park. Through the years we have dreamed of having an opportunity to prepare a book that would meet the needs of such Park visitors. This volume is the result of such dreams.

The book has a twofold purpose: to furnish professional botanists with as complete and accurate a checklist of the seed plants of the Park as our present knowledge permits; and to aid Park visitors, whether with or without botanical training, to answer the question, "What is that plant?" Throughout the book we have avoided technical terms as far as possible.

With few exceptions the scientific names in the book are those used by Kearney and Peebles in *Arizona Flora.* At the request of the National Park Service we have, as far as possible, used the common names that are found in *Standardized Plant Names* by Kelsey and Dayton.

We have omitted the authorities for scientific names because we believe they would be more confusing than helpful to the great majority of users of the book. Such authorities may be found in *Arizona Flora* or in the Grand Canyon Herbarium or the Herbarium of the Museum of Northern Arizona.

Deep appreciation is hereby expressed for the continuous cooperation and support of Dr. E. B. Danson, Director of the Museum of Northern Arizona, and of Mr. Dave Beal, Chief Naturalist, Grand Canyon National Park, throughout the preparation of the book.

The line drawings that illustrate the glossary are by Mr. Barton A. Wright, Curator of the Museum of Northern Arizona. The photographs are individually credited. The author feels deeply obligated to all of these illustrators as well as to all others who have in any way aided in the preparation and publication of the book.

W. B. McDougall

Table of Contents

Figures

Index of Photographs
Black and White

Color

INTRODUCTION

The plant life in the Grand Canyon National Park furnishes more color and beauty than any other one feature, aside from the Grand Canyon itself. The great variation in climate and habitat from the higher parts of the North Rim which support coniferous forests to the bottom of the Canyon which supports desert vegetation, creates not only a great variety of plant communities but also a very long blooming season. In fact there is scarcely a time during the year when plants cannot be found in bloom somewhere in the Park. It is not surprising therefore that for large numbers of Park visitors the plant life constitutes one of the chief attractions and that there is a constant demand for an illustrated book to aid in identifying the various kinds of plants seen. This book is intended to supply that demand.

THE NAMES OF PLANTS

In addition to a common name each plant has a scientific name which usually consists of two words, a generic or genus name and a specific or species name. Thus the name of the white sweet-clover is *Melilotus alba*, *Melilotus* being the genus name which is applied to all sweet-clovers and *alba* the species name which is applied to white sweet-clover only. Other sweet-clovers have different specific names. Yellow sweet-clover, for example, is *Melilotus officinalis*.

Some of the plants in the Park have never acquired common names. In such a case the genus name is often used as a common name. This same practice often is used with cultivated plants, such as aster and chrysanthemum which are genus names. Common names often are confusing because the same name may be used for wholly unrelated plants in different localities, or the same plant may be known by several different names. Most or all of the species of a genus often are called by the same common name. For example there are eight different species of *Eriogonum* in the Park that are called simply wild-buckwheat. We have no other common name for them. A specific scientific name, on the other hand, is applied to only one kind of plant and it can be understood by botanists anywhere in the world even though they may be wholly unfamiliar with the English language. When first we encounter a new scientific name it may seem quite unpronounceable. Actually most of them are no more difficult than the last names of some of our close friends but they may seem more difficult to pronounce or remember because they are less familiar. However, if you wish, you can disregard the scientific names entirely and still have just as much fun identifying plants.

HOW TO USE THE KEYS

About 975 different kinds of plants are described in this book. Obviously if it were necessary to search through the entire lot every time we wished to learn the name of a plant the task would be most difficult. The keys have been provided to make such a task unnecessary. With a little practice in the use of the keys we should be able to find the names of any plants that are inclu‹ in the book. At each numbered step in a key there are two or more alternativ‹ to choose from and we must decide which alternative fits the plant that w‹ are trying to identify. If we make the correct decision in each case we shall find the correct name of the plant, and the correctness of our decisions will depend upon the accuracy of our observations. Therefore we must learn to make accurate observations.

In order to see just how the keys are to be used let us take an example. Suppose that on a sunny morning in June we are walking along the Rim Trail west of Bright Angel Lodge and we find a slender plant about 18 inches tall with numerous small leaves on the stem and several bright blue flowers each about ½ inch across. A closer examination of a flower shows that it has 5 small, green sepals, 5 rather large petals, 5 stamens and 1 pistil with 5 styles. We note also that the sepals, petals and stamens are attached at the base of the ovary. That is, the ovary is superior. We are now ready to use the key.

Turning to the beginning of the key on page 10 we are confronted at once with two alternatives. These are, "Woody plants (Trees, shrubs or woody vines)" and "Non-woody plants (herbs)." Since our plant is not at all woody we readily choose the second alternative which is followed by the number 87. This means that our next step in the key is number 87 and we can skip numbers 2 to 86. At 87 we again have two alternatives and since our plant has numerous green leaves we again choose the second alternative which takes us to 92. In a similar manner we pass to 93, 96, 97, 102, 106, 125 where we choose the first alternative, 126, 130, 134, 135, 137 where we choose the second alternative since the leaves on the stem, although close together, are alternate, 141, 146 where we choose the first of four alternatives, and 147. At 147 we again choose the second alternative since the petals of our flowers are blue and do not have appendages on the back. This alternative is not followed by another number but by the name of the flax family. If we have not made a mistake this should be the family to which our plant belongs and since the name is followed by a page number we will turn to that page and by reading the brief description of the family we will decide that our plant does indeed belong to the flax family. Only two species are described for this family, one with blue flowers and one with yellow flowers, and the description of the blue-flowered one tells us that our plant is the blue flax.

In some cases the key will lead us to a family that contains more than three species. In such a case there will be a key to the species of the family and that key should be used in the same way the general key was used. It will lead us to the name of our plant.

GLOSSARY

ACORN. The nutlike fruit of oak trees and shrubs.

AKENE. A small, dry, hard, 1-seeded fruit.

ALTERNATE. One in a place at different levels on the axis. (Fig. 1).

ANTHER. The pollen bearing part of a stamen. (Fig. 2).

AWN. A bristlelike appendage, especially on the spikelets of grasses and the akenes of composites. (Fig. 3).

AXIL. The upper angle between a leaf and a stem. (Fig. 1).

AXILLARY. Borne in an axil.

AXIS. The central structure about which organs are borne, such as that part which bears the flowers.

BASAL. At or very near the base of a stem.

BEAK. A narrow projection such as occurs at the tip of some akenes. (Fig. 2).

BEARDED. Bearing hairs.

BERRY. A fleshy fruit such as a grape or a currant.

BLADE. The expanded portion of a leaf. (Fig. 1).

BRACT. A modified and reduced leaf subtending a flower or a cluster of flowers. (Fig. 2).

BUSHY. Widely branched like a bush.

CALYX. The outermost set of organs of a complete flower. (Fig. 2, 3).

CAPSULE. A dry fruit developed from a compound ovary and thus having more than one cell. Opening at maturity. (Fig. 3).

CATKIN. A modified spike in which the flowers are of one sex, either male or female.

CHAFFY. Like chaff. Applied to the dry bracts found between the flowers on the receptacle of some composites. (Fig. 2).

CLASPING. Embracing the stem. Applied to the bases of some sessile leaves. (Fig. 1).

COMPLETE FLOWER. A flower that has sepals, petals, stamens and pistils. (Fig. 2).

COMPOSITE. A member of the composite family in which several or many flowers are together on one receptacle.

COMPOUND LEAF. A leaf in which the blade is divided into leaflets. (Fig. 1).

CONE. The fruit of cone-bearing trees such as pines.

COROLLA. The set of floral organs next within the calyx. Usually not green. (Fig. 2).

DISK. The central portion of the head of a composite as distinguished from the rays. (Fig. 2).

DISSECTED. Deeply cut or lobed into many fine divisions.

DRUPE. A fruit with a central, stony seed and a fleshy covering such as a plum.

ENTIRE LEAF. A leaf with the blade neither toothed nor lobed. (Fig. 1).

FEATHERY. Having fine hairs like a feather.

FILAMENT. The part of a stamen which supports the anther. (Fig. 2).

FLORET. A grass flower with its lemma and palea. (Fig. 3).

GLANDULAR. Bearing secreting structures, sometimes making the plant or plant part sticky.

GLUME. One of the two empty bracts at the base of a grass spikelet. (Fig. 3).

HERBACEOUS PLANT. A plant with no woody stem above ground. A herb.

IMPERFECT FLOWER. A flower that lacks either stamens or pistils.

INFERIOR OVARY. An ovary that is below the place of attachment of the sepals and petals. (Fig. 2).

INVOLUCRE. A circle of bracts around a flower or cluster of flowers, such as the head of a composite. (Fig. 2).

IRREGULAR FLOWER. A flower in which the petals are not all of the same size and shape. (Fig. 3).

KEEL. The two lowest, more or less united, petals of a flower of the pea family. (Fig. 3).

LANCEOLATE. Shaped like a lance head. (Fig. 1).

LEAF. One of the primary organs of a plant. (Fig. 1).

LEAFLET. One of the divisions of a compound leaf. (Fig. 1).

LEMMA. The lower of the 2 bracts enclosing the flower of a grass. (Fig. 3).

LOBED LEAF. A leaf in which the blade is lobed. (Fig. 1).

NERVE. An unbranched vein.

NET-VEINED. The veins of a leaf arranged like a net. (Fig. 1).

NODE. The place on a stem where a leaf is borne.

OBLANCEOLATE. Lanceolate with the narrowest part toward the attached end. (Fig. 1).

OBLONG. Broader than linear but with sides nearly parallel. (Fig. 1).

OBOVATE. Shaped like the longitudinal section through an egg and attached at the small end. (Fig. 1).

OPPOSITE. Arranged at the same level on opposite sides of an axis. (Fig. 2).

OVAL. Broadly elliptical. (Fig. 1).

OVARY. The lower part of the pistil which contains the ovules. (Fig. 2).

OVATE. Shaped like the longitudinal section through an egg and attached at the large end. (Fig. 1).

PALEA. The upper of the 2 bracts that enclose a grass flower. (Fig. 3).

PALMATE. Arranged, or projecting, from a common base, like the fingers of a hand.

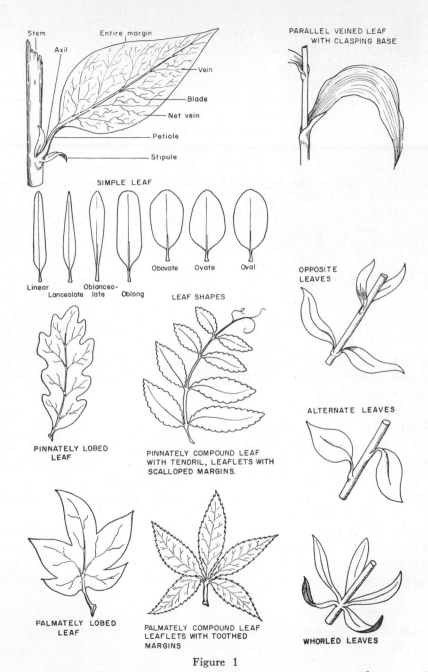

PARALLEL VEINED LEAF
WITH CLASPING BASE

Stem
Axil
Entire margin
Vein
Blade
Net vein
Petiole
Stipule

SIMPLE LEAF

Linear
Lanceolate
Oblanceo-
late
Oblong
Obovate
Ovate
Oval

LEAF SHAPES

OPPOSITE
LEAVES

ALTERNATE LEAVES

PINNATELY LOBED
LEAF

PINNATELY COMPOUND LEAF
WITH TENDRIL, LEAFLETS WITH
SCALLOPED MARGINS.

PALMATELY LOBED
LEAF

PALMATELY COMPOUND LEAF
LEAFLETS WITH TOOTHED
MARGINS

WHORLED LEAVES

Figure 1

PALMATELY COMPOUND LEAF. A compound leaf with the leaflets palmate. (Fig. 1).

PALMATELY LOBED LEAF. A leaf with the lobes palmate. (Fig. 1).

PANICLE. A compound flower cluster with the flowers stalked. (Fig. 2).

PAPPUS. The modified calyx of a composite flower. (Fig. 2).

PARALLEL-VEINED LEAF. A leaf with the main veins extending lengthwise of the leaf and nearly parallel. (Fig. 1).

PERFECT FLOWER. A flower having both stamens and pistils. (Fig. 2).

PETAL. One of the parts of a corolla. (Fig. 2).

PETIOLE. The stalk part of a leaf. (Fig. 1).

PINNATE. Arranged like the pinnae of a feather.

PINNATELY COMPOUND LEAF. A leaf with the leaflets pinnate. (Fig. 1).

PINNATELY LOBED LEAF. A leaf with the lobes pinnate. (Fig. 1).

PISTIL. The female organ of a flower. (Fig. 2, 3).

PISTILLATE. Having pistils but not stamens.

RACEME. A simple flower cluster with the flowers stalked. (Fig. 2).

RAY FLOWER. A composite flower with a strap-shaped corolla. (Fig. 2).

RECEPTACLE. The upper end of a flower stalk upon which numerous flowers or the organs of a single flower are borne. (Fig. 2).

REGULAR FLOWER. A flower in which the petals, whether distinct or united, are all the same size and shape. (Fig. 2).

SCALE. The bract subtending the flower or fruit of a sedge. (Fig. 3).

SCALLOPED. A leaf margin that is deeply wavy. (Fig. 1).

SEPAL. One of the parts of a calyx. (Fig. 2).

SESSILE. Without a stalk.

SHEATH. That part of a leaf that envelops a stem. (Fig. 1).

SIMPLE LEAF. A leaf that is not compound. (Fig. 1).

SINUS. The cleft or indentation between 2 lobes.

SPIKE. A simple, elongated flower cluster with the flowers sessile. (Fig. 2).

SPIKELET. A unit of a grass flower cluster, usually consisting of 2 glumes and 1 or more florets. (Fig. 3).

SPUR. A hollow projection of a flower part. (Fig. 3).

STAMEN. The male organ of a flower. (Fig. 2, 3).

STAMINATE FLOWER. A flower having stamens but not pistils.

STERILE. Unproductive, as a flower without pistils or a stamen without an anther.

STIGMA. That part of a pistil that receives the pollen. (Fig. 2).

STIPULES. Appendages at the base of the petiole of some leaves. (Fig. 1).

STYLE. That portion of the pistil between the ovary and the stigma. (Fig. 2).

GRAND CANYON WILD FLOWERS

Seed Plants of Grand Canyon
National Park

CRIMSON MONKEYFLOWER *(Mimulus cardinalis)*

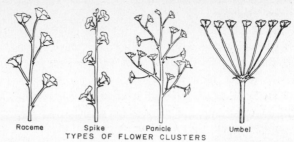

Raceme Spike Panicle Umbel

TYPES OF FLOWER CLUSTERS

COMPLETE PERFECT REGULAR FLOWER

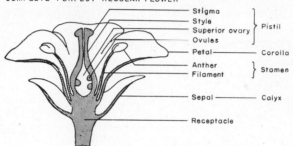

Stigma
Style
Superior ovary Pistil
Ovules

Petal Corolla

Anther Stamen
Filament

Sepal Calyx

Receptacle

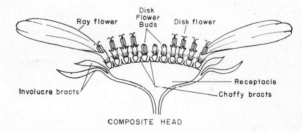

Ray flower Disk Flower Buds Disk flower

Involucre bracts Receptacle

Chaffy bracts

COMPOSITE HEAD

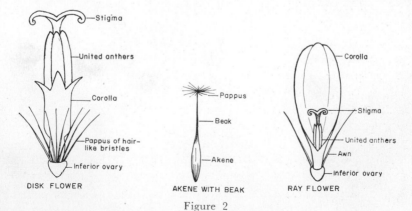

Stigma

United anthers

Corolla

Pappus of hair-like bristles

Inferior ovary

DISK FLOWER

Pappus

Beak

Akene

AKENE WITH BEAK

Corolla

Stigma

United anthers

Awn

Inferior ovary

RAY FLOWER

Figure 2

Glossary 7

SUBTEND. Under or supporting, as a bract or leaf subtends a flower that is borne in its axil.

SUPERIOR OVARY. An ovary that is above the place of attachment of the sepals and petals. (Fig. 2).

TENDRIL. A modified leaf or branch that serves as a climbing organ. (Fig. 1).

TERMINAL. At the upper end.

TOOTHED LEAF. A leaf with teeth along the margin. (Fig. 1).

UMBEL. A flat-topped flower cluster with the flower stalks all attached at the same level, like the ribs of an umbrella. (Fig. 2).

WHORLED. Arranged in a circle around the stem. (Fig. 1).

WING. One of the petals of a pea flower. (Fig. 3). Also any expanded portion of a fruit or stem.

WOODY PLANT. A plant that has a woody stem above ground.

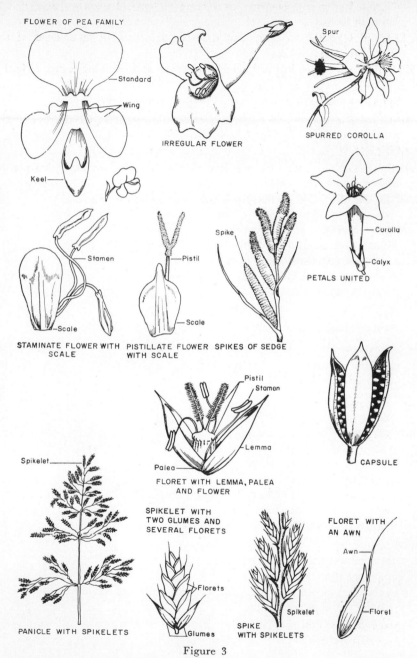

FLOWER OF PEA FAMILY

Standard

Wing

Keel

IRREGULAR FLOWER

Spur

SPURRED COROLLA

Stamen

Scale

STAMINATE FLOWER WITH SCALE

Pistil

Scale

PISTILLATE FLOWER WITH SCALE

Spike

SPIKES OF SEDGE

Corolla

Calyx

PETALS UNITED

Pistil
Stamen

Lemma

Palea

FLORET WITH LEMMA, PALEA AND FLOWER

CAPSULE

Spikelet

PANICLE WITH SPIKELETS

SPIKELET WITH TWO GLUMES AND SEVERAL FLORETS

Florets

Glumes

Spikelet

SPIKE WITH SPIKELETS

FLORET WITH AN AWN

Awn

Floret

Figure 3

Key To The Seed Plants Of Grand Canyon National Park

1. Woody plants (trees, shrubs or woody vines). 2.
   Non woody plants (herbs). 87.

2. Stems climbing or trailing. 3.
   Stems not climbing or trailing. 5.

3. Stems rather stout, woody throughout, usually climbing by means
   of tendrils opposite the leaves.
   GRAPE FAMILY (VITACEAE) 150
   Stems rather weak, woody only near the base. 4.

4. Stems twining, often tangled.
   SLENDER JANUSIA (*Janusia gracilis*) 145
   Stems trailing, forming loose mats.
   TWINFLOWER (*Linnaea borealis*) 208
   Stems straggling over other plants.
   ARIZONA HONEYSUCKLE (*Lonicera arizonica*) 208
   Stems climbing by means of tenrillike petioles.
   VIRGINS BOWER (*Clematis ligusticifolia*) 94

5. Plants without green leaves. 6.
   Plants with green leaves, at least in summer. 8.

6. Stems very fleshy and very prickly.
   CACTUS FAMILY (CACTACEAE) 155
   Stems not very fleshy. 7.

7. A large shrub with numerous, usually spine-tipped branches;
   flowers small and inconspicuous.
   CANOTIA (*Canotia holacantha*) 148
   A large shrub with several or many long, unbranched stems, these
   beset with many short spines; flowers bright red and conspicuous.
   OCOTILLO (*Fouquieria splendens*) 171
   A small shrub, 12 to 20 inches high, with broomlike branches and
   a strong odor of turpentine; flowers dark purple or blue.
   TURPENTINE-BROOM (*Thamnosma montana*) 145

8. Leaves needlelike or very narrow, arranged spirally or in 2's or 3's,
   never simply alternate or opposite.
   PINE FAMILY (PINACEAE) 29
   Leaves awl-shaped, ½ inch long or less, in whorls of 3; plant low,
   forming dense, evergreen patches.
   DWARF JUNIPER (*Juniperus communis* var. *saxatilis*) 32
   Leaves scalelike. 9.

Leaves neither needlelike, awl-shaped, nor scalelike, arranged alternate, opposite or all basal. 11.

9. Scalelike leaves only at the joints of the stem, not crowded nor overlapping, opposite or in 3's.
JOINTFIR FAMILY (EPHEDRACEAE) 32
Scalelike leaves crowded and overlapping, covering the young stem. 10.

10. Flowers very small and numerous, conspicuous, pink to nearly white; fruit a capsule.
TAMARIX *(Tamarix pentandra)* 153
Flowers greenish, inconspicuous, fruit a berrylike cone.
CYPRESS FAMILY (CUPRESSACEAE) 30

11. Leaves parallel-veined; all basal or nearly so; flower parts in 3's or 6's. 12.
Leaves net-veined; flower parts mostly in 4's or 5's. 13.

12. Flowers with inferior ovary; leaf margins with spinelike teeth.
AMARYLLIS FAMILY (AMARYLLIDACEAE) 68
Flowers with superior ovary; leaf margins entire or with threadlike fibers.
LILY FAMILY (LILIACEAE) 65

13. Flowers in heads surrounded by involucres of bracts.
COMPOSITE FAMILY (COMPOSITAE) 212
Flowers not in heads surrounded by involucres. 14.

14. Leaves compound. 15.
Leaves simple. 31.

15. Leaflets spiny-toothed, thick, evergreen.
BARBERRY FAMILY (BERBERIDACEAE) 96
Leaflets not spiny-toothed. 16.

16. Leaves opposite. 17.
Leaves alternate. 21.

17. Plant usually unbranched, woody only near the base; usually with only 1 flower.
CLEMATIS *(Clematis hirsutissima)* 94
Plant branched, woody throughout. 18.

18. Fruit conspicuously winged. 19.
Fruit not winged. 20.

19. Fruit double, with 2 wings.
BOX-ELDER *(Acer negundo)* 149

Fruit single, with a single wing.
OLIVE FAMILY (OLEACEAE) 171

20. Fruit a capsule, densely white-hairy; leaflets 2, thick, evergreen, sessile, appearing like a 2-lobed leaf.
CREOSOTE-BUSH *(Larrea tridentata)* 144
Fruit berrylike, not hairy; leaflets more than 2, not evergreen.
HONEYSUCKLE FAMILY (CAPRIFOLIACEAE) 207

21. Leaflets mostly 3.   22.
Leaflets more than 3.   25.

22. Stems armed with prickles.
HIMALAYA BERRY *(Rubus procerus)* 115
Stems not armed with prickles.   23.

23. Leaflets coarsely scalloped or shallowly lobed; fruit red, hairy, sticky, not winged.
SKUNKBUSH *(Rhus trilobata)* 147
Leaflets with small teeth or nearly entire, not scalloped or lobed; fruit nearly round, flat, winged, not hairy or sticky.   24.

24. Bark of the twigs straw color to light olive; leaves yellowish-green; terminal leaflets usually 3 times as long as the others or more.
HOPTREE *(Ptelea pallida)* 145
Bark of twigs brown or dark purple; leaves bright green or bluish-green; terminal leaflets usually less than 3 times as long as the others.
HOPTREE *(Ptelea angustifolia)* 145

25. Leaves large, often 1 foot long or more, with large leaflets and a pronounced odor of black walnut.
ARIZONA WALNUT *(Juglans major)* 72
Leaves and leaflets smaller, without odor of walnut.   26.

26. Flowers very irregular.
PEA FAMILY (LEGUMINOSAE) 116
Flowers regular or nearly so.   27.

27. Flowers yellow; stems usually armed with short spines.
CATCLAW *(Acacia greggii)* 120
Flowers white.   28.
Flowers pink or red; fruit red.   30.

28. Stems armed with prickles.
RED RASPBERRY *(Rubus strigosus)* 116

Stems not armed with prickles.   29.

29. Leaves fernlike; fruit a podlike capsule.
FERNBUSH (*Chamaebatiaria millefolium*) 113
Leaves not fernlike; fruit berrylike.
MOUNTAIN-ASH (*Sorbus dumosa*) 116

30. Leaflets wedge-shaped, toothed at or near the tip;
flowers usually solitary on the branches.
DESERT ROSE (*Rosa stellata*) 115
Leaflets not wedge-shaped, toothed well below the tip;
flowers usually several together on the branches.
ARIZONA ROSE (*Rosa arizonica*) 115

31. Leaves in whorls of 4.   32.
Leaves opposite.   33.
Leaves alternate, sometimes in dense clusters.   55.

32. Plant woody well above the base with many short,
spreading branches.
BEDSTRAW (*Galium stellatum*) 207
Plant woody only near the base, the branches longer and
more upright.
MUNZ BEDSTRAW (*Galium munzii*) 207

33. Plants growing as parasites on the stems of other
woody plants.
MISTLETOE FAMILY (LORANTHACEAE) 74
Plants growing in soil.   34.

34. Leaf margins scalloped.   35.
Leaf margins toothed or lobed or both, not scalloped.   36.
Leaf margins entire or nearly so.   41.

35. Stems creeping, forming loose mats; leaves thick,
evergreen, nearly round; flowers nodding, nearly
regular, white or pinkish.
TWINFLOWER (*Linnaea borealis*) 208
Stems upright; leaves ovate to nearly round, bright
green and rough above, whitish beneath; flowers somewhat irregular, 2-lipped, whitish to bluish.
LIPPIA (*Aloysia wrightii*) 189

36. Fruit winged.   37.
Fruit not winged.   39.

37. Fruit single with a single wing.
SINGLE LEAF ASH (*Fraxinus anomala*) 172
Fruit double with 2 wings.   38.

38. Leaves thin, smooth, with numerous teeth, often lobed; flower clusters long-stalked.

MOUNTAIN MAPLE *(Acer glabrum)* 148

Leaves thickish, usually hairy beneath, with few, blunt teeth; flower clusters short-stalked,

BIGTOOTH MAPLE *(Acer grandidentatum)* 148

39. Petals united; fruit a berry.

MOUNTAIN SNOWBERRY *(Symphoricarpos oreophilus)* 209

Petals distinct; fruit a capsule. 40.

40. A large shrub; flowers showy with 4 large, white petals.

MOCK-ORANGE *(Philadelphus microphyllus)* 109

A low shrub, 10 inches high or less, with some of the stems creeping; flowers small, not showy, red.

MOUNTAIN-LOVER *(Pachystima myrsinites)* 148

41. Flowers irregular. 42.
Flowers regular or nearly so. 45.

42. Flowers red.

BRIDGES BEARDTONGUE *(Penstemon bridgesii)* 201

Flowers blue or purple. 43.

43. Stamens with anthers 2; plants erect.

DESERT SAGE *(Salvia carnosa)* 192

Stamens with anthers 4; plants partly prostrate and spreading; leaves linear. 44.

44. Throat of corolla 2-ridged and densely hairy on the lower side.

MAT BEARDTONGUE *(Penstemon caespitosus)* 201

Throat of corolla rounded, not 2-ridged, and lightly if at all hairy.

TOADFLAX BEARDTONGUE *(Penstemon linarioides)* 202

45. Petals united.

HONEYSUCKLE FAMILY (CAPRIFOLIACEAE) 207

Petals distinct or none. 46.

46. Flowers large and showy, often 1 inch across or more, mostly white. 47.
Flowers much smaller, not showy. 48.

47. Stamens 8.

FENDLERBUSH *(Fendlera rupicola)* 108

Stamens 20 or more.

MOCK-ORANGE *(Philadelphus microphyllus)* 109

14 Grand Canyon Wild Flowers

PHOTO EVANS

ENGLEMANN SPRUCE
(Picea engelmannii)

PHOTO MERKLE

SEGO-LILY
(Calochortus nuttallii)

PHOTO MERKLE

DEATH-CAMAS
(Zigadenus elegans)

PHOTO MERKLE

SPOTTED CORALROOT
(Corallorhiza maculata)

48. Leaves linear or nearly so. 49.
    Leaves broader. 50.

49. Stems slender, twining, often tangled, woody only near
    the base.
    SLENDER JANUSIA (*Janusia gracilis*) 145
    Stems stout, woody throughout; flowers yellowish.
    BLACKBRUSH (*Coleogyne ramosissima*) 113

50. Fruit with a long wing at the end.
    SINGLE LEAF ASH (*Fraxinus anomala*) 172
    Fruit not winged. 51.

51. Flowers with petals. 52.
    Flowers without petals. 53.

52. Stamens 4; leaves 1 to 3 inches long.
    RED-OZIER DOGWOOD (*Cornus stolonifera*) 168
    Stamens 5; leaves less than 1 inch long.
    DESERT CEANOTHUS (*Ceanothus greggii*) 149
    Stamens 10; leaves less than 1 inch long.
    FENDLERELLA (*Fendlerella utahensis*) 108

53. Leaves densely covered with silvery, star-shaped hairs.
    BUFFALOBERRY (*Shepherdia rotundifolia*) 159
    Leaves hairy or smooth but without star-shaped hairs. 54.

54. Leaves densely hairy beneath.
    YELLOWLEAF SILKTASSEL (*Garrya flavescens*) 168
    Leaves smooth beneath or nearly so.
    WRIGHTS SILKTASSEL (*Garrya wrightii*) 168

55. Plant densely woolly all over, the flowers
    hidden in the wool.
    WINTERFAT (*Eurotia lanata*) 83
    Plant smooth or hairy but not woolly. 56.

56. Bark conspicuously warty; flowers mostly imperfect but
    usually some of them perfect.
    NETLEAF HACKBERRY (*Celtis reticulata*) 73
    Bark not conspicuously warty. 57.

57. Flowers imperfect. 58.
    Flowers perfect. 64.

58. Male flowers in catkins; female flowers solitary or in
    small clusters; fruit an acorn.
    BEECH FAMILY (FAGACEAE) 72
    Both male and female flowers in catkins; male and female

flowers on separate plants except in the birch family. 59.
None of the flowers in catkins. 62.

59. Fruit fleshy, resembling a blackberry; usually some of
the leaves palmately lobed.
TEXAS MULBERRY (*Morus microphylla*) 73
Fruit dry. 60.

60. Winter buds covered by a single scale.
WILLOW FAMILY (SALICACEAE) 70
Winter buds covered with more than one scale. 61.

61. Bark dark gray or brown; leaves deeply toothed; fruit
a nutlet.
BIRCH FAMILY (BETULACEAE) 72
Bark light gray or nearly white; leaves bluntly or roundly
toothed; fruit a capsule; seeds with tufts of hair.
WILLOW FAMILY (SALICACEAE) 70

62. Leaves mostly 1 to 2 inches long, entire or nearly so;
fruits winged.
FOURWING SALTBUSH (*Atriplex canescens*) 82
Leaves mostly less than 1 inch long, scalloped; fruit
not winged. 63.

63. Leaves oval or ovate; fruit 3-angled, not hairy.
BERNARDIA (*Bernardia incana*) 146
Leaves nearly round; fruit not 3-angled, red, hairy.
SKUNKBUSH (*Rhus trilobata* var. *simplicifolia*) 147

64. Flowers irregular. 65.
Flowers regular or nearly so. 66.

65. Flowers white, usually with purple spots.
DESERT-WILLOW (*Chilopsis linearis*) 203
Flowers red.
REDBUD (*Cercis occidentalis*) 139
Flowers purple.
RATANY (*Krameria parvifolia*) 139

66. Corolla lacking (Note: when only one set of organs
representing calyx and corolla is present it is always
called a calyx even though it may look like a corolla). 67.
Corolla present. 69.

67. Flowers several together within a calyxlike involucre.
BUCKWHEAT FAMILY (POLYGONACEAE) 76
Flowers not within an involucre; flowers white or
whitish. 68.

68. Plant woody only near the base; fruit nutlike, without a tail.
BASTARD-TOADFLAX *(Comandra pallida)* 74
Plant woody throughout; fruit an akene with a long
feathery tail.
ROSE FAMILY (ROSACEAE) 110

69. Petals united. 70.
Petals distinct. 75.

70. Plants woody only near the base. 71.
Plants woody throughout. 72.

71. Flowers yellow; leaves entire; stamens 2 or 4.
MENODORA *(Menodora scabra)* 172
Flowers white or whitish; leaves divided into very
narrow, sharp-pointed lobes; stamens 5.
LEPTODACTYLON *(Leptodactylon pungens)* 178

72. Plant a dwarf, much-branched, matted shrub; leaves
evergreen, linear or nearly so, crowded.
MOUNTAIN-HEATH *(Phyllodoce empetriformis)* 169
Plant not dwarf, 1 to several feet high, not matted. 73.

73. Leaves evergreen, not in clusters; stamens 10.
HEATH FAMILY (ERICACEAE) 168
Leaves not evergreen, mostly in clusters in the axils
of spines. 74.

74. Stamens 10.
OCOTILLO *(Fouquieria splendens)* 171
Stamens 5.
NIGHTSHADE FAMILY (SOLANACEAE) 192

75. Stamens numerous. 76.
Stamens 6 to 10. 78.
Stamens with anthers 5 or fewer. 82.

76. Fruits like a small pea pod, ¼ inch long or less;
flowers solitary on the branches.
CROSSOSOMA *(Crossosoma parviflorum)* 110
Fruit not like a small pea pod or, if so, then the flowers
numerous on the branches and the leaves fernlike. 77.

77. Pistil 1; fruit a capsule.
MOCK-ORANGE *(Philadelphus microphyllus)* 109
Pistils more than 1 or, if only 1, then the fruit
berrylike or cherrylike or an akene.
ROSE FAMILY (ROSACEAE) 110

78. Flowers blue; plant somewhat spiny.
   TURPENTINE-BROOM *(Thamnosma montana)* 145
   Flowers white. 79.

79. Plant woody only near the base.
   DESERT PEPPERWEED *(Lepidium fremontii)* 103
   Plant woody throughout. 80.

80. Plant somewhat spiny; fruit a small pod.
   GREASEBUSH *(Glossopetalon nevadense)* 148
   Plant not spiny; fruit a capsule. 81.

81. Stamens 8; flowers large and showy.
   FENDLERBUSH *(Fendlera rupicola)* 108
   Stamens 10; flowers small and inconspicuous.
   FENDLERELLA *(Fendlerella utahensis)* 108

82. Stamens united to form a column with 5 small teeth
   alternating with the 5 anthers; petals purplish,
   attached to the stamen column, each with a hornlike
   structure on its back.
   AYENIA *(Ayenia californica)* 152
   Stamens distinct; petals white or whitish. 83.

83. Leaves rounded, toothed and more or less lobed; fruit
   a berry. 84.
   Leaves lanceolate to ovate, oval, elliptic or oblong,
   entire or toothed but not lobed; fruit cherrylike or
   a capsule. 85.

84. Berries smooth or prickly but not hairy.
   SAXIFRAGE FAMILY (SAXIFRAGACEAE) 107
   Berries hairy.
   SKUNKBUSH *(Rhus trilobata* var. *simplicifolia)* 148

85. Leaves rough to the touch; flowers in spikes each
   subtended by a broad bract.
   SANDPAPER PLANT *(Petalonyx parryi)* 154
   Leaves not rough to the touch; flowers axillary or in
   panicles. 86.

86. Leaves small, leathery, crowded on the many, stiff,
   nearly erect branches.
   MORTONIA *(Mortonia utahensis)* 148
   Leaves not leathery, not noticeably crowded; branches
   spreading.
   BUCKTHORN FAMILY (RHAMNACEAE) 149

87. Plants without green color. 88.
    Plants with green color in leaves or stems or both. 92.

88. Stems twining about the stems of other plants.
    DODDER *(Cuscuta campestris)* 176
    Stems not twining. 89.

89. Plants growing as parasites on the stems of cone-bearing
    trees such as pine, spruce and fir.
    MISTLETOE FAMILY (LORANTHACEAE) 74
    Plants growing in soil, parasitic on roots or fungi. 90.

90. Ovary inferior; flowers irregular.
    ORCHID FAMILY (ORCHIDACEAE) 69
    Ovary superior. 91.

91. Flowers regular.
    PINEDROPS *(Pterospora andromedea)* 169
    Flowers irregular.
    BROOMRAPE FAMILY (OROBANCHACEAE) 204

92. Stems very fleshy and very prickly; usually seen
    without leaves.
    CACTUS FAMILY (CACTACEAE) 155
    Stems not very fleshy and very prickly at the same time;
    usually seen with leaves. 93.

93. Plants grasslike or rushlike; flowers not conspicuously
    colored. 94.
    Plants not grasslike or rushlike or, if so, then the
    flowers conspicuously colored. 96.

94. Flowers not in the axils of dry or chaffy bracts.
    RUSH FAMILY (JUNCACEAE) 63
    Flowers in the axils of dry or chaffy bracts. 95.

95. Leaves in 3 rows on the stem, their lower parts forming
    tubes around the stem; stems solid and usually triangular;
    one bract to each flower.
    SEDGE FAMILY (CYPERACEAE) 57
    Leaves in 2 rows on the stem, their lower parts forming
    sheaths around the stem but their margins not united to
    form tubes; stems often hollow except at the nodes, not
    triangular; 2 bracts to each flower.
    GRASS FAMILY (GRAMINEAE) 34

96. Flowers in heads surrounded by involucres of bracts
    (rarely solitary); ovary inferior.
    COMPOSITE FAMILY (COMPOSITAE) 212

Flowers not in heads surrounded by involucres or, if so, then the ovary superior or the involucre calyxlike. 97.

97. Plants growing in marshes, ponds, lakes or slow-running streams. 98.
Plants growing in dry or wet places but not in water. 102.

98. Stems and leaves entirely immersed in water or floating on the surface; flower clusters sometimes projecting above the water. 99.
Some parts of the stems or leaves projecting above the water. 100.

99. Leaves alternate.
PONDWEED FAMILY (POTAMOGETONACEAE) 33
Leaves opposite.
WATER STARWORT *(Callitriche heterophylla)* 147

100. Leaves opposite; flowers axillary.
WATERWORT FAMILY (ELATINACEAE) 153
Leaves all basal; oblong or ovate with petioles longer than the blades; flowers in panicles.
WATER-PLANTAIN *(Alisma triviale)* 34
Leaves alternate, linear, sessile; flowers in spikes or heads. 101.

101. Flowers in a dense, cylindrical spike, the male flowers in the upper part, the female in the lower part.
CATTAIL FAMILY (TYPHACEAE) 33
Flowers in dense heads, the male and female flowers in separate heads on the same plant.
BURREED *(Sparganium multipedunculatum)* 33

102. Leaves parallel-veined; flower parts mostly in 3's or 6's. 103.
Leaves net-veined; flower parts mostly in 4's or 5's. 106.

103. Ovary superior.
LILY FAMILY (LILIACEAE) 65
Ovary inferior. 104.

104. Flowers irregular.
ORCHID FAMILY (ORCHIDACEAE) 69
Flowers regular. 105.

105. Leaves all basal; flowers white; stamens 6.
AMARYLLIS FAMILY (AMARYLLIDACEAE) 68
Leaves not all basal; flowers blue or violet; stamens 3.
IRIS FAMILY (IRIDACEAE) 68

Key To Seed Plants 21

106. Flowers without a corolla (Note: when only one set of organs representing calyx and corolla is present it is called a calyx even if it looks like a corolla).   107.
Flowers with a corolla.   125.

107. Flowers without a calyx.   108.
Flowers with a calyx.   109.

108. Flowers in small clusters of 1 female and several male flowers surrounded by a calyxlike involucre, the whole resembling a perfect flower; plants with milky juice.
SPURGE FAMILY (EUPHORBIACEAE) 145
Flowers in dense, cylindrical spikes subtended by large white, petallike bracts.
YERBA-MANSA (*Anemopsis californica*) 70

109. Calyx not colored like a corolla, usually green.   110.
Calyx colored more or less like a corolla.   117.

110. Flowers subtended by rigid, sharp-pointed bracts.   111.
Bracts subtending flowers, if present, not rigid or sharp-pointed.   112.

111. Leaves very narrow, somewhat spiny-tipped.
RUSSIAN-THISTLE (*Salsola kali* var. *tenuifolia*) 83
Leaves broader, not spiny-tipped.
AMARANTH FAMILY (AMARANTHACEAE) 83

112. Flowers imperfect, the male and female flowers on separate plants.   113.
Flowers perfect or, if imperfect, then the male and female flowers on the same plant.   114.

113. Leaves compound.
MEADOWRUE (*Thalictrum fendleri*) 96
Leaves simple.
SHEEP SORREL (*Rumex acetosella*) 81

114. Leaves with stipules.   115.
Leaves without stipules, alternate.   116.

115. Leaves alternate, the stipules united to form a sheath around the stem; calyx 6-parted; stamens 6.
BUCKWHEAT FAMILY (POLYGONACEAE) 76
Leaves opposite, the stipules not forming sheaths around the stem; calyx 4-parted; stamens 4; plants armed with stinging hairs.
NETTLE (*Urtica serra*) 73

116. Styles 2 or 3.

GOOSEFOOT FAMILY (CHENOPODIACEAE) 81
Style 1, short.

NETTLE FAMILY (URTICACEAE) 73

117. Flowers borne within calyxlike involucres. 118.
Flowers not borne within calyxlike involucres. 119.

118. Ovary appearing inferior because of a constriction
of the calyx above the ovary.
FOUR-O'CLOCK FAMILY (NYCTAGINACEAE) 84
Ovary obviously superior.
BUCKWHEAT FAMILY (POLYGONACEAE) 76

119. Leaves opposite. 120.
Leaves alternate or whorled or all basal. 123.

120. Leaves compound.
CROWFOOT FAMILY (RANUNCULACEAE) 92
Leaves simple. 121.

121. Leaves mostly 2-lobed.
PTEROSTEGIA (*Pterostegia drymarioides*) 80
Leaves entire. 122.

122. Ovary appearing inferior although actually superior.
FOUR-O'CLOCK FAMILY (NYCTAGINACEAE) 84
Ovary obviously superior.
HORSE-PURSLANE (*Trianthema portulacastrum*) 86

123. Stamens more than 10.
CROWFOOT FAMILY (RANUNCULACEAE) 92
Stamens fewer than 10. 124.

124. Ovary superior.
BUCKWHEAT FAMILY (POLYGONACEAE) 76
Ovary inferior.
BASTARD-TOADFLAX (*Comandra pallida*) 74

125. Petals distinct. 126.
Petals united, at least below. 153.

126. Ovary inferior or partly so. 127.
Ovary superior. 130.

127. Ovary only partly inferior. 128.
Ovary wholly inferior. 129.

128. Sepals or calyx lobes 2.
PURSLANE (*Portulaca oleracea*) 87
Sepals or calyx lobes 5.

SAXIFRAGE FAMILY (SAXIFRAGACEAE) 107

129. Flowers in simple compound umbels; petals 5; stamens 5.

PARSLEY FAMILY (UMBELLIFERAE) 164
Flowers not in umbels; petals 4; stamens 8.

EVENING-PRIMROSE FAMILY (ONAGRACEAE) 159
Flowers not in umbels; petals 5 or more; stamens many.

LOASA FAMILY (LOASACEAE) 153

130. Flowers irregular. 131.
Flowers regular or nearly so. 134.

131. Stamens more than 10.

CROWFOOT FAMILY (RANUNCULACEAE) 92
Stamens 10, usually 9 of them united.

PEA FAMILY (LEGUMINOSAE) 116
Stamens 6 or 8. 132.
Stamens 5. 133.

132. Leaves compound, much dissected; flowers yellow.

GOLDEN CORYDALIS (*Corydalis aurea*) 96
Leaves simple, linear; flowers white.

WHITE MILKWORT (*Polygala alba*) 145

133. Leaves compound; plants tall.

PEA FAMILY (LEGUMINOSAE) 116
Leaves simple; plants low.

VIOLET FAMILY (VIOLACEAE) 153

134. Stems prostrate; flowers yellow.

CALTROP FAMILY (ZYGOPHYLLACEAE) 144
Stems not prostrate or, if so, then the flowers not
yellow. 135.

135. Sepals 2 or 3. 136.
Sepals more than 3. 137.

136. Stems prickly; leaves alternate; flowers large, white.

POPPY FAMILY (PAPAVERACEAE) 96
Stems not prickly; leaves opposite or basal; flowers small.

PORTULACA FAMILY (PORTULACACEAE) 87

137. Leaves opposite. 138.
Leaves alternate or basal. 141.

138. Flowers yellow. 139.
Flowers not yellow. 140.

139. Stamens numerous; stems not twining or tangled.

24 Grand Canyon Wild Flowers

ST. JOHNSWORT FAMILY (GUTTIFERAE) 152
Stamens 5 or 6; stems twining, often tangled.
SLENDER JANUSIA *(Janusia gracilis)* 145

140. Styles 3 (rarely 2), distinct.
PINK FAMILY (CARYOPHYLLACEAE) 88
Styles 5, united around a central column, separating at
maturity to form 5 long-tailed, 1-seeded fruits.
GERANIUM FAMILY (GERANIACEAE) 143

141. Pistils several to many.   142.
Pistil 1, simple or compound.   146.

142. Flowers in dense, spikelike racemes.
ROCKMAT *(Petrophytum caespitosum)* 114
Flowers not in dense, spikclike racemes.   143.

143. Pistils arranged spirally on a long, cylindrical
receptacle, the whole resembling a dense spike.
MOUSETAIL *(Myosurus minimus)* 95
Pistils and receptacles not resembling a cylindrical
spike.   144.

144. Calyx with sepallike bracts alternating with the 5
calyx lobes, the whole resembling a 10-lobed calyx.
ROSE FAMILY (ROSACEAE) 110
Calyx without bracts between the calyx lobes.   145.

145. Leaves short, fleshy, linear, almost cylindrical.
STONECROP *(Sedum stenopetalum)* 107
Leaves various but not fleshy and cylindrical.
CROWFOOT FAMILY (RANUNCULACEAE) 92

146. Stamens 5.   147.
Stamens 6.   148.
Stamens 8 to 12.   149.
Stamens more than 12.   151.

147. Petals with a hornlike appendage on the back, white
or whitish.
AYENIA *(Ayenia californica)* 152
Petals without hornlike appendages on the back,
blue or yellow.
FLAX FAMILY (LINACEAE) 144

148. Stamens all about the same length.
CAPER FAMILY (CAPPARIDACEAE) 106
Two of the stamens shorter than the other 4.

MUSTARD FAMILY (CRUCIFERAE) 97

149. Leaves compound with 3 leaflets; flowers yellow.
    WOOD-SORREL *(Oxalis pilosa)* 144
    Leaves simple; flowers white or greenish. 150.

150. Styles 5.
    DITAXIS *(Ditaxis neomexicana)* 146
    Style 1.
    HEATH FAMILY (ERICACEAE) 168

151. Petals 12 or more, pink or white.
    BITTERROOT *(Lewisia rediviva)* 87
    Petals 5. 152.
    Petals 4; stamens purple; plant ill-smelling.
    CLAMMYWEED *(Polanisia trachysperma)* 107

152. Stamens distinct; flowers yellow, creamy or orange.
    LOASA FAMILY (LOASACEAE) 153
    Stamens united in a column around the styles; flowers
    not yellow.
    MALLOW FAMILY (MALVACEAE) 150

153. Stems trailing, twining or climbing by tendrils. 154.
    Stems not trailing, twining or climbing by tendrils. 157.

154. Flowers imperfect, the male and female flowers on the
    same plant; plants with tendrils.
    BUFFALO GOURD *(Cucurbita foetidissima)* 210
    Flowers perfect; plants without tendrils. 155.

155. Stems prickly.
    FIESTA FLOWER *(Pholistoma auritum* var. *arizonicum)* 183
    Stems not prickly. 156.

156. Stems trailing but not twining; leaves evergreen.
    TWINFLOWER *(Linnaea borealis)* 208
    Stems trailing or twining; leaves not evergreen.
    MORNING GLORY FAMILY (CONVOLVULACEAE) 175

157. Ovary inferior or partly so. 158.
    Ovary superior. 161.

158. Stamens 2.
    MENODORA *(Menodora scabra)* 172
    Stamens usually 3; leaves opposite.
    VALERIAN FAMILY (VALERIANACEAE) 209
    Stamens 4; leaves opposite or whorled.
    MADDER FAMILY (RUBIACEAE) 205

Stamens 5; leaves alternate or basal. 159.

159. Flowers irregular.
BELLFLOWER FAMILY (CAMPANULACEAE) 210
Flowers regular. 160.

160. Flowers small, numerous, white.
WATER PIMPERNEL *(Samolus floribundus)* 171
Flowers medium-sized, few, violet-blue.
PARRY BELLFLOWER *(Campanula parryi)* 210

161. Flowers irregular. 162.
Flowers regular. 166.

162. Stamens 6 to 8.
WHITE MILKWORT *(Polygala alba)* 145
Stamens with anthers 5; corolla slightly irregular.
FLANNEL MULLEIN *(Verbascum thapsus)* 203
Stamens with anthers 2 or 4. 163.

163. Fruit breaking into 2 or 4 nutlets. 164.
Fruit a capsule. 165.

164. Ovary conspicuously 4-lobed; fruit of 4 nutlets.
MINT FAMILY (LABIATAE) 190
Ovary not 4-lobed or only slightly so; fruit of 2 or
4 nutlets.
VERBENA FAMILY (VERBENACEAE) 189

165. Ovary 1-celled; fruit large, ending in a long,
hooked beak.
UNICORN PLANT FAMILY (MARTYNIACEAE) 203
Ovary 2-celled; fruit without a long, hooked beak.
FIGWORT FAMILY (SCROPHULARIACEAE) 196

166. Stamens 2 or 4; corolla greenish-white or nearly
colorless; flowers in dense, long-stalked spikes.
PLANTAIN FAMILY (PLANTAGINACEAE) 204
Stamens 5; corollas conspicuously colored. 167.

167. Plants with milky juice; pistils 2, the ovaries distinct,
the styles or stigmas united; fruit a pair of pods. 168.
Plants without milky juice. 169.

168. Stamens distinct.
DOGBANE FAMILY (APOCYNACEAE) 173
Stamens united with the styles to form a central column,
this attached to the base of the corolla.
MILKWEED FAMILY (ASCLEPIADACEAE) 174

169. Fruits breaking up into 4 or fewer nutlets.
BORAGE FAMILY (BORAGINACEAE) 183
Fruit a berry.
NIGHTSHADE FAMILY (SOLANACEAE) 192
Fruit a capsule. 170.

170. Capsule about 1 inch long and about as wide, very
prickly.
SACRED DATURA *(Datura meteloides)* 194
Capsule much smaller, not prickly. 171.

171. Leaves opposite or whorled. 172.
Leaves alternate or basal. 173.

172. Style unlobed or none; stigmas 1 or 2 or stigma 2-lobed.
GENTIAN FAMILY (GENTIANACEAE) 172
Style 3-lobed, a stigma on each lobe.
PHLOX FAMILY (POLEMONIACEAE) 176

173. Styles 2 or style 2-lobed.
WATERLEAF FAMILY (HYDROPHYLLACEAE) 179
Style 3-lobed.
PHLOX FAMILY (POLEMONIACEAE) 176
Style 1, not lobed. 174.

174. Plants low; leaves all basal or nearly so; flowers
not in spikes. 175.
Plants tall, stout; leaves not all basal; flowers in
a dense, stout spike, yellow.
FLANNEL MULLEIN *(Verbascum thapsus)* 203

175. Stamens 4 or 5; leaves not evergreen.
PRIMROSE FAMILY (PRIMULACEAE) 170
Stamens 10; leaves evergreen.
HEATH FAMILY (ERICACEAE) 168

FAMILIES OF PLANTS

With Keys and Descriptions of Species

PINE FAMILY (PINACEAE)

A male flower in this family consists of a single stamen and nothing else and a female flower consists of a single pistil in the axil of a little bract or modified leaf. The male and female flowers are in separate clusters but on the same plant. A female flower matures into the familiar cone scale with 2 seeds at its base.

1. Leaves with a sheath at the base, needlelike, single or in
   2's or 3's; cones maturing in the second season. 2.
   Leaves without a sheath at the base, linear and flat or
   4-sided; cones maturing the first season. 3.

2. Leaves mostly single.
   SINGLELEAF PINE (*Pinus monophylla*) 30
   Leaves mostly in clusters of 2.
   PINYON PINE (*Pinus edulis*) 30
   Leaves mostly in clusters of 3.
   PONDEROSA PINE (*Pinus ponderosa*) 30

3. Leaves 4-sided. 4.
   Leaves flat, linear. 5.

4. Leaves not rigid, pointed at the tip but not spiny-tipped;
   cones about 2 inches long.
   ENGELMANN SPRUCE (*Picea engelmannii*) 30
   Leaves rigid, spiny-tipped; cones about 3 inches long.
   COLORADO BLUE SPRUCE (*Picea pungens*) 30

5. Leaves short-stalked; cones drooping, shaggy.
   DOUGLAS-FIR (*Pseudotsuga menziesii* var. *glauca*) 30
   Leaves sessile; cones erect, not shaggy. 6.

6. Twigs smooth when 1 year old; cones grayish-green; bracts
   of cone scales with a short, triangular tip.
   WHITE FIR (*Abies concolor*). 29
   Twigs hairy when 1 year old; cones dark purple; bracts
   of cone scales with a long, awl-shaped tip.
   ALPINE FIR (*Abies lasiocarpa*) 29

WHITE FIR (*Abies concolor*). A tree, 60 to 100 feet tall; leaves 2 to 3 inches long on the lower branches; male flowers rose to dark red; cones oblong, 3 to 5 inches long.

ALPINE FIR (*Abies lasiocarpa*). A tree, 60 to 120 feet tall; leaves 1 to 2 inches long on lower branches; male flowers dark blue; cones oblong, 2 to 4 inches long.

ENGELMANN SPRUCE *(Picea engelmannii)*. A tree, 60 to 120 feet tall; leaves about 1 inch long; male flowers dark purple; cones oblong, drooping.

COLORADO BLUE SPRUCE *(Picea pungens)*. A tree, 75 to 90 feet tall; leaves about 1 inch long; male flowers yellow or tinged with red; cones oblong, drooping.

PINYON PINE *(Pinus edulis)*. A small tree, 15 to 45 feet tall; leaves 1 to 2 inches long, rigid, often curved, sharp-pointed, mostly in clusters of 2; male flowers dark red when fresh; cones 1 to 2 inches long and nearly as wide.

SINGLELEAF PINE *(Pinus monophylla)*. Very similar to the preceding except that the leaves are single instead of in clusters of 2.

PONDEROSA PINE *(Pinus ponderosa)*. A tree, 45 to 135 feet tall; leaves 3 to 10 inches long, mostly in clusters of 3; male flowers yellow; cones mostly 3 to 6 inches long.

DOUGLAS-FIR *(Pseudotsuga menziesii* var. *glauca)*. A tree, 60 to 100 feet tall; leaves about 1 inch long; male flowers orange-red; cones 2 to 10 inches long, the subtending bracts longer than the cone scales and giving the cone a unique, shaggy appearance.

CYPRESS FAMILY (CUPRESSACEAE)

Our representatives of this family are junipers. They are cone-bearing shrubs and small trees, but their little cones are so fleshy that they resemble berries and commonly are called juniper berries.

1. Leaves awl-shaped, in whorls of 3, the upper surfaces
   conspicuously white.

   DWARF JUNIPER *(Juniperus communis* var. *saxatilis)* 32
   Leaves mostly scalelike, opposite and overlapping like
   shingles, their upper surfaces not exposed to view.   2.

2. Small branches flattened and often drooping; berries less
   than ¼ inch in diameter, usually 2-seeded.

   ROCKY MOUNTAIN JUNIPER *(Juniperus scopulorum)* 32
   Small branches not flattened, not drooping; berries
   usually 1-seeded.   3.

3. Main trunk usually lacking, limbs arising at or below the
   ground level; berries ¼ inch in diameter or less.

   ONE SEED JUNIPER *(Juniperus monosperma)* 32
   Main trunk usually present, limbs arising above the
   ground level; berries ¼ to ½ inch in diameter.

   UTAH JUNIPER *(Juniperus osteosperma)* 32

LADY'S-TRESSES
(Spiranthes romanzoffiana)

QUAKING ASPEN
(Populus tremuloides)

REDROOT WILD-BUCKWHEAT
(Eriogonum racemosum)

SULPHUR FLOWER
(Eriogonum umbellatum)

Families Of Plants 31

DWARF JUNIPER *(Juniperus communis* var. *saxatilis).* A shrub, usually less than 3 feet high, the branches partly prostrate, often forming dense, circular patches; leaves ½ inch long or less; berries about ¼ inch in diameter, dark blue.

ONE SEED JUNIPER *(Juniperus monosperma).* A spreading shrub or small tree, the larger branches usually arising at or below the ground level; leaves scalelike, opposite; male and female flowers on separate plants.

UTAH JUNIPER *(Juniperus osteosperma).* A shrub or small tree, the branches usually arising above the ground level; leaves scalelike, opposite; male and female flowers on the same plant.

ROCKY MOUNTAIN JUNIPER *(Juniperus scopulorum).* A bushy shrub or small tree, usually less than 35 feet tall; leaves scalelike, opposite; male and female flowers on separate plants.

JOINTFIR FAMILY (EPHEDRACEAE)

Low or medium-sized shrubs, usually growing in dry places, with opposite or whorled, scalelike leaves. The male and female flowers are on separate plants and the fruits resemble very small cones.

1. Leaves in whorls of 3.
   TORREY JOINTFIR *(Ephedra torreyana)* 33
   Leaves opposite; plants all looking much alike and often difficult to distinguish. 2.

2. Bases of leaves brown, persistent. 3.
   Bases of leaves gray, often dropping off soon. 4.

3. Flower clusters and fruits of female plants sessile or nearly so; stems never sticky.
   GREEN JOINTFIR *(Ephedra viridis)* 33
   Flower clusters and fruits of female plants definitely stalked; stems often sticky.
   CUTLER JOINTFIR *(Ephedra cutleri)* 32

4. Seeds usually in pairs, brown, the surface smooth.
   NEVADA JOINTFIR *(Ephedra nevadensis)* 33
   Seeds usually solitary, gray or light brown, the surface wrinkled.
   JOINTFIR *(Ephedra fasciculata)* 32

CUTLER JOINTFIR *(Ephedra cutleri).* Stems usually 20 to 40 inches high, much-branched, bright green, often sticky; leaves opposite, scalelike; stalks of female flower clusters and conelike fruits often ¼ to ½ inch long.

JOINTFIR *(Ephedra fasciculata).* Stems yellowish-green, minutely rough; leaves opposite.

NEVADA JOINTFIR *(Ephedra nevadensis)*. Very similar to the preceding except for the difference given in the key.

TORREY JOINTFIR *(Ephedra torreyana)*. Stems bluish-green, 10 to 40 inches high; bracts of the conelike flower clusters in whorls of 3 like the leaves.

GREEN JOINTFIR *(Ephedra viridis)*. Very similar to the cutler jointfir except for the differences given in the key.

CATTAIL FAMILY (TYPHACEAE)

Marsh or shallow water plants with tall, erect stems and creeping, underground stems; leaves alternate, linear, sheathing the stem at the base; flowers in a dense, terminal spike, imperfect, the male flowers in the upper part of the spike, the female flowers in the lower part; fruit a nutlike akene.

NARROWLEAF CATTAIL *(Typha angustifolia)*. Stems 3 to 7 feet tall; leaves less than ½ inch wide, nearly as long as the stem; spike 8 to 20 inches long, about 10 times as long as thick, the upper part usually separated from the lower by a sterile portion.

COMMON CATTAIL *(Typha latifolia)*. Stems 3 to 8 feet tall, stout; leaves often more than ½ inch wide, often longer than the stem; spike 8 to 24 inches long, usually about 6 times as long as wide, the upper part not separated from the lower by a sterile portion.

BURREED FAMILY (SPARGANIACEAE)

Herbs growing in shallow water; leaves alternate, sessile, linear; flowers imperfect, the male and female in separate, dense, spherical heads on the same plant; in fruit the pistillate heads are burlike.

BURREED *(Sparganium multipedunculatum)*. Stems 1 to 2 feet long, usually floating; leaves about ¼ inch wide, flat; pistillate heads nearly 1 inch in diameter.

PONDWEED FAMILY (POTAMOGETONACEAE)

Herbs growing in water; leaves floating or immersed; flowers perfect, in spikes, these often above water.

PONDWEED *(Potamogeton diversifolius)*. Submersed leaves narrowly linear, about 2 inches long or less; floating leaves with an elliptic blade, 2 inches long or less, and a petiole from as long to twice as long; spikes more or less headlike, those in the axils of submersed leaves 1- to 5-flowered, those in the axils of floating leaves few- to 50-flowered.

LEAFY PONDWEED *(Potamogeton foliosus* var. *macellus)*. Stems slender, forming a dense mat, often rooting in the mud; branches sometimes 3 feet long but often short, much-branched and bushy; spikes usually short and more or less headlike; leaves all alike, narrowly linear, 4 inches long or less.

FLOATINGLEAF PONDWEED *(Potamogeton natans)*. Stems branching from a horizontal stem that roots in the mud, otherwise mostly unbranched; submersed leaves usually consisting only of a petiole which may be 1 foot long but without a blade; floating leaves consisting of a rather short, broadly oblong blade and a much longer petiole.

WATER-PLANTAIN FAMILY (ALISMACEAE)

Herbaceous plants growing in shallow water, the leaves all basal but the blades usually above the surface of the water, the stem bearing only a panicle of flowers.

WATER-PLANTAIN *(Alisma triviale)*. Stem 4 to 40 inches high; leaf blades 1 to 6 inches long, lanceolate or elliptic, the petioles often longer than the blades; flowers small, in a large, compound panicle; sepals 3; petals 3, white or pinkish; stamens 6; pistils numerous; fruit an akene.

GRASS FAMILY (GRAMINEAE)

The flowers of grasses are wind-pollinated and are usually small and not very conspicuous. Grasses often are considered difficult to identify but once one becomes familiar with the structure of a grass flower, or floret (Fig. 3), these plants can be identified quite readily, especially with the aid of a good lens.

1. Spikelets sessile in groups of 3 borne in loose terminal spikes, the groups falling entire at maturity.
   GALLETA *(Hilaria jamesii)* 52
   Spikelets not in groups of 3 or, if so, then some of the spikelets not sessile and the groups not falling entire.   2.

2. Axis of spikelets jointed below the glumes so that when the spikelets fall, the glumes fall with them.   3.
   Axis of spikelets jointed above the glumes so that when the spikelets fall the glumes remain on the plant.   19.

3. Spikelets subtended by 1 or more bristles.   4.
   Spikelets not subtended by bristles.   8.

4. Bristles united below, forming a bur and falling with the spikelets.
   SANDBUR *(Cenchrus pauciflorus)* 50
   Bristles distinct, remaining on the plant after the spikelets fall; spikelets borne in spikelike panicles.   5.

5. Bristles below each spikelet numerous.
   YELLOW BRISTLEGRASS *(Setaria lutescens)* 55
   Bristles below each spikelet 1 to 3.   6.

6. Bristles more or less rough when rubbed upward.
   HOOKED BRISTLEGRASS *(Setaria verticillata)* 55
   Bristles rough only when rubbed downward.   7.

7. Panicle rather loosely flowered, 4 to 10 inches long.

PLAINS BRISTLEGRASS *(Setaria macrostachya)* 55
Panicle compactly flowered, usually less than 4 inches long.

GREEN BRISTLEGRASS *(Setaria viridis)* 55

8. Flower clusters very conspicuously hairy. 9.
Flower clusters not conspicuously hairy. 13.

9. Lemmas awned. 10.
Lemmas not awned. 12.

10. Racemes 2.

BUSHY BLUESTEM *(Andropogon glomeratus)* 46
Racemes more than 2. 11.

11. Nodes of the stem densely hairy.

CANE BLUESTEM *(Andropogon barbinodis)* 46
Nodes of the stem smooth or nearly so.

SILVER BLUESTEM *(Andropogon saccharoides)* 47

12. Panicle usually 6 to 12 inches long.

SATINTAIL *(Imperata brevifolia)* 52
Panicle usually 2 to 4 inches long.

ARIZONA COTTONTOP *(Trichachne californica)* 57

13. First glume 2-awned; second glume 1-awned.

WOLFTAIL *(Lycurus phleoides)* 52
Both glumes 1-awned or awn-tipped. 14.
Both glumes awnless. 16.

14. Glumes very unequal in length.

BARNYARD GRASS *(Echinochloa crusgalli)* 50
Glumes equal in length. 15.

15. Panicle spikelike, very dense.

RABBITFOOT GRASS *(Polypogon monspeliensis)* 55
Panicle with short branches, not spikelike.

DITCH POLYPOGON *(Polypogon interruptus)* 55

16. Lemmas not awned. 17.
Lemmas awned. 18.

17. Spikelets in an open panicle.

HUACHUCA PANICUM *(Panicum huachucae)* 54
Spikelets in several racemes which are palmately arranged.

HAIRY CRABGRASS *(Digitaria sanguinalis)* 50
Spikelets in numerous short spikes in a narrow panicle,
each with 2 rows of spikelets along one side.

AMERICAN SLOUGHGRASS *(Beckmannia syzigachne)* 47

18. Lemma awned from below the middle of the back.

SHORT-AWN FOXTAIL *(Alopecurus aequalis)* 46
Lemma awned from the tip, the awn long, bent, hairy.

TANGLEHEAD *(Heteropogon contortus)* 51

19. Spikelets sessile or nearly so, in spikes or spikelike racemes, or in headlike clusters.   20.
Spikelets definitely stalked, in open or spikelike panicles.   40.

20. Spikelets borne on opposite sides of the axis of the spike.   21.
Spikelets borne on one side of the axis of the spike.   35.

21. Spikelets solitary at each place of attachment to the axis.   22.
Spikelets more than 1 at each place of attachment to the axis.   27.

22. First glume lacking; spikelet placed edgewise to the axis of the spike.
RYEGRASS *(Lolium perenne)* 52
First glume present; spikelet placed flatwise to the axis of the spike.   23.

23. Glumes 1-nerved; plants annual.
RYE *(Secale cereale)* 55
Glumes 2- to several-nerved; plants perennial.   24.

24. Plants without creeping underground stems, bunchgrasses.
SLENDER WHEATGRASS *(Agropyron trachycaulum)* 46
Plants with creeping underground stems, sod-forming grasses.   25.

25. Glumes rigid, tapering to a short awn.
BLUESTEM WHEATGRASS *(Agropyron smithii)* 46
Glumes not rigid, sharp-pointed but not awned.   26.

26. Glumes shorter than the spikelet; axis of the spike smooth or nearly so.
QUACKGRASS *(Agropyron repens)* 46
Glumes nearly as long as the spikelets; axis of spike hairy, especially at the nodes.
FALSE QUACKGRASS *(Agropyron pseudorepens)* 46

27. Spikelets 3 at each place of attachment to the axis, the middle one with a perfect flower, the lateral ones usually reduced to awns only.   28.
Spikelets mostly 2 at each place of attachment to the axis.   32.

28. Awns slender; plants perennial.   29.
Awns stout; plants annual, branching from the base.   30.

29. Awns 1 to 2 inches long; spike nodding.
FOXTAIL BARLEY *(Hordeum jubatum)*
Awns less than ½ inch long; spike erect.
MEADOW BARLEY *(Hordeum brachyantherum)*

30. Glumes not fringed with hairs along the margins.
MEDITERRANEAN BARLEY *(Hordeum hystrix)*
Glumes, or some of them, fringed with hairs along the margins. 31.

31. Floret of lateral spikelets longer and broader than that of the central spikelet.
BARLEY *(Hordeum leporinum)*
Floret of lateral spikelets not longer than that of the central spikelet.
BARLEY *(Hordeum stebbinsii)*

32. Glumes without awns. 33.
Glumes with long, spreading awns. 34.

33. Plants with slender, creeping, underground stems; some of the spikelets often solitary.
CREEPING WILD-RYE *(Elymus triticoides)*
Plants without underground stems; none of the spikelets solitary.
BLUE WILD-RYE *(Elymus glaucus)*

34. Glumes cleft into 3 or more awnlike divisions.
BIG SQUIRRELTAIL *(Sitanion jubatum)*
Glumes entire or 2-cleft.
BOTTLEBRUSH SQUIRRELTAIL *(Sitanion hystrix)*

35. Spike enclosed in broad, crowded sheaths forming small headlike structures at the ends of the branches.
FALSE BUFFALOGRASS *(Munroa squarrosa)*
Spikes arranged palmately at the ends of the branches, not enclosed.
BERMUDA GRASS *(Cynodon dactylon)*
Spikes arranged in the form of a raceme, not enclosed. 36.

36. Spikelets not arranged like the teeth of a comb; spikelets falling entire at maturity. 37.
Spikelets arranged like the teeth of a comb; florets falling separately at maturity. 38.

37. Spikelets fewer than 20; plants annual.
NEEDLE GRAMA *(Bouteloua aristidoides)*
Spikelets more than 20; plants perennial.

SIDE-OATS GRAMA *(Bouteloua curtipendula)* 48

38. Spikes usually 2, sometimes 1 or 3.
    BLUE GRAMA *(Bouteloua gracilis)* 48
    Spikes usually 3 to 7. 39.

39. Spikelets 25 to 40 to each spike; plants annual.
    SIX-WEEKS GRAMA *(Bouteloua barbata)* 48
    Spikelets about 12 to each spike, purplish; plants perennial.
    RED GRAMA *(Bouteloua trifida)* 48

40. Spikelets 1-flowered. 41.
    Spikelets 2- to several-flowered. 78.

41. First glume 2-awned.
    WOLFTAIL *(Lycurus phleoides)* 52
    First glume awnless or with a single awn. 42.

42. Lemma with a 3-branched awn. 43.
    Lemma awnless or with an unbranched awn. 48.

43. Panicle open, the branches wide-spreading.
    THREE-AWN *(Aristida hamulosa)* 47
    Panicle narrow, the branches not spreading. 44.

44. Awn branches 2 to 3 inches long.
    RED THREE-AWN *(Aristida longiseta)* 47
    Awn branches 1 inch long or less. 45.

45. Stem conspicuously branched from the base; plant annual.
    SIX-WEEKS THREE-AWN *(Aristida adscensionis)* 47
    Stem not conspicuously branched from the base; plant
    perennial. 46.

46. Glumes nearly equal in length; awn distinctly twisted
    below the branches.
    ARIZONA THREE-AWN *(Aristida arizonica)* 47
    Glumes unequal in length; awn not twisted below the
    branches or only slightly so. 47.

47. Lemma narrowed into a slender beak.
    BLUE THREE-AWN *(Aristida glauca)* 47
    Lemma not narrowed into a beak.
    WRIGHT THREE-AWN *(Aristida wrightii)* 47

48. Lemma awnless. 49.
    Lemma awned. 60.

49. Glumes longer than the lemma. 50.
    Glumes as long as or shorter than the lemma. 53.

50. Panicle spikelike. 51.
Panicle not spikelike. 52.

51. Stems usually more than 20 inches high, from a swollen
bulblike base; panicle several times as long as wide.
TIMOTHY *(Phleum pratense)* 54
Stems 10 to 20 inches high, from a somewhat creeping
base; panicle usually not more than twice as long as wide.
ALPINE TIMOTHY *(Phleum alpinum)* 54

52. Panicle narrow, densely flowered, the short branches
whorled.
WATER BENT *(Agrostis semiverticillata)* 46
Panicle very open, the branches wide-spreading.
BENTGRASS *(Agrostis scabra)* 46

53. Lemma densely hairy on the nerves.
PINE-DROPSEED *(Blepharoneuron tricholepis)* 48
Lemma not densely hairy on the nerves. 54.

54. Lemma 3-nerved. 55.
Lemma 1-nerved; glumes very unequal in length. 57.

55. Panicle very open, the branches wide-spreading.
ALKALI MUHLY *(Muhlenbergia asperifolia)* 53
Panicle narrow, sometimes almost spikelike, the branches
short. 56.

56. Plant annual, without creeping underground stems;
panicle few-flowered.
PULL-UP MUHLY *(Muhlenbergia filiformis)* 53
Plant perennial, with creeping underground stems;
panicle many-flowered.
MAT MUHLY *(Muhlenbergia richardsonis)* 53

57. Panicle narrow and spikelike.
SPIKE DROPSEED *(Sporobolus contractus)* 56
Panicle open, not spikelike. 58.

58. Panicle loosely flowered, the spikelets solitary at the
ends of the branches.
TEXAS DROPSEED *(Sporobolus texanus)* 56
Panicle more densely flowered, the spikelets crowded or
at least close together. 59.

59. Panicle branches straight, the secondary branches short
and densely flowered.
SAND DROPSEED *(Sporobolus cryptandrus)* 56
Panicle branches curved, more or less tangled, the

secondary branches longer and more loosely flowered.

MESA DROPSEED *(Sporobolus flexuosus)* 56

60. Lemma awned from near the middle of the back. 61.
Lemma awned from the tip or between teeth at the tip. 62.

61. Lemma bearded at the base with long hairs.

JONES REEDGRASS *(Calamagrostis scopulorum)* 50
Lemma not bearded at the base.

SHORT-AWN FOXTAIL *(Alopecurus aequalis)* 46

62. Glumes longer than the lemma. 63.
Glumes about as long or shorter than the lemma. 74.

63. Glumes awned. 64.
Glumes blunt- or sharp-pointed but not awned. 65.

64. Panicle spikelike.

RABBITFOOT GRASS *(Polypogon monspeliensis)* 55
Panicle narrow with short branches but not spikelike.

DITCH POLYPOGON *(Polypogon interruptus)* 55

65. Awn straight or sometimes bent but not tightly twisted,
easily falling off. 66.
Awn once or twice bent, at least the lower part tightly
twisted, usually not easily falling off. 68.

66. Lemma smooth.

SMILO GRASS *(Oryzopsis miliacea)* 54
Lemma densely hairy. 67.

67. Panicle rather narrow, the branches not wide-spreading;
awn nearly ½ inch long.

BLOOMER RICEGRASS *(Oryzopsis bloomeri)* 54
Panicle loose, the branches wide-spreading; awn less
than ¼ inch long.

INDIAN RICEGRASS *(Oryzopsis hymenoides)* 54

68. Terminal segment of awn feathery; awn 5 to 7 inches long.

NEW MEXICO FEATHERGRASS *(Stipa neomexicana)* 56
Terminal segment of awn not feathery. 69.

69. Lower segment of awn conspicuously feathery.

DESERT NEEDLEGRASS *(Stipa speciosa)* 57
Lower segment of awn smooth, rough, or short-hairy
but not feathery. 70.

70. Lemma densely soft-hairy with long, white hairs all
over the back.

CRESTED NEEDLEGRASS *(Stipa coronata* var. *depauperata)* 56

Lemma conspicuously long-hairy at the tip, short hairy elsewhere.

SCRIBNER NEEDLEGRASS *(Stipa scribneri)* 57
Lemma short-hairy all over the back. 71.

71. Panicle open, the slender branches spreading; awn 4 to 6 inches long.

NEEDLE-AND-THREAD *(Stipa comata)* 56
Panicle narrow, rather dense; awn less than 3 inches long. 72.

72. Awn usually about 2 inches long, the terminal segment somewhat zigzag.

MORMON NEEDLEGRASS *(Stipa arida)* 56
Awn usually less than 2 inches long, the terminal segment straight. 73.

73. Hairs at tip of lemma about as long as elsewhere; awn usually about 1 inch long.

SUBALPINE NEEDLEGRASS *(Stipa columbiana)* 56
Hairs at tip of lemma longer than elsewhere; awn usually less than 1 inch long.

LETTERMAN NEEDLEGRASS *(Stipa lettermani)* 56

74. Glumes very small, much less than ¼ as long as the lemma; plants annual.

LITTLESEED MUHLY *(Muhlenbergia microsperma)* 53
Glumes more than ½ as long as the lemma; plants perennial. 75.

75. Plants with creeping underground stems at the base. 76.
Plants without creeping underground stems. 77.

76. Stems 4 to 8 inches tall; panicle narrow, the branches short.

UTAH MUHLY *(Muhlenbergia curtifolia)* 53
Stems 15 to 25 inches tall; panicle narrow but with long, slender branches.

FOREST MUHLY *(Muhlenbergia sylvatica)* 53

77. Panicle open and loose.

BUSH MUHLY *(Muhlenbergia porteri)* 53
Panicle narrow and dense.

MESA MUHLY *(Muhlenbergia monticola)* 53

78. Glumes longer than the lowest floret, often longer than the spikelet. 79.
Glumes not longer, usually shorter, than the lowest floret. 82.

79. Lemmas awned from the back. 80.

Lemmas awnless or awned from between 2 lobes at the tip. 81.

80. Spikelets large, the glumes about 1 inch long.
WILD OAT *(Avena fatua)* 47
Spikelets small, the glumes less than ¼ inch long.
SLENDER HAIRGRASS *(Deschampsia elongata)* 50

81. Lemma awnless or merely awn-tipped.
JUNE GRASS *(Koeleria cristata)* 52
Lemma awned from between 2 lobes at the tip.
TIMBER OATGRASS *(Danthonia intermedia)* 50

82. Stout plants 6 to 12 feet tall; panicles plumelike.
COMMON REED *(Phragmites communis)* 54
Low or medium-sized plants less than 6 feet tall. 83.

83. Lemmas 3-nerved. 84.
Lemmas 5- to many-nerved. 87.

84. Lemmas smooth, awnless.
SPREADING LOVEGRASS *(Eragrostis diffusa)* 51
Lemma more or less hairy on the nerves or at the base. 85.

85. Plants with runnerlike stems which root at the nodes; panicles small, headlike.
FLUFFGRASS *(Tridens pulchellus)* 57
Plants without runners; panicles not headlike. 86.

86. Glumes shorter than the lowest floret; lemma awned.
HAIRY TRIDENS *(Tridens pilosa)* 57
Glumes about as long as the lowest floret; lemma awnless.
SLIM TRIDENS *(Tridens muticus)* 57

87. Lemma awnless. 88.
Lemma awned or at least awn-tipped from between very small teeth at the tip. 94.

88. Nerves of the lemmas usually prominent, parallel, not converging toward the tip or slightly so. 89.
Nerves of lemmas often not prominent, definitely converging toward the tip. 90.

89. Spikelets linear, not flattened; panicle narrow, the branches not spreading.
NORTHERN MANNAGRASS *(Glyceria borealis)* 51
Spikelets ovate or oblong, more or less flattened; panicle open, the branches spreading and somewhat drooping.
FOWL MANNAGRASS *(Glyceria striata)* 51

90. Panicle open, the branches spreading and few-flowered.
ANNUAL·BLUEGRASS *(Poa annua)* 54
Panicle narrow and dense, the branches not spreading. 91.

91. Plants with creeping underground stems. 92.
Plants without creeping underground stems. 93.

92. Stems strongly flattened, 2-edged.
CANADA BLUEGRASS *(Poa compressa)* 54
Stems not strongly flattened, not 2-edged.
PLAINS BLUEGRASS *(Poa arida)* 54

93. Lemma cobwebby at the base.
BIGELOW BLUEGRASS *(Poa bigelovii)* 54
Lemma hairy on the lower part of the nerves but not
cobwebby at the base.
LONGTONGUE MUTTON BLUEGRASS *(Poa longiligula)* 55

94. Spikelets densely clustered toward the ends of the
branches; lemmas awn-tipped or very short-awned.
ORCHARD GRASS *(Dactylis glomerata)* 50
Spikelets not noticeably clustered, rather evenly distributed
on the branches of narrow or open panicles. 95.

95. Lemmas awned from the tip, sometimes the awn very short
or almost lacking. 96.
Lemmas awned from between 2 small teeth at the tip,
sometimes the awn very short or almost lacking. 98.

96. Lemma merely awn-tipped or almost awnless.
ARIZONA FESCUE *(Festuca arizonica)* 51
Lemma definitely awned. 97.

97. Spikelets usually more than 5-flowered; plant annual.
SIX-WEEKS FESCUE *(Festuca octoflora)* 51
Spikelets mostly 4- or 5-flowered; plant perennial.
SHEEP FESCUE *(Festuca ovina)* 51

98. Spikelets flattened; lemmas with a central ridge along
the back. 99.
Spikelets not conspicuously flattened; lemmas rounded
on the back. 102.

99. Lemmas merely awn-tipped or almost awnless.
RESCUE BROME *(Bromus catharticus)* 48
Lemmas definitely awned. 100.

100. Lemmas hairy on the margins, the teeth at the tip
rather prominent.

ARIZONA BROME *(Bromus arizonicus)* 48
Lemmas smooth or evenly hairy over the back, the
teeth at the tip very small. 101.

101. Panicle with slender, spreading branches; awn usually
more than ¼ inch long.
MOUNTAIN BROME *(Bromus carinatus)* 48
Panicle with stiff, more erect branches; awn usually
less than ¼ inch long.
BROME *(Bromus marginatus)* 49

102. Annual, more or less weedy plants. 103.
Perennial plants, not weedy. 107.

103. Lemmas broad, short-pointed or blunt at the tip.
BALD BROME *(Bromus racemosus)* 49
Lemmas narrow, rather long-pointed. 104.

104. Panicle narrow, more or less dense. 105.
Panicle open, the branches spreading. 106.

105. Stems hairy below the panicle.
FOXTAIL BROME *(Bromus rubens)* 49
Stems smooth below the panicle.
SPANISH BROME *(Bromus madritensis)* 49

106. Panicle branches slender; awns ½ inch long or less.
CHEATGRASS *(Bromus tectorum)* 49
Panicle branches stout; awns 1 to 5 inches long.
RIPGUT BROME *(Bromus rigidus)* 49

107. Lemmas awn-tipped or very nearly awnless; creeping
underground stems present.
SMOOTH BROME *(Bromus inermis)* 49
Lemmas definitely awned; creeping underground stems
absent. 108.

108. Lemmas hairy on the lower part of the back and margins,
the upper part smooth.
FRINGED BROME *(Bromus richardsoni)* 49
Leaves evenly hairy all over the back. 109.

109. Stems usually less than 2 feet tall; panicle usually less
than 4 inches long, drooping.
NODDING BROME *(Bromus porteri)* 49
Stems about 2½ to 3½ feet tall; panicle usually more
than 4 inches tall, erect, the branches somewhat drooping.
WEEPING BROME *(Bromus frondosus)* 48

BUTTERCUP
(Ranunculus cardiophyllus)

PHOTO MERKLE

PRICKLY-POPPY
(Argemone munita subsp. *rotundata)*

PHOTO MERKLE

WESTERN WALLFLOWER
(Erysimum capitatum)

PHOTO MERKLE

FERNBUSH
(Chamaebatiaria millefolium)

PHOTO MERKLE

FALSE QUACKGRASS *(Agropyron pseudorepens)*. Stems 1 to 4 feet tall, smooth, with creeping, underground stems at the base; leaf blades 5 to 8 inches long, rough, sometimes short-hairy above; spikes 3 to 12 inches long; spikelets about ¼ inch long, 3- to 7-flowered; glumes awn-pointed, nearly as long as the spikelets, lemmas sharp-pointed or short awned.

QUACKGRASS *(Agropyron repens)*. Stems 2 to 4 feet tall with creeping underground stems at the base; leaf blades flat, about ¼ inch wide or more; spike 2 to 6 inches long; spikelets 4- to 6-flowered; glumes awn-pointed, somewhat shorter than the spikelet; awn of lemmas varying from very short to nearly as long as the lemma.

BLUESTEM WHEATGRASS *(Agropyron smithii)*. Stems 1 to 2 feet tall or more, with creeping underground stems at the base; leaf blades narrow, firm, stiff, flat when fresh; sheaths smooth; spikes 3 to 6 inches long; spikelets ½ inch long or more, 6- to 10-flowered.

SLENDER WHEATGRASS *(Agropyron trachycaulum)*. Stems 1½ to 4 feet high, smooth; leaf blades 3 to 8 inches long, flat when fresh; sheaths smooth or the lower ones somewhat hairy; spikes 3 to 10 inches long, usually slender; spikelets 3- to 7-flowered; glumes nearly as long as the spikelets, awn-pointed; lemma smooth or nearly so, awn-pointed.

BENTGRASS *(Agrostis scabra)*. Stems 1 to 2½ feet tall, in small, dense bunches; leaf blades flat, 3 to 8 inches long; sheaths smooth; panicle 6 to 10 inches long, very open, the branches in whorls; spikelets 1-flowered; glumes unequal, both longer than the lemma.

WATER BENT *(Agrostis semiverticillata)*. Stems 6 to 24 inches tall, partly prostrate at the base; leaf blades rather short and broad; panicle narrow with short, dense, somewhat whorled branches; spikelets very small, 1-flowered; glumes equal, longer than the lemma; lemma awnless.

SHORT-AWN FOXTAIL *(Alopecurus aequalis)*. Stems 6 to 24 inches tall, erect or spreading; leaf blades short and narrow; panicle spikelike, slender, 1 to 3 inches long; spikelets very small, 1-flowered; awn of lemma scarcely visible beyond the glumes.

CANE BLUESTEM *(Andropogon barbinodis)*. Stems in bunches, 1 to 5 feet tall, with short spreading hairs at the nodes; leaves smooth or nearly so except for a few hairs in the throat of the sheath; panicle usually 3 to 4 inches long, silvery to creamy white, silky, somewhat fan-shaped; racemes several to many; awns nearly 2 inches long, bent near the middle.

BUSHY BLUESTEM *(Andropogon glomeratus)*. Stems 2 to 5 feet tall, often in dense clumps, bushy-branched toward the top; leaf blades rather long, the sheaths often soft-hairy; panicle dense, feathery, fan-shaped or oblong; each pair of racemes subtended by a bract which is about as long as the racemes; awns about ½ inch long.

SILVER BLUESTEM *(Andropogon saccharoides).* Very similar to the cane bluestem but the nodes of the stems are usually not hairy and the panicle is 3 to 6 inches long and not fan-shaped.

SIX-WEEKS THREE-AWN *(Aristida adscensionis).* An annual plant; stems 4 to 30 inches tall, branched from the base, erect or spreading, smooth; leaf blades very narrow, 2 to 6 inches long; panicle narrow, 2 to 4 inches long, rather compact, the branches short, not spreading; awn branches about ½ inch long.

ARIZONA THREE-AWN *(Aristida arizonica).* Plant perennial; stems 1 to 3 feet tall; leaf blades mostly flat but narrowed to a fine, rolled point, the old ones usually curled or bent; panicle narrow, 4 to 10 inches long, rather dense; glumes and lemma equal in length; awn branches ½ inch long or more.

BLUE THREE-AWN *(Aristida glauca).* Plant perennial; stems 4 to 8 inches tall; leaf blades 2 to 4 inches long, very narrow, rolled, mostly curved or bent; panicle narrow, rather few-flowered, the branches short, stiff, not spreading; second glume about twice as long as the first; lemma tapering into a twisted beak; awn branches ½ to 1 inch long.

THREE-AWN *(Aristida hamulosa).* Plant perennial; stems 1 to 2 feet long, erect or spreading and partly prostrate; leaf blades flat or more or less rolled; panicle large and open, usually ½ as long as the entire stem, the branches spreading or drooping; central awn branch nearly 1 inch long, the lateral ones a little shorter.

RED THREE-AWN *(Aristida longiseta).* Plant perennial, often in large bunches; stems 8 to 12 inches tall; leaf blades curved or bent, less than 6 inches long; second glume about twice as long as the first and longer than the lemma; awn branches about 2 to 3 inches long.

WRIGHT THREE-AWN *(Aristida wrightii).* Plant perennial; stems in bunches, 1 to 2 feet tall; leaf blades rolled, curved or bent, the sheaths somewhat hairy in the throat; panicle narrow, 6 to 8 inches long; second glume about twice as long as the first and a little longer than the lemma; awn branches a little less than 1 inch long.

WILD OAT *(Avena fatua).* Stems 1 to 2½ feet tall, stout; leaves numerous, the blades flat; panicle 6 to 12 inches long, loose and open, the branches spreading; spikelets about 1 inch long, usually 3-flowered; lemma clothed below with stiff, brownish or whitish hairs; awn 1 to 1½ inches long, bent in the middle and twisted below. The twisting and untwisting of the awn, with varying amounts of moisture, often serves to plant the floret with its seed in the soil.

AMERICAN SLOUGHGRASS *(Beckmannia syzigachne).* Stems 8 to 40 inches tall, rather coarse; leaf blades 3 to 4 inches long, flat; panicle 2 to 8 inches long; spikes 2 inches long or less; glumes rounded at the end but with a very small, pointed tip; lemma about as long as the glumes, sharp-pointed.

PINE-DROPSEED *(Blepharoneuron tricholepis)*. Stems 8 to 24 inches tall, in dense bunches; leaves crowded on the basal shoots, mostly less than ½ as long as the stems, the blades slender, flat or rolled; panicle grayish, 2 to 8 inches long, 1 to 2 inches wide, the branches not spreading, many-flowered; glumes a little shorter than the abruptly pointed lemma.

NEEDLE GRAMA *(Bouteloua aristidoides)*. Stems slender, 4 to 12 inches tall; leaf blades small and few, up to 6 inches long on large plants but usually much shorter; spikes 9 to 14 on a slender axis; spikelets 2 to 4 on each spike, each spikelet bearing 3 awns that are longer than the floret.

SIX-WEEKS GRAMA *(Bouteloua barbata)*. Stems 8 to 12 inches long, erect to nearly prostrate, often forming mats; leaf blades few, very narrow, less than 2 inches long; spikes 3 to 7, each with 25 to 40 spikelets; lemma densely hairy, awns as long as the body of the lemma or shorter.

SIDE-OATS GRAMA *(Bouteloua curtipendula)*. Stems in bunches, 20 to 32 inches tall; leaf blades flat or rolled, 2 to 8 inches long; spikes 35 to 50, purplish, spreading or hanging downward, each with 5 to 8 spikelets; glumes and lemma sharp-pointed but not awned.

BLUE GRAMA *(Bouteloua gracilis)*. Stems 8 to 20 inches tall, in dense bunches, leafy at the base; leaf blades 1 to 6 inches long, flat or loosely rolled; spikes 1 to 3, usually 2, with numerous spikelets, often as many as 80; lemma hairy; awns short, slender.

RED GRAMA *(Bouteloua trifida)*. Stems 4 to 8 inches tall, in bunches, leafy at the base; leaf blades less than 1 inch long; spikes 3 to 7, each with about 12 purplish spikelets; lemma hairy toward the base, cleft more than ½ its length; awns winged toward the base.

ARIZONA BROME *(Bromus arizonicus)*. Stems mostly 15 to 36 inches tall; leaf blades 8 to 12 inches long; panicle 6 to 12 inches long and relatively narrow; spikelets mostly 5- to 7-flowered; glumes only slightly unequal and not much shorter than the lemmas; lemmas conspicuously hairy along the margins; awns ¼ to 1½ inches long.

MOUNTAIN BROME *(Bromus carinatus)*. Very similar to the preceding but the panicle wider with more spreading or drooping branches; spikelets larger, 6- to 10-flowered; glumes more unequal; lemmas either smooth or slightly hairy all over the back.

RESCUE BROME *(Bromus catharticus)*. Stems 15 to 40 inches tall, stout; leaf blades narrow, smooth or nearly so; panicle 6 inches long or less, open, the branches up to 6 inches long; spikelets about 1 inch long, 6- to 12-flowered; glumes about equal, shorter than the lemmas; lemmas varying from smooth to hairy, awnless or very short-awned.

WEEPING BROME *(Bromus frondosus)*. Stems 2 to 3 feet tall or more, rather weak; leaf blades rough but not hairy; panicle very open, the slender branches drooping; spikelets rather few near the ends of the branches; glumes slightly unequal; lemmas usually hairy all over the back.

SMOOTH BROME *(Bromus inermis)*. Stems 20 to 40 inches tall from creeping underground stems; leaf blades smooth or nearly so, relatively wide; panicle 4 to 8 inches long, the branches in whorls, spreading when in flower, more erect in fruit; spikelets about 1 inch long; glumes quite unequal; lemmas smooth or nearly so, awnless or awn-pointed.

SPANISH BROME *(Bromus madritensis)*. Stems 6 to 16 inches tall, smooth below the panicle; leaves smooth or nearly so; panicle 2 to 4 inches long with rather few, large spikelets; spikelets about 6- to 8-flowered; glumes somewhat unequal; lemmas with prominent teeth at the tip; awns rather stout, ½ inch long or more.

BROME *(Bromus marginatus)*. Stems 1 to 4 feet tall, hairy below the panicle; leaf blades and sheaths hairy; panicle 4 to 16 inches long, the branches somewhat spreading; spikelets 1 inch long or more, 3- to 10-flowered; glumes nearly equal; lemmas somewhat hairy; awns less than ¼ inch long.

NODDING BROME *(Bromus porteri)*. Stems 1 to 2 feet tall, nodes hairy; leaf blades often 6 to 12 inches long; panicle about 4 inches long or less with rather few spikelets, drooping; spikelets 5- to 10-flowered; glumes somewhat unequal, both shorter than the lemmas; lemmas densely and evenly hairy on the back.

BALD BROME *(Bromus racemosus)*. Stems 8 to 12 inches tall, usually smooth below the panicle; leaf blades and sheaths short-hairy; panicle 2 to 4 inches long, dense; spikelets about ½ inch long, 5- to 9-flowered; glumes unequal; lemmas smooth or nearly so; awns about ½ inch long.

FRINGED BROME *(Bromus richardsoni)*. Stems 2 to 4 feet tall, slender, hairy at the nodes; leaf blades often nearly ¼ inch wide; panicle 6 to 10 inches long, the slender branches up to 6 inches long, drooping; first glume 1-nerved; lemmas hairy along the margins except near the tip, smooth on the back.

RIPGUT BROME *(Bromus rigidus)*. Stems 16 to 28 inches tall; leaf blades and sheaths hairy; panicle open, nodding, with rather few spikelets, 3 to 6 inches long, the lower branches less than 1 inch long; spikelets 5- to 7-flowered; glumes somewhat unequal, the second as long as the lemmas; lemmas 1 inch long or more, rough or with short hair; awn stout, 2 inches long or less.

FOXTAIL BROME *(Bromus rubens)*. Stems 6 to 16 inches tall, short-hairy below the panicle; leaf blades and sheaths hairy; panicle erect, dense, 1½ to 3 inches long, usually purplish; spikelets about 1 inch long, 4- to 11-flowered; glumes unequal; lemmas about ½ inch long, rough or somewhat hairy; awn ½ to ¾ inch long.

CHEATGRASS *(Bromus tectorum)*. Stems erect or spreading, 1 to 2 feet tall; leaf blades and sheaths soft-hairy; panicle 2 to 6 inches long, rather dense, soft, drooping, often purplish; spikelets nodding, about ½ inch long; glumes soft-hairy, quite unequal; lemmas soft-hairy.

JONES REEDGRASS *(Calamagrostis scopulorum)*. Stems 20 to 32 inches tall; leaf blades rough but not hairy, flat; panicle pale or purplish, narrow and rather dense, 3 to 6 inches long; glumes equal, awn-pointed; lemmas about as long as the glumes, minutely short-hairy, with long hairs at the base; awn about as long as the lemma, attached above the middle of the back.

SANDBUR *(Cenchrus pauciflorus)*. Stems 8 to 36 inches long, spreading and often forming large mats; leaf blades usually flat; racemes 1 to 3 inches long, the burs somewhat crowded; body of the bur usually densely hairy; spines numerous, spreading; spikelets usually 2 in each bur.

BERMUDA GRASS *(Cynodon dactylon)*. Extensive creeping by scaly stems on or within the soil, the upright flowering stems 4 to 16 inches tall; leaf blades flat, with a conspicuous ring of white hairs at the base; spikes usually 4 or 5, 1 to 2 inches long; spikelets small, crowded, overlapping; lemma boat-shaped.

ORCHARD GRASS *(Dactylis glomerata)*. Stems in large bunches, 2 to 4 feet tall; leaf blades 1 foot long or less; panicle 2 to 8 inches long, the few branches more or less spreading when in bloom; spikelets 2- to 5-flowered, in one-sided clusters near the ends of the branches; glumes and lemmas with stiff hairs on the margins and on the ridge along the back; lemmas awn-pointed.

TIMBER OATGRASS *(Danthonia intermedia)*. Stems 4 to 20 inches tall; leaf blades and sheaths smooth or nearly so but with long hairs in the throat of the sheath; panicle 1 to 2 inches long, narrow, purplish, the short branches each with a single spikelet, not at all spreading; glumes equal; lemmas about ½ as long as the glumes, hairy at the base and along the lower part of the margins; awns nearly as long as the lemmas, twisted below.

SLENDER HAIRGRASS *(Deschampsia elongata)*. Stems densely clustered, slender, erect, 1 to 4 feet tall; leaf blades soft, very narrow, flat or folded; panicle narrow, up to 1 foot long, the hairlike branches not at all spreading; spikelets on very short stalks; glumes about equal, twice as long as the lemma; awn from below the middle of the back of the lemma, somewhat longer than the lemma.

HAIRY CRABGRASS *(Digitaria sanguinalis)*. Stems 8 to 40 inches tall, freely branching, rooting at the lower nodes; leaf blades and sheaths more or less hairy; racemes several; spikelets very small, in 2 rows along 1 side of the axis; first glume very small, the second about ½ as long as the spikelet, fringed with hairs; lemma about twice as long as the second glume.

BARNYARD GRASS *(Echinochloa crusgalli)*. Stems 8 to 40 inches tall, often branching from the base; leaf blades ½ inch wide or less, 4 to 12 inches long; panicle 4 to 8 inches long, pale green to purple, the branches more or less spreading; spikelets awned or awnless, more or less hairy with stiff hairs.

BLUE WILD-RYE *(Elymus glaucus).* Stems in bunches, often bent at the base, 2 to 4 feet tall, leafy; leaf blades flat, ¼ to ½ inch wide; spike 2 to 8 inches long, usually dense; glumes awn-pointed; lemma awned, the awn 1 to 2 times as long as the body of the lemma.

CREEPING WILD-RYE *(Elymus triticoides).* Stems 2 to 4 feet tall, often in large colonies from extensively creeping underground stems; leaf blades narrow, flat or rolled; spike rather slender; spikelets about ½ inch long; glumes very narrow, awn-tipped; lemma smooth, brownish or purplish, awn-tipped.

SPREADING LOVEGRASS *(Eragrostis diffusa).* Stems 1 to 2 feet tall, in clusters; leaf blades narrow, 2 to 6 inches long; panicle 2 to 8 inches long; spikelets about ¼ inch long, slender, 6- to 12-flowered.

ARIZONA FESCUE *(Festuca arizonica).* Stems 20 to 36 inches tall; leaf blades hairlike, rolled, 6 to 10 inches long; panicle 3 to 8 inches long, narrow, somewhat 1-sided; spikelets between ¼ and ½ inch long; glumes somewhat unequal; lemma about as long as the second glume, awnless or awn-pointed.

SIX-WEEKS FESCUE *(Festuca octoflora).* Stems 6 to 12 inches tall or more; leaf blades narrow, rolled, 1 to 4 inches long; panicle narrow, the branches short, sometimes spreading; spikelets about ¼ inch long, densely 5- to 12-flowered; first glume 1-nerved, the second 3-nerved; lemma with a short awn.

SHEEP FESCUE *(Festuca ovina).* Stems densely clustered, 8 to 16 inches tall; leaf blades slender, rolled, 2 to 4 inches long or more; panicle narrow, sometimes almost spikelike, 2 to 3 inches long; spikelets mostly 4- to 5-flowered; lemmas short-awned.

NORTHERN MANNAGRASS *(Glyceria borealis).* Stems 2 to 3 feet tall or more; leaf blades rather narrow, flat or folded; panicle 8 to 16 inches long, the branches up to 4 inches long, each bearing several spikelets; spikelets about 1 inch long, 5- to 12-flowered; glumes a little shorter than the lemmas; lemmas strongly 7-nerved.

FOWL MANNAGRASS *(Glyceria striata).* Stems 1 to 3 feet tall or more, in large clusters; leaf blades usually wider than in the preceding species, flat or folded; panicle 4 to 8 inches long, open, nodding, the branches drooping; spikelets 3- to 7-flowered, often purplish; glumes often less than ½ as long as the lemmas; lemmas prominently 7-nerved.

TANGLEHEAD *(Heteropogon contortus).* Stems 8 to 32 inches tall; leaf blades flat or folded; racemes 2 to 3 inches long, 1-sided; spikelets in pairs, 1 sessile, the other stalked, the stalked spikelets and some of the lower sessile ones are staminate and awnless, the remaining sessile ones have perfect flowers and are long-awned; first glume of the fertile spikelets brown-hairy, wrapped around the second glume and the flower; awns 2 to 5 inches long, bent and curved, often tangled.

GALLETA *(Hilaria jamesii).* Stems 6 to 24 inches high, with creeping underground stems at the base, smooth except at the nodes; leaf blades mostly 1 to 2 inches long, soon rolled; spike 1 to 3 inches long; each group of spikelets long-hairy at the base; glumes of the central spikelet fringed with hairs; lemmas 3- to 5-nerved, short-awned.

MEADOW BARLEY *(Hordeum brachyantherum).* Stems in bunches, 8 to 28 inches high or more; leaf blades 2 to 5 inches long; spike 1 to 3 inches long, slender; central spikelet sessile, with a perfect flower, lateral ones stalked and sterile; glumes all awnlike; lemma of central spikelet short-awned.

MEDITERRANNEAN BARLEY *(Hordeum hystrix).* Stems 6 to 16 inches tall, freely branching; leaf blades and sheaths more or less hairy; spike about 1 inch long or less and ½ as wide or more; glumes awnlike; lemma of central spikelet with an awn somewhat longer than the glumes.

FOXTAIL BARLEY *(Hordeum jubatum).* Stems 1 to 2 feet tall; leaf blades 1 to 6 inches long, flat; spike 2 to 4 inches long and about as wide, nodding, soft; glumes awnlike; lemma with an awn as long as the glumes.

BARLEY *(Hordeum leporinum).* Stems 6 to 20 inches tall; leaf blades relatively broad, somewhat hairy; spikes 2 to 4 inches long, rather narrow; outer glumes awnlike, the inner ones broader but with an awn about 1 inch long; lemma of central spikelet with an awn 1 inch long or more.

BARLEY *(Hordeum stebbinsii).* Very similar to the preceding but the spike usually narrower, the stems shorter, and the awns shorter and more slender.

SATINTAIL *(Imperata brevifolia).* Stems 2 to 4 feet tall, smooth; leaf blades 4 to 12 inches long or more, ¼ to ½ inch wide, smooth; panicle 6 to 12 inches long, narrow and spikelike, soft and silky; spikelets surrounded by silky hairs 3 times as long as the spikelets.

JUNE GRASS *(Koeleria cristata).* Stems in small bunches, 1 to 2 feet tall, short-hairy below the panicle; at least the lower leaf blades and sheaths hairy; panicle more or less spikelike, 2 to 6 inches long; glumes and lemmas awnless or awn-pointed.

RYEGRASS *(Lolium perenne).* Stems 1 to 2 feet tall, often reddish at the base; leaf blades 2 to 8 inches long, flat, smooth or nearly so; spike 6 to 10 inches long; spikelets not crowded, about 6- to 10-flowered; glumes about as long as the first floret; lemmas awnless or nearly so.

WOLFTAIL *(Lycurus phleoides).* Stems 8 to 24 inches tall; leaf blades very narrow, mostly less than 4 inches long; panicle 1 to 2 inches long, spikelike; spikelets crowded; first glume 2-awned, the second 1-awned; lemma longer than the glumes, hairy on the margins, short-awned.

ALKALI MUHLY *(Muhlenbergia asperifolia)*. Stems slender, 4 to 20 inches tall from slender, creeping underground stems; leaf blades very narrow, 1 to 2 inches long; panicle 2 to 6 inches long and about as wide, open and much-branched, breaking off at maturity; spikelets very small, at the ends of the branches, awnless.

UTAH MUHLY *(Muhlenbergia curtifolia)*. Stems 4 to 8 inches tall, loosely clustered from creeping underground stems; leaf blades narrow, mostly less than 1 inch long, rigidly spreading, sharp-pointed, more or less hairy; panicle 1 to 3 inches long, slender, the branches short, not spreading; lemma and palea hairy on the lower half, the lemma short-awned.

PULL-UP MUHLY *(Muhlenbergia filiformis)*. Stems soft and hairlike, 2 to 6 inches tall or more; leaf blades about 1 inch long or more; panicle narrow with few spikelets, usually less than 2 inches long; spikelets very small, awnless.

LITTLESEED MUHLY *(Muhlenbergia microsperma)*. Stems densely clustered, branching and spreading at the base, often purple, 4 to 12 inches tall; leaf blades mostly less than 1 inch long, very narrow; panicle 2 to 6 inches long, the branches rather far apart, not spreading; spikelets on short, thick stalks; glumes about equal, very short; lemma much longer and awned.

MESA MUHLY *(Muhlenbergia monticola)*. Stems in bunches, slender, 12 to 20 inches tall, leafy throughout; leaf blades 1 to 3 inches long, flat or rolled; panicle narrow, soft, rather dense, 2 to 4 inches long or more; lemma hairy at the base, tapering to an awn that is about ½ inch long.

BUSH MUHLY *(Muhlenbergia porteri)*. Stems almost woody at the base, wiry, widely spreading and branching from nearly all nodes, 1 to 3 feet tall or more; leaf blades very narrow, 1 to 3 inches long, soon dropping off from the sheaths; panicle 2 to 4 inches long, open, with slender, brittle, wide-spreading branches, bearing rather few, long-stalked spikelets; lemma purple, somewhat hairy, with a delicate awn.

MAT MUHLY *(Muhlenbergia richardsonis)*. Stems wiry, 2 to 24 inches tall, from numerous underground stems; leaf blades usually rolled, mostly 2 inches long or less; panicle narrow, rather loose or almost spikelike, 1 to 4 inches long; glumes about ½ as long as the lemmas; lemma pointed but awnless.

FOREST MUHLY *(Muhlenbergia sylvatica)*. Stems 16 to 40 inches tall, slender, rather sparingly branched from the middle and upper nodes, the branches often drooping; leaf blades 3 to 6 inches long; panicle 3 to 7 inches long, narrow, the branches slender but not spreading; lemma slightly longer than the glumes, hairy at the base, tapering into a slender awn.

FALSE BUFFALOGRASS *(Munroa squarrosa)*. Stems forming mats as much as 20 inches in diameter with short, leafy branches; leaf blades mostly less than 1 inch long; spikelets 2- to 4-flowered, in headlike, leafy clusters, at the ends of the branches; lemmas with a tuft of hairs on the margin near the middle.

BLOOMER RICEGRASS *(Oryzopsis bloomeri)*. Stems 1 to 2 feet tall; leaf blades narrow, rolled, firm; panicle 3 to 6 inches long, the branches slender but rather stiff, not spreading, the longer ones 2 to 3 inches long; glumes rather broad; lemma densely long-hairy; awn nearly ½ inch long, slightly twisted.

INDIAN RICEGRASS *(Oryzopsis hymenoides)*. Stems densely clustered, 1 to 2 feet tall; leaf blades slender, rolled, nearly as long as the stems; panicle 3 to 6 inches long, the slender branches all spreading and forked; spikelets solitary at the ends of the many branchlets; glumes abruptly pointed; lemma nearly black at maturity, densely hairy with long, white hairs.

SMILO GRASS *(Oryzopsis miliacea)*. Stems rather stout, 2 to 5 feet tall; leaf blades flat and relatively broad for a grass; panicle 6 to 12 inches long, the branches spreading with numerous short-stalked spikelets beyond the middle; glumes pointed; lemma smooth; awn short and straight.

HUACHUCA PANICUM *(Panicum huachucae)*. Stems 8 to 24 inches high, the nodes bearded with spreading hairs; leaf blades 2½ to 3½ inches long and about ½ inch wide, hairy on both sides; panicle about 2 inches long and about as wide; second glume as long as the spikelet, hairy, the first glume about ½ as long; lemma smooth and shining.

ALPINE TIMOTHY *(Phleum alpinum)*. Stems 8 to 20 inches tall, in bunches; leaf blades mostly less than 4 inches long; panicle spikelike, bristly, about 1 inch long and nearly ½ as wide; glumes fringed with hairs along the ridge on the back, awned; lemma much shorter, smooth, awnless.

TIMOTHY *(Phleum pratense)*. Similar to the preceding but the plant usually twice as tall and the panicle 2 to 4 inches long and slender.

COMMON REED *(Phragmites communis)*. Our largest grass; stem 6 to 12 feet tall from stout, creeping underground stems; leaf blades 6 to 15 inches long, 1 inch wide or less; panicle 6 to 15 inches long, rather dense; spikelets about ½ inch long, hairy.

ANNUAL BLUEGRASS *(Poa annua)*. Stems 2 to 8 inches tall or more, forming bright green mats; leaf blades 1 to 4 inches long, soft, flat; panicle 1 to 3 inches long, open; spikelets 3- to 6-flowered; lemmas 5-nerved, more or less hairy on the lower part of the nerves.

PLAINS BLUEGRASS *(Poa arida)*. Stems 8 to 24 inches tall; leaf blades 1 to 6 inches long, folded or rolled, mostly basal; panicle 1 to 4 inches long, narrow, the branches not spreading; spikelets 4- to 8-flowered; lemma densely hairy on the nerves.

BIGELOW BLUEGRASS *(Poa bigelovii)*. Stems 3 to 6 inches tall; leaf blades short and narrow; panicle 3 to 6 inches long, narrow, the branches short, not spreading; spikelets 3- to 6-flowered; lemma webbed at the base.

CANADA BLUEGRASS *(Poa compressa)*. Stems solitary or few, 6 to 30 inches tall, strongly flattened; leaf blades 1 to 4 inches long; panicle 1 to 4 inches long, narrow; spikelets crowded, 3- to 6-flowered; lemmas sparsely hairy on the nerves toward the base.

LONGTONGUE MUTTON BLUEGRASS *(Poa longiligula).* Stems 1 to 2 feet tall; leaf blades 3 to 5 inches long, narrow, with a conspicuous appendage at the upper end of the sheath; panicle 3 to 5 inches long, narrow; spikelets 3- to 6-flowered; lemma hairy on the nerves.

DITCH POLYPOGON *(Polypogon interruptus).* Stems 1 to 3 feet tall, in bunches; leaf blades 3 to 10 inches long; panicle 3 to 6 inches long, narrow but not spikelike; glumes equal, awned; lemma much shorter than the glumes with a slender awn about as long as the glumes.

RABBITFOOT GRASS *(Polypogon monspeliensis).* Stems usually 6 to 20 inches tall; leaf blades 2 to 6 inches long, flat; panicle 1 to 6 inches long, dense, spikelike, yellowish when mature; glumes equal, with awns 3 or 4 times as long as the body, somewhat hairy; lemma about ½ as long as the glumes, with an awn just a little longer.

RYE *(Secale cereale).* This is an escape from cultivation. It resembles wheat but is usually taller and the spike is more slender, often nodding, and always "bearded," that is, the glumes have long awns.

YELLOW BRISTLEGRASS *(Setaria lutescens).* Stems 20 to 40 inches tall, branching from the base; leaf blades up to 10 inches long and nearly ¼ inch wide, flat but often twisted in a loose spiral; panicle spikelike, yellow at maturity, 2 to 4 inches long, the axis densely hairy; bristles 5 to 20 at the base of each spikelet, 2 or 3 times as long as the spikelet.

PLAINS BRISTLEGRASS *(Setaria macrostachya).* Stems 1 to 4 feet tall, in dense bunches; leaf blades 6 to 16 inches long, flat or folded; panicle spikelike, 4 to 10 inches long, more or less interrupted or lobed; bristles about ½ inch long.

HOOKED BRISTLEGRASS *(Setaria verticillata).* Stems often much-branched from the base and spreading, up to 3 feet long; leaf blades 4 to 8 inches long, flat; panicle spikelike, 2 to 6 inches long, ¼ to ½ inch wide, erect but not stiff; bristles solitary at the base of each spikelet, 1 to 3 times as long as the spikelet.

GREEN BRISTLEGRASS *(Setaria viridis).* Stems 8 to 16 inches tall or more, branching from the base; leaf blades usually less than 6 inches long, flat; panicle erect or nodding, densely flowered, green or purple, usually less than 4 inches long; bristles 1 to 3 below each spikelet, 3 or 4 times as long as the spikelets.

BOTTLEBRUSH SQUIRRELTAIL *(Sitanion hystrix).* Stems 4 to 20 inches tall, erect or spreading, rather stiff; leaf blades 2 to 8 inches long, flat or rolled, varying from smooth to densely white-hairy; spike 1 to 3 inches long or more; glumes very narrow, extended into a rough awn, sometimes 2-lobed to the middle or with a bristle or awn from 1 margin; lemma awned, the awns of both lemma and glumes wide-spreading, 1 to 4 inches long.

BIG SQUIRRELTAIL *(Sitanion jubatum)*. Very similar to the preceding but the glumes split into 3 or more awns.

SPIKE DROPSEED *(Sporobolus contractus)*. Stems 1 to 3 feet tall, in bunches; leaf blades 1 to 8 inches long, mostly flat, the sheaths smooth except for a ring of hairs at the upper end; panicle spikelike, a few inches to 1 foot long or more, often partly enclosed by the uppermost leaf sheath; spikelets very small, the glumes very unequal, both glumes and lemma awnless.

SAND DROPSEED *(Sporobolus cryptandrus)*. Stems 1 to 3 feet tall, erect or spreading, usually in rather small bunches; leaf blades 2 to 6 inches long, mostly flat, tapering to a fine point, the sheath with a conspicuous ring of long white hairs at the top; panicles up to 9 inches long, open but often partly enclosed by the uppermost leaf sheath; glumes very unequal.

MESA DROPSEED *(Sporobolus flexuosus)*. Very similar to the preceding but the panicle usually longer, more open and more loosely flowered.

TEXAS DROPSEED *(Sporobolus texanus)*. Stems 12 to 20 inches tall, slender, wiry, in dense bunches; leaf blades flat, or rolled when dry, mostly less than 4 inches long; panicle very open, 6 to 12 inches long and nearly as wide; spikelets solitary at the ends of the numerous, hairlike branches; glumes very unequal.

MORMON NEEDLEGRASS *(Stipa arida)*. Stems 16 to 32 inches tall; leaf blades narrow, 4 to 8 inches long, flat or rolled; panicle 4 to 6 inches long, narrow, compact, pale or silvery; glumes between ¼ and ½ inch long; lemma about ½ as long as the glumes; awn 1½ to 2½ inches long, loosely twisted below.

SUBALPINE NEEDLEGRASS *(Stipa columbiana)*. Stems 1 to 2 feet tall or more; leaf blades 4 to 10 inches long, mostly rolled but sometimes flat; panicle 3 to 8 inches long, rather dense, often purplish; glumes nearly ¼ inch long; lemma 2/3 as long as the glumes, hairy; awn about 1 inch long.

NEEDLE-AND-THREAD *(Stipa comata)*. Stems 1 to 3 feet tall or more; leaf blades 4 to 12 inches long, narrow, flat, or rolled; panicle 4 to 8 inches long, narrow; glumes about ¾ inch long; lemma about ½ as long as the glumes, pale or brownish; awn 4 to 6 inches long, loosely twisted below.

CRESTED NEEDLEGRASS *(Stipa coronata var. depauperata)*. Stems 1 to 2 feet tall; leaf blades 4 to 8 inches long; panicle 4 to 6 inches long, narrow, purplish; glumes slightly unequal; lemma about ½ as long as the second glume, densely hairy; awn about 1 inch long, bent once.

LETTERMAN NEEDLEGRASS *(Stipa lettermani)*. Stems 1 to 2 feet tall; leaf blades slender, rolled, 2 to 8 inches long; panicle slender, loose, 4 to 6 inches long; glumes less than ¼ inch long; lemmas slightly shorter than the glumes, hairy; awn about ¾ inch long.

NEW MEXICO FEATHERGRASS *(Stipa neomexicana)*. Stems 16 to 32 inches tall; leaf blades 4 to 12 inches long, very narrow, rolled; panicle 1 to 4 inches long, narrow; glumes 1 to 2 inches long; lemma about ½ inch long; awn 5 to 7 inches long.

SCRIBNER NEEDLEGRASS *(Stipa scribneri)*. Stems 12 to 28 inches tall; leaf blades 6 to 10 inches long, mostly flat; panicle 4 to 12 inches long, narrow, the rather stiff branches not spreading; glumes nearly ½ inch long; lemma covered with white hairs, those at the summit longer, forming a brushlike tip; awn ½ to ¾ inch long.

DESERT NEEDLEGRASS *(Stipa speciosa)*. Stems numerous, 1 to 2 feet tall; leaf blades 4 to 10 inches long; very narrow and closely rolled, almost hairlike, mostly basal; panicle 4 to 6 inches long, narrow, dense; glumes smooth, about ½ inch long; lemma about ¼ inch long, densely short-hairy; awn about 2 inches long or less, densely long-hairy near the base.

ARIZONA COTTONTOP *(Trichachne californica)*. Stems 16 to 40 inches tall, from a knotty, felty-hairy base, freely branching; leaves numerous, the blades less than 5 inches long, smooth to densely short-hairy; panicle 2 to 4 inches long, narrow, the few racemes 1 to 2 inches long, not spreading; spikelets small, somewhat crowded, the white or purplish hairs much longer than the spikelets.

SLIM TRIDENS *(Tridens muticus)*. Stems slender, in dense bunches, 12 to 20 inches tall; leaf blades mostly 2 to 4 inches long, very narrow, rolled; panicle narrow, the short branches not spreading; spikelets 6- to 8-flowered, pale to purplish; lemma densely hairy on the lower half.

HAIRY TRIDENS *(Tridens pilosa)*. Stems 4 to 12 inches tall, in dense bunches; leaf blades very narrow, flat or folded, mostly in short basal clusters, those on the stem less than 1 inch long; panicles long-stalked but less than 1 inch long with 3 to 10 large, 6- to 12-flowered spikelets; lemmas densely hairy toward the base.

FLUFFGRASS *(Tridens pulchellus)*. Stems slender, clustered, usually less than 6 inches high, with a cluster of short leaves at the base and another cluster at the top, the stems finally bending over and rooting at the leaf clusters and producing other stems; panicle headlike, usually not longer than the blades of the leaf cluster, consisting of 1 to 5, rather large, white-woolly spikelets.

SEDGE FAMILY (CYPERACEAE)

A large family of grasslike or rushlike plants of little economic importance. The fruit is an akene.

1. Flowers all imperfect, the male and female flowers in separate spikes or at opposite ends of the same spike.   2.
   Flowers all perfect or, if some of them imperfect, the male and female flowers not sharply separated.   18.

2. Spike 1; male and female flowers on separate plants.
   SEDGE *(Carex curatorium)* 60

Spikes more than 1; male and female flowers on the same plant. 3.

3. Stigmas mostly 3; akenes mostly 3-angled. 4.
   Stigmas mostly 2; akenes mostly lens-shaped. 6.

4. Bracts enclosing akene not hairy.
   SEDGE *(Carex thurbori)* 62
   Bracts enclosing akene hairy. 5.

5. Pistillate spikes 25- to 75-flowered; tall plants of wet places.
   WOOLLY SEDGE *(Carex lanuginosa)* 60
   Pistillate spikes 3- to 10-flowered; low plants of dry places.
   ROSS SEDGE *(Carex rossii)* 60

6. Lateral spikes stalked.
   NEBRASKA SEDGE *(Carex nebraskensis)* 60
   Lateral spikes sessile, short. 7.

7. Stems solitary or a few together from a long-creeping underground stem. 8.
   Stems loosely or densely clustered, the underground stem not long-creeping. 9.

8. Bracts enclosing akene wing-margined.
   SILVERTOP SEDGE *(Carex siccata)* 62
   Bracts enclosing akene not wing-margined, blackish in age.
   SEDGE *(Carex praegracilis)* 60

9. Spikes with the male flowers above the female or with the flowers all female. 10.
   Spikes with the male flowers below the female. 11.

10. Scales subtending flowers conspicuously tinged with reddish-brown.
    SEDGE *(Carex occidentalis)* 60
    Scales subtending flowers at most only slightly tinged with reddish-brown.
    SEDGE *(Carex rusbyi)* 62

11. Leaflike bracts conspicuously surpassing the head.
    SLENDER-BEAK SEDGE *(Carex athrostachya)* 60
    Leaflike bracts not conspicuously surpassing the head. 12.

12. Beak of bract enclosing akene flattened.
    BROOM SEDGE *(Carex scoparia)* 62
    Beak of bract enclosing akene slender, not flattened. 13.

13. Bract enclosing akene less than ⅛ inch long, ovate.
    SEDGE *(Carex subfusca)* 62

Bract enclosing akene more than ⅛ inch long, the body flattened. 14.

14. Bract enclosing akene not much over ⅛ inch long; stems usually tall and slender. 15.
Bract enclosing akene usually about ¼ inch long; stems shorter and stouter. 16.

15. Bract enclosing akene with a strong, wide margin.
OVALHEAD SEDGE *(Carex festivella)* 60
Bract enclosing akene with a very narrow margin.
SMALLWING SEDGE *(Carex microptera)* 60

16. Scales subtending flowers with very narrow or almost no whitish margins.
SEDGE *(Carex haydeniana)* 60
Scales subtending flowers with wide, white margins. 17.

17. Bracts enclosing akene many-nerved on both back and front.
LIDDONS SEDGE *(Carex petasata)* 60
Bracts enclosing akene nerved only on the back.
SEDGE *(Carex wootoni)* 62

18. Base of style noticeably enlarged. 19.
Base of style not noticeably enlarged. 23.

19. Spikes several in a simple or compound umbel.
FIMBRISTYLIS *(Fimbristylis thermalis)* 62
Spike solitary at the end of the stem; leaves consisting of basal sheaths only. 20.

20. Swollen base of style continuous with tip of akene.
BEAKED SPIKE-SEDGE *(Eleocharis rostellata)* 62
Swollen base of style evidently distinct from the tip of the akene. 21.

21. Akene smooth or nearly so, not cross-ribbed.
SPIKE-SEDGE *(Eleocharis parishii)* 62
Akene cross-ribbed between the longitudinal ribs. 22.

22. Bristles at base of akene none.
NEEDLE SPIKE-SEDGE *(Eleocharis acicularis)* 62
Bristles at base of akene several, longer than the akene.
SPIKE-SEDGE *(Eleocharis radicans)* 62

23. Flowers all perfect; leaf margins not spiny-toothed.
OLNEY BULRUSH *(Scirpus olneyi)* 63
Flowers partly staminate, only 1 or 2 of the uppermost perfect; leaf margins spiny-toothed.
CALIFORNIA SAWGRASS *(Cladium californicum)* 62

Families Of Plants 59

SLENDER-BEAK SEDGE *(Carex athrostachya)*. Stems in small or large bunches, 2 to 24 inches long; leaf blades flat, longer or shorter than the stems; spikes in a headlike cluster, the lowest subtended by leaflike bracts that are longer than the head.

SEDGE *(Carex curatorium)*. Evidently rare, known only from the Grand Canyon area. Our only sedge in which the male and female flowers are entirely on separate plants.

OVALHEAD SEDGE *(Carex festivella)*. Stems 12 to 40 inches tall, in rather large bunches from short underground stems; leaves flat, shorter than the stems; spikes in a dense head which is 1 inch long or less.

SEDGE *(Carex haydeniana)*. Stems 4 to 16 inches tall, in dense bunches; leaves narrow, flat, as long as the stems or shorter; spikes in roundish or ovate heads which are less than 1 inch long.

WOOLLY SEDGE *(Carex lanuginosa)*. Stems 12 to 40 inches tall, loosely clustered, from long-creeping underground stems; leaf blades flat, about as long as the stems or longer; spikes usually 4 to 6, the upper 2 usually entirely staminate and the lower ones pistillate.

SMALLWING SEDGE *(Carex microptera)*. Stems 12 to 40 inches tall, smooth; leaf blades flat, much shorter than the stem; spikes 5 to 10, in an egg-shaped or nearly spherical head, 15- to 30-flowered, the head about ½ inch long; male and female flowers in the same spike, the female above, the male below.

NEBRASKA SEDGE *(Carex nebraskensis)*. Stems 6 to 48 inches tall, clustered from rather long underground stems; leaf blades flat, longer or shorter than the stems; staminate spikes only 1 or 2, broadly linear; pistillate spikes 5 or 6, more oblong.

SEDGE *(Carex occidentalis)*. Stems 1 to 2 feet tall; leaf blades rather narrow, nearly as long as the stems; spikes more or less clustered into a very narrow head which is about 1 inch long but the lowest 1 or 2 spikes usually are entirely separate from the head; spikes brownish and somewhat chaffy in appearance.

LIDDONS SEDGE *(Carex petasata)*. Stems 12 to 32 feet tall, somewhat clustered from short underground stems; leaf blades flat, narrow, shorter than the stems; spikes in an oblong head which is 1 to 1½ inches long.

SEDGE *(Carex praegracilis)*. Stems 8 to 30 inches tall, loosely clustered, from blackish, long-creeping underground stems; leaf blades narrow, flat, usually shorter than the stems; spikes few to numerous in an oblong or ovate head which may be 2 inches long or less.

ROSS SEDGE *(Carex rossii)*. Stems 2 to 12 inches tall, loosely clustered, from short underground stems; leaf blades very narrow, flat or folded, as long as the stems or shorter; spikes 3 to 5, the uppermost 2 or 3 near the end of the stem, the others basal and long-stalked.

CLIFFROSE
(Cowania mexicana)

PHOTO MERKLE

DEER-VETCH
(Lotus utahensis)

PHOTO MERKLE

HILLS LUPINE
(Lupinus hillii)

PHOTO MERKLE

WHITE SWEET-CLOVER
(Melilotus alba)

PHOTO HAMILTON

Families Of Plants 61

SEDGE *(Carex rusbyi).* Stems 8 to 15 inches tall, somewhat clustered; leaf blades narrow, flat or folded, mostly shorter than the stems; spikes mostly 4 or 5, clustered near the end of the stem but the cluster not headlike.

BROOM SEDGE *(Carex scoparia).* Stems 6 to 40 inches tall, loosely clustered; leaf blades narrow, flat; spikes 3 to 12, in a narrowly oblong or nearly spherical head

SILVERTOP SEDGE *(Carex siccata).* Stems 8 to 36 inches tall, single or 2 or 3 together from long-creeping underground stems; leaf blades narrow, flat or nearly so; spikes 6 to 12 in a narrowly oblong head but with some of the lowermost ones separated from the head, these spikes are pistillate and few-flowered while in the head proper the lower spikes are staminate and the upper ones pistillate.

SEDGE *(Carex subfusca).* Stems 8 to 26 inches tall, densely clustered, the underground stem very short; spikes in an oblong or ovate head which may be 1½ inches long or less.

SEDGE *(Carex thurberi).* Stems 6 to 40 inches tall, in clusters from short underground stems; leaf blades flat, longer or shorter than the stems, very narrow to more than ¼ inch wide; spikes usually 2 to 5, not clustered into a head.

SEDGE *(Carex wootoni).* Stems mostly 16 to 20 inches tall; leaf blades nearly as long as the stems; spikes usually 4 or 5, clustered near the end of the stem but not in heads.

CALIFORNIA SAWGRASS *(Cladium californicum).* Stems stout, 3 to 6 feet tall; leaf blades 3 to 6 feet long, flat, about ¼ inch wide, with toothed margins; spikes in an axillary, compound umbel with 3 to 6 spikes at the end of each branch of the umbel.

NEEDLE SPIKE-SEDGE *(Eleocharis acicularis).* Stems matted, hairlike, 2 to 8 inches tall; spike 5- to 10-flowered, the scales with brown sides, a green midrib, and colorless margins.

SPIKE-SEDGE *(Eleocharis parishii).* Stems slender, clustered, 4 to 8 inches tall; spike narrowly lanceolate, about ¼ inch long, many-flowered, the scales pale or chestnut-brown.

BEAKED SPIKE-SEDGE *(Eleocharis rostellata).* Stems 6 to 50 inches tall, wiry, sometimes bending over and rooting at the tip; spike 10- to 20-flowered, the scales light brown, the midrib lighter.

SPIKE-SEDGE *(Eleocharis radicans).* Stems spongy, pale green, ½ to 3 inches tall, forming a close cover on the wall; spike ⅛ inch long or less, few-flowered, the scales green with colorless margins.

FIMBRISTYLIS *(Fimbristylis thermalis).* Stems slender, 8 to 28 inches tall; leaves basal, flat, narrow, shorter than the stem; spikes several in a simple or somewhat compound umbel subtended by one or more leaflike bracts, the spikes oblong, ¼ to ½ inch long, many-flowered.

OLNEY BULRUSH *(Scirpus olneyi)*. Stems stout, sharply triangular, the sides concave, 20 to 100 inches tall; leaf blades 1 to 5 inches long; spikes 5 to 12 in a headlike cluster subtended by a short, leaflike bract, the scales flecked with brown, short-awned.

RUSH FAMILY (JUNCACEAE)

The flowers of this family are similar in structure to lily flowers but the sepals and petals are scalelike and not brightly colored. The number of stamens may be either 3 or 6 but is usually 6.

1. Flower cluster appearing lateral, the subtending bract cylindric like the stem, stiffly erect and appearing like a continuation of the stem.   2.
   Flower cluster obviously terminal, the subtending bract leaflike, not strictly erect and not appearing like a continuation of the stem.   3.

2. Stems rather slender, not very rigid; flower cluster not headlike; each flower subtended by 2 small bracts.
   BALTIC RUSH *(Juncus balticus* var. *montanus)* 64
   Stems very stout and rigid; flower cluster headlike, the heads in an open panicle subtended by a single bract; individual flowers without subtending bracts.
   RUSH *(Juncus acutus* var. *sphaerocarpus)* 64

3. Leaves flattened with the flat surface facing the stem.   4.
   Leaves flattened in such a way that one edge faces the stem.   6.
   Leaves cylindric, not flattened.   7.

4. Flowers in heads, the individual flowers not subtended by bracts.
   RUSH *(Juncus longistylus)* 64
   Flowers not in heads, each flower subtended by 2 bracts.   5.

5. Flower cluster more than ½ the height of the plant; low annual plants.
   RUSH *(Juncus confusus)* 64
   Flower cluster much less than ½ the height of the plant; taller, perennial plants.
   INLAND RUSH *(Juncus interior)* 64

6. Styles much longer than the sepals and petals; seeds with tails.
   RUSH *(Juncus tracyi)* 65

Styles little if any longer than the sepals and petals; seeds without tails.

ROCKY MOUNTAIN RUSH *(Juncus saximontanus)* 65

7. Capsule awl-shaped, very narrow.

TORREY RUSH *(Juncus torreyi)* 65

Capsules oblong or egg-shaped. 8.

8. Anthers shorter than the stalk part of the stamens; styles shorter than the sepals and petals; heads usually solitary.

RUSH *(Juncus mertensianus)* 64

Anthers much longer than the stalk part of the stamens; styles longer than the sepals and petals; heads usually 2 or more.

RUSH *(Juncus badius)* 64

RUSH *(Juncus acutus* var. *sphaerocarpus).* Stems 2 to 4 feet tall, stout, rigid, in large clusters; leaves all basal, cylindric, nearly as long as the stems, the sheaths inflated, brownish; flowers 2 to 4 in small clusters in a panicle with unequal branches 2 to 8 inches long; sepals and petals pale brown.

RUSH *(Juncus badius).* Stems 8 to 20 inches tall; leaves cylindric, 1 short leaf more than halfway up the stem, the others basal; flower cluster 1 to 2 inches long with 4 to 12 heads, each 5- to 10-flowered; sepals and petals dark brown.

BALTIC RUSH *(Juncus balticus* var. *montanus).* Stems 4 to 8 inches tall, slender, wiry; leaves all basal, consisting of sheaths only without blades; flowers in a rather dense, many-flowered panicle; sepals and petals purplish-brown often with a greenish center.

RUSH *(Juncus confusus).* Stems 12 to 20 inches tall, very slender; leaves basal, the blades almost hairlike; flower cluster very small and compact; sepals and petals with a green center, lateral brown stripes, and wide, colorless margins.

INLAND RUSH *(Juncus interior).* Stems 20 to 40 inches tall, rather stout; leaves 1/3 as long as the stems, the blades flat or somewhat rolled; flower cluster large and open, 1 to 4 inches long, many-flowered.

RUSH *(Juncus longistylus).* Stems 8 to 20 inches tall, slender, loosely clustered; leaves flat, grasslike, basal ones ½ as long as the stems or more, 1 to 3 shorter ones on the stem; flowers in 1 to 8 heads each 3- to 12-flowered; sepals and petals brown with usually whitish margins.

RUSH *(Juncus mertensianus).* Stems 4 to 12 inches tall, very slender, clustered; leaves 1 to 3 per stem, flattened laterally, 2 to 5 inches long; heads usually solitary but sometimes 2 or 3, usually many-flowered; sepals and petals dark brown or almost black.

ROCKY MOUNTAIN RUSH (*Juncus saximontanus*). Stems 16 to 24 inches tall, somewhat flattened; leaf blades flat, 4 to 10 inches long; heads few, in an open panicle, each 15- to 25-flowered; sepals and petals light brown.

TORREY RUSH (*Juncus torreyi*). Stems stout, 16 to 40 inches tall, from a slender underground stem with tuberlike thickenings; leaves cylindric; heads 1 to 20, about ½ inch in diameter, many-flowered; sepals and petals brownish to greenish, narrowly awl-shaped.

RUSH (*Juncus tracyi*). Stems up to 2 feet tall; leaf blades mostly 3 to 5 inches long with 1 or 2 shorter ones higher on the stem; flowers in small, headlike clusters, in a simple or compound umbel.

LILY FAMILY (LILIACEAE)

Mostly herbaceous plants with parallel-veined leaves and perfect, regular flowers having 3 sepals, 3 petals, 6 stamens, and a 3-celled, superior ovary.

1. Plants with a short, woody stem, mostly below ground;
   leaves numerous, in a large rosette at the end of the stem.   2.
   Plants entirely herbaceous; leaves not in large rosettes.   5.

2. Flowers much less than ½ inch long, many of them imperfect.
   BEARGRASS or **SACAHUISTA** (*Nolina microcarpa*) 67
   Flowers more than 1 inch long, all perfect.   3.

3. Leaves mostly more than ½ inch wide; capsule large, often
   6 to 8 inches long; flower cluster branched.
   DATIL YUCCA (*Yucca baccata*) 67
   Leaves less than ½ inch wide; capsule about 2 inches long.   4.

4. Flower cluster branched, borne high above the rosette
   of leaves.
   UTAH YUCCA (*Yucca utahensis*) 68
   Flower cluster mostly unbranched, starting just above the
   rosette of leaves.
   FINELEAF YUCCA (*Yucca angustissima*) 67

5. Sepals and petals very unlike in shape and color.   6.
   Sepals and petals alike or nearly so.   7.

6. Stems bent and curved in a zigzag manner, branched.
   WEAKSTEM MARIPOSA (*Calochortus flexuosus*) 66
   Stems erect, straight or nearly so, not much-branched
   if any.
   SEGO-LILY (*Calochortus nuttallii*) 67

7. Styles 3, distinct.
   DEATH-CAMAS (*Zigadenus elegans*) 68
   Style 1 or the styles united, at least toward the base.   8.

Families Of Plants   65

8. Fruit berrylike.   9.
Fruit a capsule.   10.

9. Flowers solitary or 2 or 3 together in an umbellike cluster
at the end of the stem; berry somewhat lobed.
FAIRYBELLS *(Disporum trachycarpum)* 67
Flowers in a many-flowered panicle; berries red with
purplish dots.
FEATHER SOLOMON-PLUME *(Smilacina racemosa)* 67
Flowers in few-flowered racemes; berries with blue
stripes, becoming nearly black.
STARRY SOLOMON-PLUME *(Smilacina stellata)* 67

10. Plants with leafy stems; flowers solitary or few, dull
yellow spotted with brownish-purple.
FRITILLARY *(Fritillaria atropurpurea)* 67
Leaves all basal.   11.

11. Flowers in a loose raceme, orange.
CRAG-LILY *(Anthericum torreyi)* 66
Flowers in umbels.   12.

12. Sepals and petals distinct to the base or nearly so;
plants with odor of onions.   13.
Sepals and petals united below into a tube; plants
without odor of onions; flowers blue-violet.
BLUEDICKS *(Dichelostemma pulchellum)* 67

13. Umbel nodding; flowers pink to nearly white.
NODDING ONION *(Allium cernuum)* 66
Umbel erect; flowers purplish.
PALMER ONION *(Allium palmeri)* 66

NODDING ONION *(Allium cernuum)*. Stems 8 to 24 inches tall from a
narrowly egg-shaped bulb; leaves all basal, narrow, nearly flat, usually shorter
than the stem; umbel many-flowered, nodding when in flower; flowers white to
pink; stamens longer than the sepals and petals.

PALMER ONION *(Allium palmeri)*. Stems mostly 6 to 12 inches tall from
a small bulb; leaves usually 2 or more, short, narrow, nearly flat, umbel erect;
flowers rose-purple.

CRAG-LILY *(Anthericum torreyi)*. Stems mostly 10 to 24 inches tall; leaves
narrow, grasslike, usually about ½ as long as the stem or shorter; flowers in a
raceme, orange-yellow.

WEAKSTEM MARIPOSA *(Calochortus flexuosus)*. Very similar to the following species but much more branched and the stem characteristically bent and

curved, sometimes partly prostrate or intertwined with other plants; petals purple to nearly white.

SEGO-LILY *(Calochortus nuttallii).* Stems 8 to 16 inches tall; leaves few, linear, grasslike, the lower ones 4 to 6 inches long, those higher up shorter, flat but becoming rolled; flowers 1 to 4 at the end of the stem, sometimes rather long-stalked; sepals greenish; petals yellow at the base, lilac to nearly white above, with a large gland near the base and a green stripe and purple spot above the gland. In variety *aureus* the petals are lemon-yellow.

BLUEDICKS *(Dichelostemma pulchellum).* Stems 1 to 2 feet tall; leaves few, all basal, nearly as long as the stem or shorter; flowers in a few- to many-flowered, more or less headlike umbel, blue-violet.

FAIRYBELLS *(Disporum trachycarpum).* Stems 1 to 2 feet tall, branched, more or less hairy; leaves 1 to 4 inches long and ½ as wide, ovate to oblong, sessile; flowers solitary or a few in an umbellike cluster at the ends of branches, yellowish-white; fruit a red or orange berry.

FRITILLARY *(Fritillaria atropurpurea).* Stem 6 to 24 inches tall; leaves about 7 to 14, alternate or more or less whorled, ovate to lanceolate, 1 to 4 inches long and ½ as wide; flowers mostly 1 to 4, nodding, purplish-brown spotted with yellow and white.

BEARGRASS or **SACAHUISTA** *(Nolina microcarpa).* Without a visible stem above ground except when in bloom; leaves numerous, 2 feet long or more, narrow, triangular toward the tip; panicle compound, 1 to 2 feet high, many-flowered; flowers whitish.

FEATHER SOLOMON-PLUME *(Smilacina racemosa).* Stem 1 to 3 feet tall; leaves several, ovate to oblong, widest near the middle, sessile and somewhat clasping or with a short petiole, 3 to 6 inches long and 1 to 3 inches wide; flowers numerous, small, white, in a terminal panicle; berries red, usually sprinkled with purple.

STARRY SOLOMON-PLUME *(Smilacina stellata).* Stem 1 to 2 feet tall; leaves 2 to 6 inches long, usually less than 1 inch wide, lanceolate; flowers 3 to 15 in a sessile or short-stalked raceme; sepals and petals nearly ¼ inch long; berry nearly black when mature.

FINELEAF YUCCA *(Yucca angustissima).* Leaves mostly 12 to 18 inches long, usually less than ¼ inch wide, with loose fibers along the margins; flowers in a simple raceme 1 to 3 feet long with a short stalk, the raceme starting below or just above the leaf cluster; sepals and petals 1 to 2 inches long, white.

DATIL YUCCA *(Yucca baccata).* Leaves 20 to 30 inches long, mostly 1 to 1½ inches wide, often ending in a stout spine; flower cluster branched, 2 to 3 feet tall; sepals and petals 1 to 3 inches long, reddish-brown on the outside, creamy-white on the inside.

UTAH YUCCA *(Yucca utahensis)*. Leaves up to 28 inches long, usually about ¼ inch wide and with a few fibers along the margins; flower cluster branched and long-stalked, thus borne high above the leaves; flowers similar to those of the fineleaf yucca.

DEATH-CAMAS *(Zigadenus elegans)*. Stem 8 to 24 inches tall, from an egg-shaped bulb, leaves narrow, grasslike, often nearly as long as the stem; flowers about ½ inch long, pale yellow or nearly white, in a narrow panicle or, in small plants, a simple raceme.

AMARYLLIS FAMILY (AMARYLLIDACEAE)

The flowers of this family are similar to those of the lily family except that the ovary is inferior. Our representatives of the family are all agaves, often called century plants. These plants exist for about 10 or 15 years with only a rosette of thick, fleshy leaves above ground. Then they rapidly send up a stout, leafless stem and produce flowers and fruits, after which the entire plant dies.

DESERT AGAVE *(Agave deserti)*. Plants clustered, often in large colonies; flowering stem 6 to 15 feet tall; leaves 8 to 16 inches long and about 1 inch wide, with prickles along the margins and a spine at the tip; flowers in an open panicle, yellow, about 1½ to 2 inches long.

KAIBAB AGAVE *(Agave kaibabensis)*. Plants not clustered, the rosettes solitary; flowering stem 12 to 30 feet tall; leaves straight, not incurved at the tip; flowers in a spikelike raceme.

UTAH AGAVE *(Agave utahensis)*. Plants clustered with several rosettes together; flowering stem 6 to 12 feet tall; leaves 4 to 10 inches long, about 1 inch wide, curved inward at the tip, with white teeth along the margins and a slender terminal spine; flowers in a spikelike raceme, yellow, 1 to 1½ inches long, about 4 in each cluster.

IRIS FAMILY (IRIDACEAE)

Herbs with flowers having 3 sepals, 3 petals, 3 stamens, and 1 pistil with an inferior ovary, the sepals and petals colored alike.

ROCKY MOUNTAIN IRIS *(Iris missouriensis)*. Stems 8 to 20 inches tall, branched or unbranched, from a thick, underground stem; leaves mostly basal, shorter than the stem, less than ¼ inch wide, light green; flowers large and showy, violet, solitary or 2 together, subtended by partly folded, leaflike bracts; petals shorter and narrower than the sepals; stigma 3-lobed, the lobes petallike.

BLUE-EYED-GRASS *(Sisyrinchium demissum)*. Stems 6 to 12 inches tall, somewhat flattened and narrowly winged, slender; leaves about ½ as long as the stem, narrow, grasslike; flowers in a terminal cluster subtended by 2 leaflike bracts, between ¼ and ½ inch long, pale blue.

ORCHID FAMILY (ORCHIDACEAE)

Herbs with perfect, irregular flowers, the ovary inferior, the 1 or 2 stamens united with the style to form a column, the lower of the 3 petals, called the lip, very different from the other 2.

1. Plants without green color; leaves reduced to scalelike sheaths; flowers several or many in a raceme. 2.
   Plants with green leaves. 3.

2. Lip 2-lobed; 2 of the sepals forming a short spur at the upper end of the ovary.
   SPOTTED CORALROOT *(Corallorhiza maculata)* 69
   Lip not lobed; spur represented by a mere swelling at the upper end of the ovary.
   WISTER CORALROOT *(Corallorhiza wisteriana)* 69

3. Lip with a slender, cylindric spur at the base.
   CANYON HABENARIA *(Habenaria sparsiflora)* 70
   Lip without spur at the base. 4.

4. Leaf solitary, this and the flowering stem arising from a bulblike underground stem; lip bearded, much larger than the other petals.
   CALYPSO *(Calypso bulbosa)* 69
   Leaves several; flowers several or numerous; lip beardless or nearly so, not larger than the other petals. 5.

5. Leaves mostly in a basal rosette; flowers hairy.
   RATTLESNAKE-PLANTAIN *(Goodyera oblongifolia)* 70
   Leaves scattered on the stem; flowers not hairy. 6.

6. Flowers greenish or purplish, in a loose raceme.
   STREAM EPIPACTIS *(Epipactis gigantea)* 70
   Flowers yellowish-white, in a spirally twisted, spikelike raceme.
   LADY'S-TRESSES *(Spiranthes romanzoffiana)* 70

CALYPSO *(Calypso bulbosa)*. Stem 2 to 8 inches tall; leaf blade oval, veiny, 1 to 2½ inches long, on a short, slender petiole; flower very showy, crimson spotted with purple; lip shaped like a sugar scoop, nearly 1 inch long.

SPOTTED CORALROOT *(Corallorhiza maculata)*. Stem 8 to 24 inches tall, yellow or brown; raceme few- to many-flowered; flowers whitish, usually spotted with red or purple; usually blooming in June or July.

WISTER CORALROOT *(Corallorhiza wisteriana)*. Stem usually 4 to 18 inches tall; raceme lax and open; sepals reddish or purplish on the back, paler within and flecked with purple lines; petals pale, somewhat shorter and broader than the sepals, flecked with purple.

STREAM EPIPACTIS *(Epipactis gigantea)*. Stem stout, 1 to 3 feet tall, somewhat hairy; lower leaves ovate, 2 to 6 inches long, upper ones lanceolate and smaller; flowers 3 to 15 in a raceme; sepals about ½ inch long, greenish; petals shorter, purplish or reddish.

RATTLESNAKE-PLANTAIN *(Goodyera oblongifolia)*. Stems stout, 8 to 18 inches high; leaves all basal, the blades mostly 1 to 2½ inches long, oblong to ovate, on winged petioles about ½ as long; flowers whitish, in a terminal, spikelike raceme, glandular-hairy.

CANYON HABENARIA *(Habenaria sparsiflora)*. Stems 1 to 2 feet tall; lower leaves oblanceolate, 4 to 8 inches long, the upper ones smaller; flowers greenish, in a slender, sparsely flowered spike.

LADY'S-TRESSES *(Spiranthes romanzoffiana)*. Stem stout, smooth, 4 to 20 inches tall; lower leaves 3 to 5, linear, 2 to 12 inches long, the upper ones reduced to sheathing bracts; spikes 2 to 5 inches long, twisted; flowers greenish-white, about ¼ inch long.

LIZARD-TAIL FAMILY (SAURURACEAE)

A small family of herbs with numerous, small, perfect flowers in dense spikes.

YERBA-MANSA *(Anemopsis californica)*. Stem 4 to 20 inches tall, with a broadly ovate, clasping leaf above the middle and 1 to 3 petioled leaves in its axil; basal leaf blades mostly 2 to 7 inches long with petioles of about the same length; spike ½ to 1½ inches long, subtended by several white, petallike bracts, each about 1 inch long or less; each flower consists of 6 or 8 stamens and 1 pistil.

WILLOW FAMILY (SALICACEAE)

Trees and shrubs with imperfect flowers which have neither calyx nor corolla. The male and female flowers are on separate plants, both in catkins.

1. Leaf blades about as wide as long with petioles about as
long as the blades or longer.   2.
Leaf blades from 2 to several times longer than broad
with petioles usually much shorter than the blades.   3.

2. Leaf blades broadly triangular, coarsely scalloped or
toothed, not conspicuously paler beneath.
FREMONT POPLAR or **COTTONWOOD** *(Populus fremontii)* 71
Leaf blades broadly ovate to nearly round, finely toothed
or scalloped, usually conspicuously paler beneath.
QUAKING ASPEN *(Populus tremuloides)* 71

3. Leaves finely toothed.
GOODDING WILLOW *(Salix gooddingii)* 71
Leaves entire or nearly so.   4.

4. Mature leaves often more than ½ inch wide, usually less than 4 times as long as wide. **5.**
   Mature leaves less than ½ inch wide, usually more than 4 times as long as wide. **6.**

5. Leaves persistently hairy on the upper surface.
   BEBB WILLOW *(Salix bebbiana)* 71
   Leaves smooth or nearly so on the upper surface.
   SCOULER WILLOW *(Salix scouleriana)* 72

6. Mature leaves mostly less than ¼ inch wide.
   COYOTE WILLOW *(Salix exigua)* 71
   Mature leaves mostly more than ¼ inch wide. **7.**

7. Leaves more or less hairy beneath; flowers appearing before the leaves.
   ARROYO WILLOW *(Salix lasiolepis)* 71
   Leaves smooth beneath; flowers appearing with the leaves.
   RED WILLOW *(Salix laevigata)* 71

FREMONT POPLAR or **COTTONWOOD** *(Populus fremontii).* A large tree up to 100 feet tall with large, spreading branches; leaves usually 2 or 3 inches long and about as wide at the base, sharp-pointed at the tip and toothed along the margins.

QUAKING ASPEN *(Populus tremuloides).* A small or medium sized tree, usually 10 to 60 feet tall with extensive lateral roots often sending up sucker shoots; bark greenish-white; twigs slender; leaf blades mostly 1 to 2 inches long with slender, flattened petioles, becoming golden in autumn.

BEBB WILLOW *(Salix bebbiana).* A shrub or small tree, usually with a single stem and a bushy top, 5 to 24 feet tall; leaf blades elliptic to obovate, 1 to 4 inches long, more or less hairy on both sides.

COYOTE WILLOW *(Salix exigua).* A shrub, 6 to 12 feet high; leaf blades linear, usually longer and narrower than those of any of our other willows; flowers appearing with the leaves.

GOODDING WILLOW *(Salix gooddingii).* A large shrub or small tree, 18 to 30 feet tall or more, with rough, dark bark and yellowish twigs; leaf blades narrowly lanceolate, grayish-green on both sides, smooth when mature, usually with very small glands along the margins.

RED WILLOW *(Salix laevigata).* A small tree, 15 to 45 feet tall or more, with rough, dark bark and yellowish or red-brown, smooth twigs; leaf blades lanceolate, 2 to 5 inches long, light green above, paler beneath.

ARROYO WILLOW *(Salix lasiolepis).* A shrub or small tree, 6 to 30 feet tall, with smooth bark and yellow or red twigs; leaf blades narrowly to broadly oblanceolate, 2 to 4 inches long.

SCOULER WILLOW *(Salix scouleriana).* Usually a shrub, 3 to 12 feet tall but occasionally up to 30 feet tall; twigs rather stout, red-brown to almost black, smooth; leaf blades oblanceolate to obovate, 1 to 6 inches long, coarsely veiny, varying from smooth to densely hairy beneath.

WALNUT FAMILY (JUGLANDACEAE)

A small family of aromatic trees and shrubs with pinnately compound leaves and imperfect flowers. Many of the members produce edible nuts such as walnuts, hickory nuts and pecans.

ARIZONA WALNUT *(Juglans major).* A tree up to 50 feet tall but usually smaller; leaflets about 9 to 13, toothed; male flowers in long, drooping catkins; female flowers solitary or a few in a cluster; nut hard-shelled, about 1 inch in diameter.

BIRCH FAMILY (BETULACEAE)

Small trees or shrubs with alternate, simple leaves and imperfect flowers; both male and female flowers in catkins, the staminate catkins pendulous, the female flowers subtended by conspicuous bracts.

WATER BIRCH *(Betula occidentalis* syn. *B. fontinalis).* A large shrub or small tree up to 30 feet tall with smooth, dark, copper-colored bark; leaves broadly ovate, sharply toothed, 1 to 1½ inches long; nutlets wing-margined.

HOP-HORNBEAM *(Ostrya knowltoni).* Usually a shrub but sometimes a small tree up to 25 feet tall; leaves ovate, sharply doubly-toothed, 1 to 3 inches long and ½ as wide; nutlets not wing-margined, each one enclosed in an enlarged, thin-walled bract.

BEECH FAMILY (FAGACEAE)

Woody plants with simple, alternate leaves and imperfect flowers. In our members of the family the male flowers are in more or less drooping catkins and the female flowers in small, axillary clusters. The fruit is an acorn.

1. Leaves lobed. 2.
   Leaves not lobed. 3.

2. Leaves deeply lobed, the lobes rounded without a spiny tip.
   Leaves rather shallowly lobed each lobe with a spiny tip.

3. Leaves entire or with a very few teeth.
   Leaves with many spiny-tipped teeth.

GAMBEL OAK *(Quercus gambelii)*. A shrub or small tree, usually 6 to 20 feet tall but sometimes as much as 50 feet tall; leaves very variable, usually 2 to 6 inches long and lobed more than halfway to the midrib; acorn usually about ½ inch long, about ½ of it covered by the acorn cup.

GRAY OAK *(Quercus grisea)*. A tree, 45 to 65 feet tall with yellow, hairy branches; leaf blades elliptical or oblong, entire or nearly so, smooth above, hairy beneath; acorn slender, ½ to ¾ inch long.

SHRUB LIVE OAK *(Quercus turbinella)*. A shrub, 3 to 12 feet high, with brown or gray bark and hairy twigs; leaf blades about 1 inch long or less with numerous spine-tipped teeth, oblong or oval; acorn about ½ inch long or more.

WAVYLEAF OAK *(Quercus undulata)*. A low shrub, 1 to 6 feet tall but sometimes reaching 12 feet tall in moist, protected places; leaves narrowly to broadly oblong, 1 to 2 inches long, the margins shallowly lobed and spiny-toothed; acorn ½ inch long or less.

ELM FAMILY (ULMACEAE)

Trees with alternate, simple, pinnately veined leaves which are usually somewhat 1-sided at the base, and small inconspicuous flowers some of which are perfect and some staminate, none in catkins.

NETLEAF HACKBERRY *(Celtis reticulata)*. A large shrub or small tree, up to 12 or 18 feet tall, with warty bark; leaves about 3 inches long or less, toothed or sometimes nearly entire; fruit a small, orange-colored or brownish drupe.

MULBERRY FAMILY (MORACEAE)

Small trees or shrubs with simple, often deeply lobed leaves and imperfect flowers, both male and female flowers in catkins.

TEXAS MULBERRY *(Morus microphylla)*. A small tree, usually 15 to 20 feet tall or less; leaves alternate, very variable, ovate or heart-shaped, toothed, sometimes palmately lobed on one or both sides; fruits black, somewhat resembling blackberries, edible.

NETTLE FAMILY (URTICACEAE)

Herbs with opposite or alternate, simple leaves and small, inconspicuous flowers which may be either perfect or imperfect.

NETTLE *(Urtica serra)*. Stems 3 to 6 feet tall or more, both stems and leaves armed with stinging hairs; leaves opposite, lanceolate to narrowly ovate, coarsely toothed, 2 to 5 inches long, yellowish-green above, soft-hairy beneath, the petioles less than 2 inches long; flowers in axillary clusters, imperfect, greenish, the clusters of female flowers rather loose and nearly as long as the leaves, those of the male flowers denser and shorter.

PELLITORY *(Parietaria floridana)*. Stems slender, weak, 4 to 12 inches long, plant without stinging hairs; leaves ovate, 1 inch long or less, entire, short-

Families Of Plants 73

petioled; flowers in small axillary clusters subtended by small, leafy bracts that are usually less than twice as long as the greenish flowers.

PELLITORY *(Parietaria pennsylvanica)*. Very similar to the preceding but the leaves are 1 to 3 inches long with long, tapering tips and the bracts subtending the flower clusters are 2 or 3 times as long as the flowers.

MISTLETOE FAMILY (LORANTHACEAE)

Plants parasitic on the stems of trees and shrubs; leaves opposite, in ours scalelike; flowers imperfect, small and inconspicuous, the male and female flowers on separate plants.

1. Flowers in spikes; fruit sessile, whitish.
   JUNIPER MISTLETOE *(Phoradendron juniperinum)* 74
   Flowers solitary or few in the leaf axils; fruits bluish,
   greenish or purplish. 2.

2. Plants parasitic on pinyon pine, spruce and fir.
   DWARF MISTLETOE *(Arceuthobium campylopodum)* 74
   Plants parasitic on douglas-fir.
   DWARF MISTLETOE *(Arceuthobium douglasii)* 74
   Plants parasitic on ponderosa pine.
   DWARF MISTLETOE *(Arceuthobium vaginatum* forma *cryptopodum)* 74

DWARF MISTLETOE *(Arceuthobium campylopodum)*. Stems 1 to 6 inches long, much-branched, yellowish-green or brown. Forma *abietinum* occurs on white fir, North Rim; forma *divaricatum* on pinyon pine, both rims; forma *microcarpum* on spruce, North Rim.

DWARF MISTLETOE *(Arceuthobium douglasii)*. Stems very slender; plants usually scattered along the stems of the host. Otherwise similar to the preceding. North Rim, rare on South Rim.

DWARF MISTLETOE *(Arceuthobium vaginatum* forma *cryptopodum)*. Plants usually yellowish, otherwise similar to *A. campylopodum*. Both rims.

JUNIPER MISTLETOE *(Phoradendron juniperinum)*. Stems 4 to 12 inches long, the smaller branches somewhat 4-sided. Parasitic on junipers. Both rims.

SANDALWOOD FAMILY (SANTALACEAE)

A small family of herbs partly parasitic on the roots of other plants.

BASTARD-TOADFLAX *(Comandra pallida)*. Stems usually many, 4 to 16 inches tall, branched; leaves alternate, entire, sessile or nearly so, ½ to 1½ inches long; flowers greenish-white, sometimes pinkish, perfect, with calyx but no corolla, in small terminal clusters; stamens 5, the anthers with a tuft of hairs at the base; pistil 1, the ovary inferior.

GOLDEN COLUMBINE
(Aquilegia chrysantha)

PHOTO MERKLE

ROCKY MOUNTAIN BEEPLANT
(Cleome serrulata)

PHOTO MERKLE

APACHE PLUME
(Fallugia paradoxa)

PHOTO MERKLE

LEAFY ARNICA
(Arnica foliosa)

PHOTO MERKLE

Families Of Plants 75

BUCKWHEAT FAMILY (POLYGONACEAE)

A very variable family of herbaceous and woody plants with no corollas but with the calyx often colored like a corolla. The fruit in almost all cases is a triangular akene.

1. Flowers within a calyxlike involucre, the bracts more or less united. 2.
   Flowers not within a calyxlike involucre. 17.

2. Woody plants (low shrubs). 3.
   Non-woody plants (herbs). 7.

3. A low intricately branched shrub, the branches more or less spiny-tipped.

   WILD-BUCKWHEAT (*Eriogonum howellii*) 79
   Plants much less intricately branched, the branches not spiny-tipped. 4.

4. Plant woody only near the base.

   WILD-BUCKWHEAT (*Eriogonum wrightii*) 80
   Plant woody almost throughout. 5.

5. Leaves linear or narrowly lanceolate.

   BUCKWHEAT BRUSH (*Eriogonum simpsoni*) 79
   Leaves oblong to broadly ovate. 6.

6. Branches more or less erect, not spreading, not rigid; flowers pink or white.

   WILD-BUCKWHEAT (*Eriogonum corymbosum*) 78
   Branches spreading, rigid; flowers yellow, white or pink.

   WILD-BUCKWHEAT (*Eriogonum aureum*) 78

7. Plants with leafy stems, the leaves not all basal. 8.
   Leaves all basal or nearly so. 10.

8. Akenes conspicuously winged.

   WINGED WILD-BUCKWHEAT (*Eriogonum alatum*) 78
   Akenes not conspicuously winged. 9.

9. Flowers white or pink.

   WILD-BUCKWHEAT (*Eriogonum wrightii*) 80
   Flowers yellow.

   SULPHUR FLOWER (*Eriogonum umbellatum*) 80

10. Stems more or less inflated. 11.
    Stems not inflated. 12.

11. Flowers yellow.

    DESERT TRUMPET (*Eriogonum inflatum*) 79
    Flowers bright red.

WILD-BUCKWHEAT *(Eriogonum zionis* var. *coccineum)* 80

12. Flowers yellow or greenish. 13.
    Flowers white or pinkish. 15.

13. Branches hairlike; involucres very small and numerous;
    flowers very small, often only 2 in each involucre,
    yellowish or greenish.
    WILD-BUCKWHEAT *(Eriogonum trichopes)* 79
    Branches not hairlike; involucres and flowers larger,
    yellow. 14.

14. Calyx densely silky-hairy.
    YELLOW WILD-BUCKWHEAT *(Eriogonum flavum)* 79
    Calyx smooth.
    CUSHION WILD-BUCKWHEAT *(Eriogonum ovalifolium)* 79

15. Involucres sessile.
    WILD-BUCKWHEAT *(Eriogonum densum)* 79
    Involucres stalked. 16.

16. Involucres few, rather large, in terminal racemes.
    REDROOT WILD-BUCKWHEAT *(Eriogonum racemosum)* 79
    Involucres numerous, small, scattered along the branches.
    SKELETON WEED *(Eriogonum deflexum)* 79

17. Stems without swollen joints; leaves opposite, without
    sheathing stipules.
    PTEROSTEGIA *(Pterostegia drymarioides)* 80
    Stems with swollen joints; leaves alternate, with
    sheathlike stipules. 18.

18. Sepals 5, all alike and erect in fruit. 19.
    Sepals 6, the outer 3 spreading or turned down, the
    inner 3 usually enlarged and erect in fruit. 24.

19. Leaves with a hingelike joint at the base of the petiole;
    flowers in axillary clusters; bracts subtending the
    flowers with well developed blades. 20.
    Leaves without a distinct joint at the base of the petiole;
    flowers in terminal spikelike racemes; bracts subtending
    the flowers reduced to sheaths. 23.

20. Flowers crowded toward the ends of the branches, giving
    the appearance of terminal spikes.
    KELLOGG KNOTWEED *(Polygonum kelloggii)* 80
    Flowers scattered along the stems in small axillary
    clusters. 21.

21. Stems prostrate or nearly so.

PROSTRATE KNOTWEED *(Polygonum aviculare)* 80
Stems erect or nearly so. 22.

22. Flower stalks mostly bent downward.

DOUGLAS KNOTWEED *(Polygonum douglasii)* 80
Flower stalks erect or nearly so.

SAWATCH KNOTWEED *(Polygonum sawatchense)* 80

23. Raceme solitary, often ½ inch thick or more; flowers white.

AMERICAN BISTORT *(Polygonum bistortoides)* 80
Racemes at the ends of branches as well as the main stem,
narrow; flowers greenish; sepals dotted with glands.

DOTTED SMARTWEED *(Polygonum punctatum)* 80

24. Leaves, or most of them, with a single lobe on either
side at the base of the blade.

SHEEP SORREL *(Rumex acetosella)* 81
Leaves without lobes at the base of the blades. 25.

25. Stems usually without leafy shoots in the axils of leaves;
leaves usually large and thick.

CANAIGRE or **WILD-RHUBARB** *(Rumex hymenosepalus)* 81
Plants usually with leafy shoots in some of the leaf axils;
leaves entire or sometimes wavy. 26.

26. None of the inner sepals bearing grainlike swellings.

CALIFORNIA DOCK *(Rumex californicus)* 81
One or all of the inner sepals bearing a grainlike swelling. 27.

27. Plants usually more than 2 feet tall; leaves large,
broadly lanceolate.

PALE DOCK *(Rumex altissimus)* 81
Plants usually less than 2 feet tall; leaves smaller,
narrowly lanceolate to almost linear.

MEXICAN DOCK *(Rumex mexicanus)* 81

WINGED WILD-BUCKWHEAT *(Eriogonum alatum)*. Stems mostly 1 to 4 feet tall, mostly unbranched except in the flowering portion; larger leaves in a basal cluster, oblanceolate, 2 to 4 inches long, those on the stem smaller, often linear; involucres in a large, open panicle; flowers yellow, akenes 3-winged.

WILD-BUCKWHEAT *(Eriogonum aureum)*. Stems woody, 4 to 12 inches tall, branched throughout; leaves scattered on the stem, oblanceolate to lanceolate, less than 1 inch long, soft-hairy beneath, the margins often rolled, tapering to a short petiole; involucres in more or less flat-topped clusters with many short branches; flowers yellow to nearly white.

WILD-BUCKWHEAT *(Eriogonum corymbosum)*. Stems woody at the base, branched throughout, 1 to 3 feet tall; leaves scattered, 1 to 2 inches long, elliptic to ovate, short-petioled; involucres in many-branched, terminal clusters; flowers white to rose.

SKELETON WEED (*Eriogonum deflexum*). Stems 4 to 12 inches tall, widely branched, not woody; leaves all basal, round or somewhat kidney-shaped, 1 inch long or less and about as wide, the petioles longer than the blades; involucres scattered and very numerous; flowers white or pink.

WILD-BUCKWHEAT (*Eriogonum densum*). Stems 2 to 6 inches tall, repeatedly forked from the base; leaves all basal, nearly round, less than 1 inch across; involucres in all the forks and scattered on the branches; flowers white or pink.

YELLOW WILD-BUCKWHEAT (*Eriogonum flavum*). Very similar to small specimens of *Eriogonum umbellatum* with the leaves all or nearly all basal, but the sepals are soft-hairy on the outside.

WILD-BUCKWHEAT (*Eriogonum howellii*). Stems woody, 5 to 15 inches tall, intricately branched, often forming a rounded bush, somewhat spiny sometimes; leaves mostly on the middle portions of the stems, oblong or almost linear, less than 1 inch long, quite woolly, especially below; flowers yellowish-white in a much-branched panicle.

DESERT TRUMPET (*Eriogonum inflatum*). Stems 4 to 16 inches tall, conspicuously inflated below the nodes; leaves all basal, oblong to nearly round, 1 inch long or less, short-hairy, with petioles 1 to 2 inches long; flowers very small, yellow, in a much-branched panicle.

CUSHION WILD-BUCKWHEAT (*Eriogonum ovalifolium*). Flowering stems 3 to 12 inches tall; leaves crowded at the branched base, broadly oval, the blades ½ inch long or less, densely woolly on both sides, the petioles somewhat longer; flowers yellow, white or pink, in a single headlike cluster at the end of each stem.

REDROOT WILD-BUCKWHEAT (*Eriogonum racemosum*). Flowering stems 1 to 2 feet tall, 1 to several from the same base; leaves all basal, the blades 1 to 3 inches long, elliptic   , the petioles often longer; flowers white or pink, in spikelike ra   few-branched panicles.

BUCKWHEAT   *gonum simpsoni*). A much-branched shrub, 4 to 24 inches tall; leaves   on the branches, appearing linear because strongly rolled, white-woolly beneath, less than 1 inch long, the petioles short; flowers white or yellowish, in more or less flat-topped clusters.

WILD-BUCKWHEAT (*Eriogonum trichopes*). Stems 4 to 16 inches tall, with 2 or 3 branches at the first node and these repeatedly branched above; leaves all basal, the blades broadly oval, less than 1 inch long, more or less scalloped, the petioles somewhat longer; involucres few-flowered, scattered, on hairlike stalks; flowers yellow.

SULPHUR FLOWER *(Eriogonum umbellatum* syn. *E. cognatum).* Stems several from a somewhat woody base, 4 to 12 inches tall, 1 or more times forked; larger leaves all basal, the blades ovate to nearly round, mostly less than 1 inch long, petioled, those on the stem smaller and whorled; involucres long-stalked; flowers bright yellow, 10 to 20 in each involucre; sepals smooth.

WILD-BUCKWHEAT *(Eriogonum wrightii).* Stems 6 to 20 inches tall, from a somewhat woody base; leaves more or less crowded, the blades 1 inch long or less, broadly to narrowly oblanceolate, densely white-woolly on both sides, the petioles short; involucres solitary at each node but crowded near the tip of each branch because the nodes are close together; sepals white with a green or pinkish midrib.

WILD-BUCKWHEAT *(Eriogonum zionis* var. *coccineum).* Stems mostly 1 to 2 feet tall, smooth; leaves all or nearly all basal, long-petioled, the blades ovate to nearly round; involucres in long, slender racemes, few-flowered; calyx bright red.

PROSTRATE KNOTWEED *(Polygonum aviculare).* Stems 4 to 40 inches long, prostrate or nearly so; leaves lanceolate to oblong, about ¼ to ½ inch long, the stipular sheaths silvery, soon torn; flowers 1 to 5 in axillary clusters; calyx greenish with pinkish to purple margins.

AMERICAN BISTORT *(Polygonum bistortoides).* Stems 10 to 30 inches tall, unbranched; basal leaf blades oblong to lanceolate, 4 to 10 inches long, on long petioles, the few on the stems much smaller and sessile; flowers in a dense, cylindrical, terminal, spikelike raceme; calyx white or pinkish.

DOUGLAS KNOTWEED *(Polygonum douglasii).* Stems 4 to 16 inches tall, unbranched or with few branches; leaves 2 inches long or less, sessile or nearly so; flowers 1 to 3 in all but the lowest leaf axils; sepals green with pink or purple margins.

KELLOGG KNOTWEED *(Polygonum kelloggii).* Stems 12 to 32 inches tall, unbranched or branched from the base; leaves linear or nearly so, less than ¼ inch long; flowers in terminal, leafy-bracted spikelike clusters; sepals green with white margins.

DOTTED SMARTWEED *(Polygonum punctatum).* Stems 1 to 3 feet tall, branched or unbranched; leaf blades mostly lanceolate, 1 to 6 inches long, on short petioles; flowers greenish, in terminal, narrow, loosely-flowered racemes, conspicuously dotted with glands.

SAWATCH KNOTWEED *(Polygonum sawatchense).* Stems 2 to 12 inches tall, usually branched from near the base; leaves mostly oblanceolate or linear, less than 1 inch long, the margins often rolled; flowers green, in small clusters in nearly every leaf axil.

PTEROSTEGIA *(Pterostegia drymarioides).* Stems 4 to 16 inches long, slender, often prostrate; leaves opposite, mostly less than ½ inch long, often wider than long, entire or 2-lobed, short-petioled; flowers very small, greenish, solitary in the leaf axils, each subtended by a single, 2-lobed bract.

SHEEP SORREL *(Rumex acetosella)*. Stems slender, 8 to 16 inches tall, branched from the base; leaves sour to the taste because of the presence of oxalic acid, narrow, the blades 1 to 3 inches long, the upper ones nearly entire, the lower with a single lobe on either side at the base, the petioles often longer than the blades; flowers in narrow panicles which turn red in age, imperfect, the male and female flowers on separate plants.

PALE DOCK *(Rumex altissimus)*. Stems 3 to 6 feet tall; leaves ovate to lanceolate, 3 to 6 inches long, narrowed to a short petiole; flowers in a panicle of spikelike racemes, perfect, greenish.

CALIFORNIA DOCK *(Rumex californicus)*. Stems 8 to 24 inches tall, slender but firm; leaves lanceolate, to nearly linear, up to 4 inches long, the petioles about as long as the width of the blades; flowers in a panicle with slender branches; none of the enlarged sepals in fruit bearing grainlike swellings.

CANAIGRE or **WILD-RHUBARB** *(Rumex hymenosepalus)*. Stems 2 to 4 feet tall, stout, often reddish; leaves oblong or elliptic, 2 to 12 inches long; panicle rather compact, 4 to 12 inches long, pinkish; enlarged sepals in fruit ¼ to ½ inch long, the grainlike swellings conspicuous.

MEXICAN DOCK *(Rumex mexicanus)*. Very similar to California dock except that 1 or more of the enlarged sepals in fruit bear grainlike swellings.

GOOSEFOOT FAMILY (CHENOPODIACEAE)

A rather large family of herbs and shrubs with simple leaves and either perfect or imperfect flowers, none of them showy. The fruit is an akene.

1. Plant conspicuously white-hairy or woolly, somewhat woody.
   WINTERFAT *(Eurotia lanata)* 83
   Plant not conspicuously white-hairy or woolly.   2.

2. A shrub; flowers imperfect; fruit 4-winged.
   FOURWING SALTBUSH *(Atriplex canescens)* 82
   Herbs; flowers mostly perfect; fruit not 4-winged.   3.

3. Leaves linear, spiny-tipped.
   RUSSIAN-THISTLE *(Salsola kali* var. *tenuifolia)* 83
   Leaves broader, not spiny-tipped.   4.

4. Calyx and sometimes the lower leaves with yellow dots.
   RAGLEAF GOOSEFOOT *(Chenopodium incisum)* 82
   Calyx and leaves without yellow dots.   5.

5. Calyx fleshy, tinged with red and becoming bright red
   at maturity.

BLITE GOOSEFOOT *(Chenopodium capitatum)* 82
Calyx not fleshy and not bright red at maturity. 6.

6. Leaves all linear or nearly so.

SLIMLEAF GOOSEFOOT *(Chenopodium leptophyllum)* 83
Leaves broader, not linear. 7.

7. Leaves about as broad as long. 8.
Leaves considerably longer than broad. 9.

8. Leaves coarsely toothed.

NETTLELEAF GOOSEFOOT *(Chenopodium murale)* 83
Leaves nearly entire or with a single tooth or lobe on
each side near the base.

FREMONT GOOSEFOOT *(Chenopodium fremontii)* 82

9. Plant ill-scented; calyx lobes wide-spreading in fruit.

GOOSEFOOT *(Chenopodium hians)* 82
Plant not ill-scented; calyx lobes closed around the fruit.

LAMBSQUARTERS *(Chenopodium album)* 82

FOURWING SALTBUSH *(Atriplex canescens).* A shrub, 1 to 2 feet high; leaves 2 inches long or less, rather thick, narrowly elliptic to linear, sessile or nearly so; flowers imperfect, the male and female flowers mostly on separate plants; fruits conspicuously 4-winged.

LAMBSQUARTERS *(Chenopodium album).* Stems 8 to 80 inches tall; leaves ovate to lanceolate, the blades 2 inches long or less, the petioles about ½ as long; flowers in headlike clusters in rather dense spikes in most of the upper leaf axils.

BLITE GOOSEFOOT *(Chenopodium capitatum).* Stems 4 to 24 inches tall, branched from the base or unbranched; lower leaf blades triangular, coarsely toothed, often lobed at the base, upper ones narrower, the petioles about as long as the blades; flowers in headlike clusters in the upper leaf axils and in a terminal spike or raceme; sepals becoming bright red and fleshy in fruit.

FREMONT GOOSEFOOT *(Chenopodium fremontii).* Stems 8 to 23 inches tall, usually branched throughout; leaf blades thin, nearly triangular, entire or nearly so; flowers in small, headlike clusters in a panicle of spikes.

GOOSEFOOT *(Chenopodium hians).* Stems 16 to 32 inches tall, usually sparsely branched near the top; leaf blades narrowly oblong, entire or nearly so, rather thick, 1 inch long or less, the petioles about ½ as long; flowers in rather large headlike clusters in axillary or panicled spikes.

RAGLEAF GOOSEFOOT *(Chenopodium incisum).* Plant has a strong but not unpleasant odor and turns bright red in autumn; stems 4 to 24 inches tall, usually branched throughout; leaf blades 1 to 2 inches long, narrowly oblong, irregularly toothed or lobed, the petioles shorter than the blades; flowers sessile in the forks and at the ends of the branches of an ample panicle; calyx deeply lobed, the lobes covered with yellow glands.

SLIMLEAF GOOSEFOOT (*Chenopodium leptophyllum*). Stems 4 to 32 inches tall, usually branched near the top; leaves about 1 inch long or less, linear or nearly so, entire, 1-nerved; flowers in small, headlike clusters in panicled spikes.

NETTLELEAF GOOSEFOOT (*Chenopodium murale*). Stems 8 to 24 inches tall, unbranched or branched from the base; leaf blades 1 to 3 inches long, mostly ovate, the margins toothed, the petiole about as long as the blade or shorter; flowers in small, headlike clusters in axillary or terminal panicles.

WINTERFAT (*Eurotia lanata*). A shrub from a few inches to 3 feet high, densely white-woolly, usually only the lower part woody but the branches stout; leaves linear or narrowly lanceolate, 1½ inches long or less, the margins entire or often rolled; flowers imperfect, in axillary and terminal clusters.

RUSSIAN-THISTLE (*Salsola kali* var. *tenuifolia*). Very bushy, 1 to 2 feet high; leaves 1 to 2 inches long, narrowly linear, entire, sharp-pointed. After maturity the plant becomes hard and spiny and, breaking off at the surface of the soil, becomes a tumbleweed.

AMARANTH FAMILY (AMARANTHACEAE)

Mostly weedy plants with simple, entire leaves without stipules; flowers small, mostly imperfect; fruit an akene with a loose outer coat.

1. Male and female flowers on separate plants.

   Male and female flowers mostly on the same plant. 2.

2. Leaves linear or nearly so.

   Leaves broader. 3.

3. Stems mostly prostrate and purplish.

   Stems erect or nearly so. 4.

4. Plants smooth or nearly so throughout.

   Plant more or less hairy, at least on the upper part. 5.

5. Spikes stout, often ½ inch thick or more.

   Spikes slender, often less than ¼ inch thick.

AMARANTH (*Amaranthus fimbriatus*). Stems 4 to 20 inches tall, unbranched or branched above, smooth or nearly so, leaf blades linear or nearly so, mostly

1 to 2 inches long, the petioles less than 1 inch long; flowers in loose clusters, these scattered or in loose spikes.

TUMBLEWEED AMARANTH *(Amaranthus graecizans).* Stems 1 to 2 feet long, stout, prostrate, smooth or nearly so; leaf blades oval or obovate, mostly 1 inch long or less, the petioles shorter, often crowded and larger toward the ends of the branches; flowers in small, axillary clusters.

SLIM AMARANTH *(Amaranthus hybridus).* Stems 1 to 5 feet tall, stout, more or less hairy; leaf blades ovate to lanceolate, 1 to 5 inches long on somewhat shorter petioles; flowers in rather slender spikes, these axillary and in terminal panicles.

PALMER AMARANTH *(Amaranthus palmeri).* Stems 1 to 2 feet tall, stout, smooth or nearly so; leaf blades 2 inches long or less, broadly ovate to lanceolate, the petioles often somewhat longer; flowers in terminal spikes that may be 1 foot long or less.

POWELL AMARANTH *(Amaranthus powellii).* This and the following species are very similar to the slim amaranth and are often difficult to distinguish from it and from each other. Stems mostly 2 to 30 inches tall, smooth; leaf blades 1 inch long or more, the petioles slender; flowers in stiff spikes, these axillary and in a terminal panicle.

REDROOT AMARANTH *(Amaranthus retroflexus).* Stems 1 to 5 feet tall, often quite hairy in the upper part; leaf blades ovate, 1 to 4 inches long, the petioles slender, 3 inches long or less; flowers in densely crowded spikes, these in panicles or sometimes axillary.

FOUR-O'CLOCK FAMILY (NYCTAGINACEAE)

Herbaceous plants with opposite leaves; flowers subtended by bracts that sometimes form a calyxlike involucre; calyx colored like a corolla; corolla lacking. The calyx tube usually encloses the ovary so closely that the ovary appears to be inferior although it actually is superior.

1. Flowers within a calyxlike involucre. 2.
   Flowers not within a calyxlike involucre. 8.

2. Bracts of the involucre not united; flowers in umbellike heads. 3.
   Bracts of the involucre united; flowers not in umbellike heads. 4.

3. Leaves mostly basal; flowers white, sometimes pink.
   SAND-VERBENA *(Abronia nana)* 85
   Leaves not mostly basal; flowers purplish-red.
   SAND-VERBENA *(Abronia pumila)* 85

4. Fruit strongly flattened.

TRAILING ALLIONIA (*Allionia incarnata*) 85
Fruit not strongly flattened. 5.

5. Fruit not strongly 5-angled; involucre in fruit not enlarged. 6.
Fruit strongly 5-angled; involucre in fruit enlarged, thin,
conspicuously veined; flowers pink or purple. 7.

6. Calyx 1 to 2 inches long, purple.

COLORADO FOUR-O'CLOCK (*Mirabilis multiflora*) 86
Calyx about ½ inch long or less, pale pink.

WISHBONE BUSH (*Mirabilis bigelovii*) 86

7. Leaf blades scarcely longer than broad, the petioles evident.

OXYBAPHUS (*Oxybaphus pumilus*) 86
Leaf blades 5 or more times as long as broad, the petioles
short or almost none.

OXYBAPHUS (*Oxybaphus linearis*) 86

8. Calyx about 1 inch long or more.

ANULOCAULIS (*Anulocaulis leisolenus*) 86
Calyx less than ½ inch long. 9.

9. Bracts more than ½ as long as the fruits, persistent;
fruits usually 4-angled.

SPIDERLING (*Boerhaavia wrightii*) 86
Bracts much less than ½ as long as the fruits, soon
falling; fruits 5-angled. 10.

10. Fruits with narrow, longitudinal ridges and broad, open,
conspicuously rough furrows.

SPIDERLING (*Boerhaavia torreyana*) 86
Fruits with broad ridges and narrow, nearly closed,
smooth furrows.

SPIDERLING (*Boerhaavia coulteri*) 86

SAND-VERBENA (*Abronia nana*). Stems densely clustered, 3 to 6 inches
tall, leaves mostly basal, the blades oval, about ½ inch long, the petioles longer
than the blades; flowers about ½ inch long, white to pink.

SAND-VERBENA (*Abronia pumila*). Stems not densely clustered, prostrate
or nearly so, usually about 1 foot long or more; leaves opposite, one of each
pair usually larger than the other, the blades broadly lanceolate, the petioles
often shorter or as long as the blades; flowers about 1/3 inch long, purplish-red.

TRAILING ALLIONIA (*Allionia incarnata*). Stems 4 to 20 inches long, prostrate, densely short-hairy and often sticky; leaf blades ovate to oblong, somewhat rounded at the 1-sided base, petioled; flowers purplish-red, less than ¼
inch long, in clusters of 3 in the leaf axils.

ANULOCAULIS *(Anulocaulis leisolenus).* Stems 16 inches tall or more; leaves mostly basal, the blades broadly ovate to nearly round, the largest 6 inches long and broad, leathery, petioled; flowers about 1 inch long, the filaments of the stamens purple.

SPIDERLING *(Boerhaavia coulteri).* Stems erect or nearly so, 1 foot high or less, branched, somewhat hairy but usually not sticky; leaves elliptical to lanceolate, 1 inch long or less, somewhat hairy beneath; flowers very small, pink, in short, loose spikes.

SPIDERLING *(Boerhaavia torreyana).* Very similar to the preceding and often difficult to distinguish from it but the stems are usually quite sticky and often partly prostrate.

SPIDERLING *(Boerhaavia wrightii).* Stems erect or nearly so, often more than 1 foot tall, the lower part short-hairy and very sticky, the upper part smooth; leaves mostly from ½ to 1½ inches long, usually short-hairy and sticky, the petioles nearly as long as the blades; flowers similar to the 2 preceding species but the subtending bracts almost always present.

WISHBONE BUSH *(Mirabilis bigelovii).* Stems slender, 12 to 20 inches tall, much-branched, soft-hairy and sticky; leaf blades mostly about 1 inch long, ovate, the petioles shorter; involucre clusters at the ends of the branches; calyx white to pale pink.

COLORADO FOUR-O'CLOCK *(Mirabilis multiflora).* Stems 1 to 3 feet long, stout, erect or partly prostrate, forming clumps, very leafy; leaf blades 1 to 3 inches long, ovate or oblong, the petioles much shorter; involucres solitary in the leaf axils and in a terminal cluster; flowers usually 6 to 8 in each involucre, very showy, the purplish calyx up to 2 inches long or more.

OXYBAPHUS *(Oxybaphus linearis).* Stems 8 to 24 inches tall, erect or nearly so; leaf blades narrowly lanceolate, short-petioled; flowers purple, numerous, usually 3 in each involucre.

OXYBAPHUS *(Oxybaphus pumilus).* Stems few to many from a woody root, partly prostrate, 4 to 20 inches long, short-hairy throughout; leaf blades nearly triangular, 1 to 2 inches long, somewhat fleshy, short-hairy, the petioles less than 1 inch long; involucres axillary or in small, terminal clusters, hairy and sticky; calyx pale pink, hairy, less than ½ inch long.

CARPETWEED FAMILY (AIZOACEAE)

Low, often fleshy herbs with erect or prostrate stems, opposite leaves, and perfect, axillary, inconspicuous flowers.

HORSE-PURSLANE *(Trianthema portulacastrum).* Stems prostrate, smooth, branching from the base, 4 to 12 inches long; leaf blades broadly obovate to nearly round, those of opposite pairs very unequal in size, the largest nearly 1 inch long, the petioles nearly as long as the blades; flowers usually solitary and sessile in the leaf axils; calyx purplish within; corolla none.

PORTULACA FAMILY (PORTULACACEAE)

Mostly small, herbaceous, often somewhat fleshy, with simple entire leaves and perfect, regular flowers; except in bitterroot there are usually 2 sepals and 5 petals; the fruit is a capsule.

1. Sepals usually 6 to 8; petals 12 or more.
   BITTERROOT *(Lewisia rediviva)* 87
   Sepals 2; petals mostly 5. 2.

2. Sepals united below, attached to the lower part of the ovary.
   PURSLANE *(Portulaca oleracea)* 88
   Sepals distinct. 3.

3. Stem leaves several pairs.
   INDIAN-LETTUCE *(Montia chamissoi)* 87
   Stem leaves 1 pair. 4.

4. Stem leaves with bases united around the stem forming a nearly circular disk.
   MINERS-LETTUCE *(Montia perfoliata)* 88
   Bases of stem leaves not united around the stem. 5.

5. Basal leaves several; flowers white to pink.
   LEWISIA *(Lewisia pygmaea)* 87
   Basal leaves none; flowers pale pink.
   SPRING BEAUTY *(Claytonia rosea)* 87

SPRING BEAUTY *(Claytonia rosea)*. Stems 2 to 8 inches tall, 1 to several from a bulblike underground stem; basal leaves often lacking; stem leaves 1 to 2 inches long or more, linear to lanceolate, sessile; flowers white to pink, the petals between ¼ and ½ inch long.

LEWISIA *(Lewisia pygmaea)*. Flowering stems ½ to 2 inches tall with 1 pair of reduced leaves below the middle; basal leaves 1 to 2 inches long, linear; flowers solitary at the end of each stem; petals about 1/3 inch long, pink or white.

BITTERROOT *(Lewisia rediviva)*. Flowering stems 1 inch high or less, several from a thick, fleshy root; basal leaves numerous, 2 inches long or less, very fleshy, linear or almost cylindric; flowers solitary on each stem, showy; sepals 4 to 8, ½ to 1 inch long; petals 12 to 18, about 1 inch long, pink or nearly white; stamens numerous; styles 5 to 8.

INDIAN-LETTUCE *(Montia chamissoi)*. Plants of wet places with creeping or floating stems that root at the nodes and upright branches, usually 2 to 6 inches tall, that bear the flowers; leaves opposite, mostly oblanceolate, ½ to 2 inches long, sessile or nearly so; flowers in axillary or terminal racemes with about 3 to 8 flowers; petals about ¼ inch long, pink or white.

MINERS-LETTUCE *(Montia perfoliata)*. Stems more or less fleshy, erect or spreading, 2 to 12 inches long; basal leaves several, petioled, the blades lanceolate, ½ to 3 inches long; stem leaves 2, united to form a circular disk which subtends the flower cluster; flowers pink or white in a terminal raceme; petals about ⅛ inch long.

PURSLANE *(Portulaca oleracea)*. Fleshy herbs with prostrate stems 4 to 8 inches long; leaves alternate, 1 inch long or less, tending to be clustered near the ends of the branches; flowers solitary or in small clusters in the leaf axils, yellow.

PINK FAMILY (CARYOPHYLLACEAE)

Herbaceous plants with opposite, simple leaves and perfect, regular flowers. The fruit is a capsule.

1. Sepals united for most of their length; flowers white or
   tinged purple; petals 5, often with appendages at the
   base of the blade; stamens 10.   2.
   Sepals distinct or nearly so.   6.

2. Petals entire or nearly so; stem with 1 or more sticky bands.
   SLEEPY CATCHFLY *(Silene antirrhina)* 90
   Petals deeply cleft or at least 2-lobed.   3.

3. Plant annual, more or less sticky and densely hairy throughout.
   NIGHT-FLOWERING CATCHFLY *(Silene noctiflora)* 90
   Plants perennial, more or less sticky and hairy on the
   upper part.   4.

4. Petals deeply 2-lobed.
   SCOULER CATCHFLY *(Silene scouleri* subsp. *pringlei)* 90
   Petals shallowly 2-lobed.   5.

5. Flowers axillary, the flower cluster appearing very leafy.
   MENZIES CATCHFLY *(Silene menziesii)* 90
   Flowers in a terminal raceme that does not appear leafy.
   CATCHFLY *(Silene rectiramea)* 92

6. Styles usually 5.   7.
   Styles usually 3.   8.

7. Petals entire.
   PEARLWORT *(Sagina saginoides)* 90
   Petals 2-lobed.
   MOUSE-EAR CHICKWEED *(Cerastium arvense)* 90

8. Petals entire.   9.

Petals 2-lobed. 13.

9. Leaves lanceolate or broader, not rigid.

SANDWORT (*Arenaria lanuginosa* subsp. *saxosa*) 90
Leaves linear or awl-shaped, more or less rigid and
sharp-pointed. 10.

10. Sepals rounded or blunt-pointed at the tip.

SANDWORT (*Arenaria aberrans*) 89
Sepals sharp-pointed. 11.

11. Petals conspicuously longer than the sepals.

SANDWORT (*Arenaria macradenia*) 90
Petals not conspicuously longer, often shorter, than
the sepals. 12.

12. Plants bluish-green; leaves only moderately rigid and
sharply pointed.

FENDLER SANDWORT (*Arenaria fendleri*) 89
Plants light green or yellowish; leaves very rigid and
sharply pointed.

SANDWORT (*Arenaria eastwoodiae*) 89

13. Petals none or rudimentary; leaves all sessile or nearly so.

STARWORT (*Stellaria umbellata*) 92
Petals present. 14.

14. Leaves all sessile; plant glandular-hairy at least above.

TUBER STARWORT (*Stellaria jamesiana*) 92
At least the lowest leaves petioled; plants usually not
glandular. 15.

15. Leaves all petioled; flowers axillary on long stalks.

CHICKWEED (*Stellaria media*) 92
Upper leaves sessile; flowers in terminal clusters.

STARWORT (*Stellaria nitens*) 92

SANDWORT (*Arenaria aberrans*). Stems mostly 2 to 5 inches tall, several
from the base; leaves mostly basal, awl-shaped, about ½ inch long, the 1 or 2
pairs on the stem much smaller; flowers in a terminal, open cluster; petals 5,
white, longer than the sepals; stamens 12; styles 3.

SANDWORT (*Arenaria eastwoodiae*). Stems 4 to 8 inches tall, several from
a somewhat woody base; leaves almost needlelike, less than 1 inch long, sharp-
pointed; flowers in an open terminal cluster; petals white, about as long as the
sepals; stamens 10; styles 3.

FENDLER SANDWORT (*Arenaria fendleri*). Stems mostly 4 to 12 inches tall,
usually bluish-green, slender, somewhat glandular-hairy, especially above; leaves
1 to 3 inches long, almost hairlike; flowers in an open, terminal cluster; petals

white, about as long as the sepals; stamens 10; styles 3.

SANDWORT *(Arenaria lanuginosa* subsp. *saxosa).* Stems from a few inches to 2 feet tall; leaves narrowly lanceolate to oblong, less than 1 inch long, not rigid; flowers in an open panicle; petals 5, white, about as long as the sepals; stamens 10; styles 3.

SANDWORT *(Arenaria macradenia).* Stems mostly 8 to 16 inches tall, several from a somewhat woody base; leaves awl-shaped, rather stout, the basal ones 1 to 2 inches long, those on the stem much smaller; flowers in an open cluster; petals white, conspicuously longer than the sepals; stamens 10; styles 3.

MOUSE-EAR CHICKWEED *(Cerastium arvense).* A very variable species; stems 4 to 12 inches tall, simple or branched, with or without glands, smooth to densely soft-hairy; leaves 1½ inches long, narrowly oblong to linear; flowers in a loose cluster, rather few; sepals ⅛ to ¼ inch long; petals about twice as long as the sepals, 2-lobed; stamens about 10; styles 5.

PEARLWORT *(Sagina saginoides).* Stems 1 to 4 inches tall, partly prostrate and often rooting at the nodes, forming mats; leaves very narrowly linear, ½ inch long or less; flowers very small, axillary on slender stalks; sepals, petals, stamens and styles 5 each, the petals white and a little shorter than the sepals.

SLEEPY CATCHFLY *(Silene antirrhina).* Stems 4 to 30 inches tall, usually not much-branched; leaves 1 to 2½ inches long, linear or lanceolate, the lower ones narrowed to a petiole, the upper gradually reduced to bracts; flowers in an open panicle; sepals about ¼ inch long; petals white or rose-tipped, usually longer than the sepals, 2-lobed at the tip; styles 3.

MENZIES CATCHFLY *(Silene menziesii).* Stems several, 4 to 12 inches tall, glandular-hairy and repeatedly forked above; leaves numerous, narrowly lanceolate to obovate, 1 to 2 inches long; flowers in the axils of the upper leaves or terminal; calyx about ¼ inch long; petals a little longer, white, 2-lobed; styles 3.

NIGHT-FLOWERING CATCHFLY *(Silene noctiflora).* Stems 1 to 3 feet tall, stout, hairy and sticky toward the top; leaves obovate to lanceolate, 1½ to 4 inches long, the lower ones narrowed to a broad petiole, the upper ones sessile; flowers rather few in a loose panicle; calyx ½ to 1 inch long, conspicuously 10-nerved, cylindric at first, becoming enlarged in fruit; petals longer than the calyx, white or pink, 2-lobed and with toothed appendages at the base of the blade.

SCOULER CATCHFLY *(Silene scouleri* subsp. *pringlei).* Stems 8 to 16 inches tall, not much-branched; stem leaves 3 to 5 pairs, 1 to 3 inches long, linear, the basal leaves a little longer and narrowed to a petiole; flowers conspicuously stalked in a few-flowered panicle; petals white to purplish, usually a little longer than the sepals.

NEW MEXICO LOCUST
(Robinia neomexicana)

PHOTO MERKLE

CRANESBILL
(Geranium caespitosum)

PHOTO MERKLE

BLUE FLAX
(Linum lewisii)

PHOTO MERKLE

HOPTREE
(Ptelea pallida)

PHOTO HAMILTON

Families Of Plants 91

CATCHFLY *(Silene rectiramea).* Apparently a very rare species. Not known to occur anywhere except on the South Rim of Grand Canyon. It has been collected only a few times. The calyx is quite papery and the petals are very shallowly 2-lobed.

TUBER STARWORT *(Stellaria jamesiana).* Stems 8 to 20 inches tall, sharply angled, often much-branched, more or less glandular-hairy, leaves lanceolate, 2 to 4 inches long, sessile; flowers in loose, terminal and axillary clusters; petals about ¼ inch long, white; stamens 10; styles 3.

CHICKWEED *(Stellaria media).* Stems 4 to 16 inches long, partly prostrate, much-branched, smooth except for lines of hairs; leaf blades ovate or oval, 1½ inches long or less, the upper ones sessile, the others petioled; flowers small, in terminal or axillary leafy clusters; petals 2-cleft nearly to the base, shorter than the sepals.

STARWORT *(Stellaria nitens).* Stems 4 to 8 inches tall, very slender, several times forked; leaves mostly basal or near the base, linear to lanceolate or oval, about ¼ inch long or less, the basal ones petioled; flowers few, very small; petals ½ as long as the sepals or lacking entirely.

STARWORT *(Stellaria umbellata).* Stems 4 to 16 inches long, usually branched, often partly prostrate; flowers on slender stalks in the leaf axils or in open, terminal clusters; petals lacking or very small.

CROWFOOT FAMILY (RANUNCULACEAE)

A large and very variable family of mostly herbs, often with very showy flowers, the stamens and pistils often numerous.

1. Flowers irregular, mostly blue or bluish. 2.
   Flowers regular. 5.

2. Upper sepal expanded into a helmet-shaped hood.
   MONKSHOOD *(Aconitum columbianum)* 94
   Upper sepal extended into a conspicuous spur. 3.

3. Leaves mostly basal.
   BARESTEM LARKSPUR *(Delphinium scaposum)* 95
   Leaves not mostly basal. 4.

4. Flowers dark blue but the upper petals mostly white;
   plants of pine forests.
   NELSON LARKSPUR *(Delphinium nelsoni)* 95
   Flowers light blue, the upper petals pale but not white;
   plants of canyons and deserts.
   LOVELY LARKSPUR *(Delphinium amabile)* 95

5. Petals present and often showy. 6.
   Petals none or very small and inconspicuous. 13.

6. Petals with a long, slender spur at the base. 7.
   Petals not spurred. 9.

7. Flowers nodding; spurs and sepals red; spurs less than
   1 inch long.
   COLUMBINE *(Aquilegia triternata)* 94
   Flowers upright; spurs and sepals not red; spurs more
   than 1 inch long. 8.

8. Spurs and sepals blue to white.
   COLORADO COLUMBINE *(Aquilegia caerulea)* 94
   Spurs and sepals yellow.
   GOLDEN COLUMBINE *(Aquilegia chrysantha)* 94

9. Leaves entire. 10.
   Leaves scalloped, lobed or divided. 11.

10. Petals, receptacle and akenes somewhat hairy.
    BLISTER BUTTERCUP *(Ranunculus oreogenes)* 95
    Petals, receptacle and akenes smooth.
    SPEARWORT BUTTERCUP *(Ranunculus flammula)* 95

11. Nectary scale on petals not forming a pocket, its sides
    free for at least 2/3 of its length.
    BUTTERCUP *(Ranunculus uncinatus)* 95
    Nectary scale on petals forming a pocket, its sides
    attached nearly the entire length. 12.

12. Nectary scale and petal smooth.
    BUTTERCUP *(Ranunculus inamoenus)* 95
    Nectary scale and petal more or less hairy.
    BUTTERCUP *(Ranunculus cardiophyllus)* 95

13. Ovaries maturing into several-seeded pods.
    MARSH-MARIGOLD *(Caltha leptosepala)* 94
    Ovaries maturing into akenes. 14.

14. Sepals with a short spur at the base; receptacle becoming
    long and spikelike in fruit.
    MOUSETAIL *(Myosurus minimus)* 95
    Sepals not spurred at the base; receptacle not
    spikelike in fruit. 15.

15. Sepals small, less conspicuous than the stamens and
    pistils; flowers imperfect, the male and female flowers
    on separate plants.
    MEADOWRUE *(Thalictrum fendleri)* 96
    Sepals large and showy, petallike. 16.

16. Sepals 5 or more; akenes without long tails.

ANEMONE *(Anemone tuberosa)* 94

Sepals usually 4; akenes with long feathery tails. 17.

17, Stems climbing; flowers imperfect, numerous, white.

VIRGINS BOWER *(Clematis ligusticifolia)* 94

Stems not climbing; flowers solitary, perfect, purplish.

CLEMATIS *(Clematis hirsutissima)* 94

MONKSHOOD *(Aconitum columbianum)*. Stems 3 to 6 feet tall, stout, smooth below, somewhat hairy above; leaf blades palmately cleft into 3 to 5 divisions, these lobed and toothed; flowers in a loose, terminal raceme; sepals 5, purple or sometimes almost white, hooded; petals small, concealed within the hoods; stamens numerous; pistils 3 to 5; fruit a several-seeded pod.

ANEMONE *(Anemone tuberosa)*. Stems 4 to 12 inches high; leaves mostly basal with only 1 pair on the stem, 1 to 2 inches wide, divided into 3 parts with each part lobed or toothed; flowers solitary or few, about 1 inch across; sepals about 8 or 10, purple to nearly white; petals none; fruiting head cylindric, about 1 inch long; akenes densely woolly.

COLORADO COLUMBINE *(Aquilegia caerulea)*. Stems 8 to 30 inches tall; leaves mostly basal, 2 or 3 times palmately compound, the leaflets deeply lobed; flowers large, 1 to 3 inches long and about as wide; sepals deep blue, petals white; spurs 1 to 2 inches long, mostly blue.

GOLDEN COLUMBINE *(Aquilegia chrysantha)*. Leaves 1 to 3 times compound, the leaflets often hairy below; flowers 2 to 3 inches long, golden yellow throughout; spurs 1½ to 3 inches long, very slender.

COLUMBINE *(Aquilegia triternata)*. Stems 8 to 24 inches tall, slender, usually several from the same base; basal leaves mostly long-petioled and 3 times compound; leaflets rather small; stem leaves few and much smaller; flowers about 1½ inches long; sepals light red; petals mostly yellow; spurs about 1 inch long or less, pale red, stout.

MARSH-MARIGOLD *(Caltha leptosepala)*. Stems 3 to 12 inches tall; leaves all basal, the blades ovate to nearly round, up to 3 inches long, somewhat heart-shaped at the base, scalloped or nearly entire; flowers usually solitary, 1 inch across or less, whitish.

CLEMATIS *(Clematis hirsutissima)*. Stems 8 to 30 inches tall; leaves pinnately compound with 7 to 13 leaflets, these dissected into narrow divisions; flowers solitary, terminal, 1 to 1½ inches long; sepals somewhat spreading at the tip, smooth and deep purple on the inner side, densely hairy on the outside, thick; akenes hairy, with tails about 2 inches long.

VIRGINS BOWER *(Clematis ligusticifolia)*. Stems climbing, often 12 to 18 feet long; leaves pinnately compound with 5 to 7 leaflets, these lanceolate to ovate and variously toothed or lobed or nearly entire; flowers imperfect, the male and female flowers usually on separate plants; stamens and pistils numerous; akenes with long, feathery tails.

LOVELY LARKSPUR *(Delphinium amabile).* Stems 6 to 24 inches tall, 1 or several from the same base; leaves mostly basal or on the lower part of the stem, often withered at the time of flowering, the blades 1 to 3 inches wide, dissected into narrow divisions; flowers in a 5- to 25-flowered raceme; sepals lavender to blue; spur less than ½ inch long; upper petals whitish, the lower ones bluish or violet.

NELSON LARKSPUR *(Delphinium nelsoni).* Stems 8 to 20 inches tall, easily separating from the root; leaves few, the blades nearly round, palmately 3-lobed and the lobes dissected into narrow divisions; raceme 6- to 10-flowered; sepals and lower petals purple; upper petals nearly white; spur about ½ inch long, slender, nearly straight.

BARESTEM LARKSPUR *(Delphinium scaposum).* Stems 8 to 20 inches tall, smooth, unbranched; leaves all basal or nearly so, the blades palmately 3- to 7-lobed nearly to the base; flowers usually 5 to 10 in an open raceme; sepals and lower petals blue, upper petals whitish; spur much longer than the sepals.

MOUSETAIL *(Myosurus minimus).* Flowering stems 1 to 6 inches tall; leaves all basal, linear to almost hairlike, 1 to 3 inches long; flowers solitary at the ends of the stem, small and inconspicuous; akenes in a slender spike.

BUTTERCUP *(Ranunculus cardiophyllus).* Stems 6 to 16 inches tall, more or less hairy; basal leaves narrowly heart-shaped with scalloped margins, those on the stem divided into linear lobes; flowers few or several, ½ inch or more across, the petals longer than the sepals; akenes many in an oblong or cylindrical head.

SPEARWORT BUTTERCUP *(Ranunculus flammula).* Leaves mostly less than 2 inches long and less than ¼ inch wide, entire; flowers nearly ½ inch across, the petals longer than the sepals; akenes 10 to 25 in a spherical head.

BUTTERCUP *(Ranunculus inamoenus).* Stems 4 to 12 inches tall; leaves very variable, the blades ovate to nearly round, usually about 1 inch long, entire, scalloped or 3-lobed, sessile to long-petioled; flowers ¼ to ½ inch across, the petals a little longer than the sepals; akenes many in a cylindrical head.

BLISTER BUTTERCUP *(Ranunculus oreogenes).* Stems 2 to 6 inches tall; leaves narrowly oblong to nearly linear, petioled, 1 to 4 inches long, entire; flowers ½ to nearly 1 inch across; akenes numerous in an oblong or nearly spherical head.

BUTTERCUP *(Ranunculus uncinatus).* Stems 8 to 20 inches tall, more or less hairy; basal leaf blades more or less heart-shaped in outline, 1 to 3 inches broad, 3-parted, the divisions lobed, petioled, those on the stem similar but smaller; flowers small, ¼ inch across or less; akenes numerous in a spherical head.

MEADOWRUE *(Thalictrum fendleri).* Stems 1 to 2 feet tall; leaves 3 or 4 times compound, the leaflets about as wide as long, 3-lobed, the lobes more or less scalloped; flowers green and inconspicuous, imperfect, the male and female flowers on separate plants.

BARBERRY FAMILY (BERBERIDACEAE)

A small family of shrubs with compound leaves, the leaflets thick, evergreen, prickly; flowers perfect, regular, yellow; sepals, petals and stamens 6; fruit a few-seeded berry.

FREMONT MAHONIA *(Berberis fremontii).* A shrub 3 to 9 feet tall with rigid branches; leaves pinnately compound with 3 to 7 leaflets, these ½ to 1 inch long or more with about 3 large, spiny teeth on each side, the terminal leaflet seldom more than twice as long as wide; berries blue and dry at maturity.

RED MAHONIA *(Berberis haematocarpa).* Very similar to the preceding but the terminal leaflet may be as much as 5 times as long as wide and the berries are red and juicy.

CREEPING MAHONIA *(Berberis repens).* A low, evergreen shrub; stems very short or up to 10 inches long; leaves pinnately compound with 3 to 7 leaflets, these with 5 or more teeth on each side; flowers in rather dense racemes; berries blue to nearly black.

POPPY FAMILY (PAPAVERACEAE)

Herbaceous plants with very diverse characters, mostly with attractive flowers.

PRICKLY-POPPY *(Argemone arizonica).* Stems 1 foot long or more, much-branched, often partly prostrate, copiously long-prickly; leaves lobed nearly to the midrib, the lobes narrow and rather far apart, prickly on the primary and secondary veins but not between the veins; flowers large, white; sepals usually 3, each with a hornlike appendage which is not prickly; juice pale lemon-yellow. Known only from the rocky slopes on the north and south walls of Grand Canyon.

PRICKLY-POPPY *(Argemone munita* subsp. *rotundata,* formerly called *A. platyceras).* Similar to the preceding but the stems erect, the leaves lobed only about halfway to the midrib with broader lobes and prickly between the veins as well as on them, and the horns of the sepals usually prickly; juice yellow.

GOLDEN CORYDALIS *(Corydalis aurea).* Stems 4 to 16 inches tall, profusely branched; leaves twice pinnate, the leaflets lobed; juice yellow; flowers small, numerous, irregular, yellow; corolla with a short spur at the base.

MUSTARD FAMILY (CRUCIFERAE)

The flowers of this family usually have 4 sepals, 4 petals arranged in the form of a cross, 6 stamens with 2 shorter than the other 4, and 1 pistil which matures into a pod. In many cases it is necessary to have mature pods as well as flowers in order to identify a species with certainty.

1. Fruits 1-seeded, not opening at maturity; flowers very
   small and inconspicuous. 2.
   Fruits with 2 or more seeds, opening at maturity. 3.

2. Fruits with winged margins, not bearing hooked hairs.
   FRINGE POD (*Thysanocarpus laciniatus*) 106
   Fruits without wings, bearing more or less hooked hairs.
   ATHYSANUS (*Athysanus pusillus*) 101

3. Fruits flattened at right angles to the partition. 4.
   Fruits not flattened, or flattened parallel to the partition. 11.

4. Fruits 2-lobed. 5.
   TWINPOD (*Physaria chambersii*) 104
   Fruits not 2-lobed. 7.

5. Fruits with 2 or more seeds in each cell. 6.
   Fruits with a single seed in each of the 2 cells. 7.

6. Plants low; pods oval; lower leaves entire or merely toothed.
   PENNYCRESS or **WILD-CANDYTUFT** (*Thlaspi fendleri*) 106
   Plants taller; pods triangular; lower leaves usually lobed.
   SHEPHERDS PURSE (*Capsella bursa-pastoris*) 101

7. Upper leaves broadly ovate or nearly round, entire, the
   bases closely clasping the stem; lower leaves finely dissected.
   CLASPING PEPPERWEED (*Lepidium perfoliatum*) 103
   None of the leaves clasping the stem. 8.

8. Petals much longer than the sepals. 9.
   Petals well-developed but not much, if any, longer
   than the sepals.
   PEPPERWEED (*Lepidium medium*) 103
   Petals minute or lacking, never as long as the sepals. 10.

9. Stems of mature plants woody well above the base.
   DESERT PEPPERWEED (*Lepidium fremontii*) 103
   Stems not woody or only slightly so at the base.
   MOUNTAIN PEPPERWEED (*Lepidium montanum*) 103

10. Stems branched from the base, spreading, seldom erect,
    hairy with stiff, spreading hairs.
    HAIRYPOD PEPPERWEED (*Lepidium lasiocarpum*) 103

Stems erect, not branched from the base, soft-hairy or nearly smooth.
PRAIRIE PEPPERWEED *(Lepidium densiflorum)* 103

11. Fruits not more than twice as long as wide. 12.
Fruits more than twice as long as wide. 16.

12. Fruits with a distinct central nerve on each half.
FALSE-FLAX *(Camelina microcarpa)* 101
Fruits without a distinct central nerve on each half or the nerves not extending to the apex. 13.

13. Seeds plump; stems and leaves not hairy; plants of wet places.
RORIPPA *(Rorippa sphaerocarpa)* 104
Seeds flat; stems and leaves densely hairy with branched hairs; plants of dry places. 14.

14. Petals white or purplish.
BLADDERPOD *(Lesquerella purpurea)* 104
Petals yellow. 15.

15. Basal leaves mostly more than 1 inch long, usually rolled.
BLADDERPOD *(Lesquerella intermedia)* 104
Basal leaves 1 inch long or less, usually flat.
BLADDERPOD *(Lesquerella arizonica)* 103

16. Fruit long-stalked within the calyx, often ½ inch long or more.
DESERT PRINCES-PLUME *(Stanleya pinnata)* 104
Fruit sessile or very short-stalked within the calyx. 17.

17. Calyx closed or nearly so when the flower is in bloom, the sepals spreading, if at all, only at the tip. 18.
Calyx open when the flower is in bloom, the sepals more or less spreading. 25.

18. Petal blades flat or nearly so, the basal portion much narrower than the blade. 19.
Petal blades not flat, either crisped, channeled or hood-shaped, little if any wider than the basal portion. 21.

19. Flowers purple or pink.
SISYMBRIUM *(Sisymbrium linearifolium)* 104
Flowers yellow or whitish. 20.

20. Petals about ⅛ inch long; fruits 1 to 2 inches long.
DESERT MUSTARD *(Sisymbrium irio)* 104
Petals about ¼ inch long; mature fruits more than 2 inches long.

TUMBLE MUSTARD *(Sisymbrium altissimum)* 104

21. Fruits strongly flattened parallel to the partition. 22.
Fruits not flattened or only slightly so. 23.

22. Fruits erect or nearly so; stem leaves clasping at the base.
TWISTFLOWER *(Streptanthus cordatus)* 106
Fruits hanging downward; stem leaves not clasping.
STREPTANTHELLA *(Streptanthella longirostris)* 106

23. Petals purple to brown; most of the stem leaves petioled.
WILD-CABBAGE *(Caulanthus crassicaulis)* 102
Petals white to purplish-pink; stem leaves sessile. 24.

24. Sepals erect or nearly so at blooming time.
THELYPODY *(Thelypodium integrifolium)* 106
Sepals spreading or turned downward at blooming time.
THELYPODY *(Thelypodium wrightii)* 106

25. Fruits strongly flattened parallel to the partition. 26.
Fruits not flattened or only slightly so. 33.

26. Fruits less than ½ inch long, often twisted. 27.
Fruits more than ½ inch long, not twisted. 29.

27. Leaves all basal; flowers yellow.
DRABA *(Draba asprella)* 102
Leaves not all basal. 28.

28. Flowers yellow, often fading to whitish; usually found
above 6000 feet.
DRABA *(Draba rectifructa)* 102
Flowers white; usually found below 6000 feet.
DRABA *(Draba cuneifolia)* 102

29. Flowers white; fruits erect, crowded.
DRUMMOND ROCKCRESS *(Arabis drummondii)* 101
Flowers purple or pink; fruits spreading or hanging
downward. 30.

30. Fruits finely hairy; petals more than ½ inch long.
ROCKCRESS *(Arabis pulchra)* 101
Fruits not hairy. 31.

31. Stems stout, with 30 or more leaves, densely leafy below.
ROCKCRESS *(Arabis gracilipes)* 101
Stems slender, with 15 or fewer leaves, not densely
leafy below. 32.

32. Stems usually branched from the base; hairs on lower
stems and leaves branched, not bristlelike.

ROCKCRESS *(Arabis perennans)* 101
Stems usually not, or not much, branched from the base;
hairs on lower stems and leaves unbranched or merely
forked, bristlelike.

ROCKCRESS *(Arabis fendleri)* 101

33. Fruits erect or nearly so. 34.
Fruits more or less spreading, sometimes even turned
downward. 35.

34. Petals less than ¼ inch long, yellowish-white.

TOWER-MUSTARD *(Arabis glabra)* 101
Petals more than ¼ inch long, yellow or orange.

WESTERN WALLFLOWER *(Erysimum capitatum)* 103

35. Plants with forked or star-shaped hairs. 36.
Plants with unbranched hairs or none. 41.

36. Plants with entire or shallowly lobed leaves.

ERYSIMUM *(Erysimum repandum)* 103
Plants with pinnate or deeply lobed leaves. 37.

37. Upper as well as lower leaves 2 or 3 times pinnate;
fruits 1 to 2 inches long.

TANSY-MUSTARD *(Descurainia sophia)* 102
Upper leaves once pinnate; fruits less than ½ inch long. 38.

38. Seeds in 2 rows in the fruit. 39.
Seeds in 4 rows in the fruit. 40.

39. Fruits ¼ to ½ inch long; seeds more than 7.

TANSY-MUSTARD *(Descurainia richardsonii)* 102
Fruits less than ¼ inch long; seeds fewer than 7.

TANSY-MUSTARD *(Descurainia californica)* 102

40. Fruits linear; seeds 40 to 60.

TANSY-MUSTARD *(Descurainia obtusa)* 102
Fruits more or less club-shaped; seeds 12 to 20.

TANSY-MUSTARD *(Descurainia pinnata)* 102

41. Petals clear white; leaves pinnate; plants usually growing
in water.

WATERCRESS *(Rorippa nasturtium-aquaticum)* 104
Petals yellow or yellowish-white; leaves pinnately lobed;
plants usually growing in moist soil. 42.

42. Stigma 2-lobed; leaves with many lobes.

FIELDCRESS *(Rorippa obtusa)* 104
Stigma not lobed; leaves with few lobes.

DRUMMOND ROCKCRESS *(Arabis drummondii).* Stems 1 to 3 feet tall, 1 or several together; basal leaves 1 to 3½ inches long, narrowly oblanceolate or broader, petioled, entire or somewhat toothed; those on the stem oblong or lanceolate, sessile, usually with earlike lobes at the base; petals averaging about ¼ inch long, usually white but sometimes pink; fruit 1 to 3 inches long, erect, smooth, straight.

ROCKCRESS *(Arabis fendleri).* Stems 1 to 2 feet tall, 1 to several, hairy below, smooth above; basal leaves 1 to 2½ inches long, oblanceolate, toothed, hairy, those on the stem sessile, entire or toothed, usually lobed at the base; petals pink; fruits 1 to 2½ inches long, not erect.

TOWER-MUSTARD *(Arabis glabra).* Stems 1 to a few from the same base, unbranched or branched near the top, usually hairy below and smooth above, 1 to 4 feet tall; basal leaves oblanceolate to oblong, petioled, 2 to 6 inches long, more or less toothed, those on the stem lanceolate to ovate, sessile, mostly entire and smooth; sepals and petals yellow or yellowish-white; fruits erect, 1½ to 4 inches long.

ROCKCRESS *(Arabis gracilipes).* This species which is not common and is known only from Arizona is similar to *Arabis fendleri.* It can usually be distinguished by its stouter stem, larger and more numerous stem leaves, and longer fruits.

ROCKCRESS *(Arabis perennans).* Stems few to many from the same base, 4 to 24 inches tall; basal leaves oblanceolate or wider, 1½ to 2½ inches long, densely hairy with branched hairs, those of the stem smaller, lanceolate, sessile; petals purple or pink; fruits wide-spreading, 1½ to 2½ inches long.

ROCKCRESS *(Arabis pulchra).* Stems 1 to several, 8 to 24 inches tall, often somewhat woody at the base, densely hairy at least below; leaves densely hairy, 1 to 3 inches long, linear, mostly entire, the basal ones petioled, those on the stem sessile; flowers larger and more showy than in any of our other species of rockcress, usually white; fruits densely hairy, 1½ to 3 inches long.

ATHYSANUS *(Athysanus pusillus).* Stems slender, 4 to 12 inches high, branched from the base, hairy with forked, spreading hairs; leaves all near the base, ovate or oblong, about ½ inch long or less; flowers minute, in loose racemes; petals linear or sometimes none; stamens 6; fruits nearly round, 1-seeded.

FALSE-FLAX *(Camelina microcarpa).* Stems 1 to 2 feet tall; leaves entire, sessile, somewhat clasping at the base; flowers small, yellow; fruits obovate, less than ¼ inch long.

SHEPHERDS PURSE *(Capsella bursa-pastoris).* Stems 6 to 24 inches tall or more; lower leaves usually deeply lobed, the upper ones entire or merely toothed; flowers very small, white; fruits triangular, like an old-fashioned purse, about ¼ inch long or less.

WILD-CABBAGE *(Caulanthus crassicaulis).* Stems somewhat inflated, unbranched, 1 to 3 feet tall; lower leaves 2 to 6 inches long, petioled, nearly entire or somewhat toothed or lobed, the upper ones smaller, sessile; flowers in racemes; sepals purplish but densely white-hairy; petals dark purple with white margins, nearly ½ inch long; fruits erect or nearly so, rather stout, nearly ¼ inch long.

TANSY-MUSTARD *(Descurainia californica).* Stems 1 to 3 feet tall, openly branched; leaves 1 to 2½ inches long, the lower ones pinnate with 2 to 4 pairs of leaflets; flowers in racemes; fruits ¼ to ½ inch long, linear.

TANSY-MUSTARD *(Descurainia obtusa).* Stems 8 to 48 inches tall; leaves 2½ inches long or less, pinnate with 2 to 5 leaflets; petals whitish to light yellow, about twice as long as the sepals; fruits about ½ inch long.

TANSY-MUSTARD *(Descurainia pinnata).* Stems 4 to 24 inches tall; lower leaves twice pinnate, the upper ones once pinnate; petals yellow, not quite as long as the sepals; fruits wide-spreading, ¼ to ½ inch long.

TANSY-MUSTARD *(Descurainia richardsonii).* Stems slender, 1 to 4 feet tall; lower leaves once or twice pinnate, the upper one pinnate or pinnately lobed; petals bright yellow, slightly longer than the sepals; pods ¼ to ½ inch long, linear.

TANSY-MUSTARD *(Descurainia sophia).* Stems 10 to 24 inches tall, leafy, branched; leaves 1 to 3½ inches long, 2 or 3 times pinnate; sepals about as long or a little longer than the greenish-yellow petals; fruits about 1 inch long or less.

DRABA *(Draba asprella).* Stems 2 to 5 inches tall, 1 or several from the same base; leaves all basal, ½ to 1 inch long, entire, sessile or nearly so; flowers in a terminal raceme; petals yellow, often fading to whitish, less than ¼ inch long but nearly twice as long as the sepals; fruits spreading, about twice as long as wide, oblong, densely short-hairy.

DRABA *(Draba cuneifolia).* Stems 2 to 10 inches tall, simple or branched from the base; leaves not all basal, 2 inches long or less, more or less toothed; terminal racemes usually less than ½ the length of the stem; petals white, slightly longer than the sepals; fruits smooth or nearly so, linear to oblong, ½ inch long or less.

DRABA *(Draba rectifructa).* Stems 4 to 16 inches tall, branched or unbranched; leaves about 1 inch long or less, not all basal; both stems and leaves grayish-hairy; racemes more than ½ the length of the stem; petals yellow, fading to white or pink, somewhat longer than the sepals; fruit about ¼ inch long, oblong, somewhat hairy.

WESTERN WALLFLOWER *(Erysimum capitatum)*. Stems 4 to 30 inches tall, usually unbranched; basal leaves 2 to 6 inches long, linear to lanceolate, usually toothed, the upper stem leaves smaller and often entire; petals bright yellow, ½ inch long or more; fruits 2 to 4 inches long, slender, 4-angled.

ERYSIMUM *(Erysimum repandum)*. Stems 8 to 16 inches tall, often widely branched; leaves 1 to 2½ inches long, lanceolate to linear, mostly entire or shallowly lobed; petals pale yellow, about ¼ inch long; fruits 1 to 2 inches long with a short, stout beak, spreading.

PRAIRIE PEPPERWEED *(Lepidium densiflorum)*. A much-branched annual, 12 to 20 inches tall; leaves mostly oblanceolate, the basal ones 1 to 3 inches long and coarsely toothed, those on the stem entire or slightly toothed; flowers in many racemes; petals usually none; fruit narrowly notched and slightly winged at the tip.

DESERT PEPPERWEED *(Lepidium fremontii)*. Stems several, branched, somewhat woody at the base, usually 8 to 24 inches tall, sometimes up to 3 feet tall and quite shrubby; leaves linear, mostly 1 to 2 inches long, entire or with a few linear lobes; flower cluster much-branched, quite showy; petals white; fruits with wide, winged margins. All of the pepperweeds are commonly called peppergrass throughout the United States.

HAIRYPOD PEPPERWEED *(Lepidium lasiocarpum)*. A branched, spreading annual, the branches 2 to 10 inches long; leaves linear to oblanceolate, toothed or lobed, ¼ to 2 inches long or more; racemes 1 to 3½ inches long; petals narrow, usually shorter than the sepals, sometimes none, fruit nearly round, slightly winged at the tip.

PEPPERWEED *(Lepidium medium)*. A freely branched annual, 6 to 24 inches tall; basal leaves 2 to 6 inches long, pinnate or pinnately lobed, those on the stem smaller, entire or somewhat toothed; racemes numerous, many-flowered; petals white, as long as or longer than the sepals; fruits usually longer than broad, not margined, shallowly notched at the tip.

MOUNTAIN PEPPERWEED *(Lepidium montanum)*. Stems 1 to few, 8 to 12 inches tall; basal leaves pinnately divided into mostly entire, linear lobes, those on the stem smaller, entire or somewhat lobed; racemes mostly 1 to 1½ inches long, many-flowered; petals white, about twice as long as the sepals; fruit with a very narrow wing near the tip and a very small notch.

CLASPING PEPPERWEED *(Lepidium perfoliatum)*. An erect, branched annual, 8 to 20 inches tall; lower leaves twice pinnately lobed into linear lobes, the middle ones entire and somewhat clasping the stem, the upper ones completely surrounding the stem; petals yellow, slightly longer than the sepals; fruit a little longer than wide with a very small notch.

BLADDERPOD *(Lesquerella arizonica)*. Very similar to the following species except for the characters given in the key.

BLADDERPOD *(Lesquerella intermedia)*. Stems clustered from a much-branched base, 1 to 7 inches tall, hairy throughout with star-shaped hairs; flowers yellow; pods oval, hairy like the rest of the plant.

BLADDERPOD *(Lesquerella purpurea)*. Stems several to many from the same base, 8 to 20 inches tall, basal leaves 1 to 4 inches long, mostly oblanceolate, sometimes more or less scalloped or lobed, the stem leaves smaller, oval to almost linear; flowers in a terminal raceme, petals white or purplish; pods inflated, nearly spherical, less than ¼ inch thick. This is the only bladderpod in Arizona that does not have yellow flowers.

TWINPOD *(Physaria chambersii)*. A small, silvery plant with several stems 2 to 6 inches tall; leaves mostly basal, the blades nearly round, the petioles 1 to 2 inches long, the few stem leaves much smaller; flowers yellow, the petals between ¼ and ½ inch long; fruits inflated, deeply notched.

FIELDCRESS *(Rorippa islandica)*. Stems 12 to 30 inches tall, branched above, not from the base, smooth; upper leaves toothed and nearly sessile, the lower ones lobed and short petioled; flowers very small, the petals yellow; fruits linear or nearly so, less than ¼ inch long. In water or wet soil.

WATERCRESS *(Rorippa nasturtium-aquaticum)*. Growing in water or wet places; stems creeping, floating or more or less erect, 4 to 24 inches long; leaves pinnately divided into ovate or oval leaflets, the terminal one larger than the others; flowers in racemes; petals white; fruits cylindric, ¼ to ½ inch long or more.

FIELDCRESS *(Rorippa obtusa)*. Stems 4 to 12 inches tall, much-branched from the base, smooth; leaves scalloped or lobed; flowers very small, the petals yellow; fruits oblong or linear, ½ inch long or less. Moist or wet places.

RORIPPA *(Rorippa sphaerocarpa)*. Stems 4 to 12 inches tall, much-branched from the base, smooth; leaves oblong, the upper entire, the lower ones more or less lobed; flowers very small, the petals yellow; fruits nearly spherical, smaller than a pea. Often found along streams.

TUMBLE MUSTARD *(Sisymbrium altissimum)*. Stems 12 to 40 inches tall, smooth or nearly so, widely branched; leaves mostly deeply lobed, the lower 4 to 6 inches long, the upper smaller; petals pale yellow to nearly white; fruits very slender.

DESERT MUSTARD *(Sisymbrium irio)*. Similar to the preceding but usually smaller throughout and with brighter yellow petals.

SISYMBRIUM *(Sisymbrium linearifolium)*. Stems 1 to 3 feet tall; basal leaves 2 to 4 inches long, mostly oblanceolate and toothed, those on the stem linear and entire; petals nearly ½ inch long, purple or pink; fruits slender.

DESERT PRINCES-PLUME *(Stanleya pinnata)*. Stems 15 to 60 inches tall, often branched above; lower leaves 2 to 6 inches long, pinnately lobed, the

CHECKER-MALLOW
(Sidalcea neomexicana)

GLOBE-MALLOW
(Sphaeralcea parvifolia)

MAMMILLARIA
(Mammillaria arizonica)

GRIZZLY BEAR PRICKLY-PEAR
(Opuntia erinacea)

Families Of Plants 105

upper ones smaller, entire or somewhat lobed; raceme becoming 4 to 20 inches long; sepals and petals yellow or yellowish; fruits slender, 1 to 3½ inches long.

STREPTANTHELLA *(Streptanthella longirostris).* Stems 8 to 24 inches tall; lower leaves narrowly oblanceolate to ovate, mostly scalloped or toothed, the upper ones linear and usually entire; petals yellowish to nearly white; fruit 1 to 2¼ inches long, flat, narrowed to a conspicuous beak.

TWISTFLOWER *(Streptanthus cordatus).* Stems 1 to 3 feet tall, mostly un-branched above the base; basal leaves more or less toothed, especially near the tip, those on the stem entire, sessile, clasping by the heart-shaped base; flowers about ½ inch long; sepals and petals brownish-purple, the petals curved back at the tip; fruits 2 to 4 inches long, flat, linear.

THELYPODY *(Thelypodium integrifolium).* Stems 20 to 80 inches tall, branched above and sometimes below; stem leaves narrowly lanceolate or linear, sessile, entire; sepals erect, white or purple; petals purple to nearly white; fruit ½ to 1½ inches long, not flattened, irregularly twisted.

THELYPODY *(Thelypodium wrightii).* Stems 15 to 50 inches tall, much-branched; basal leaves 4 to 6 inches long, pinnately lobed, those on the stem smaller, lanceolate to linear, lobed to entire; sepals spreading or turned down-ward; petals longer than the sepals, white or purplish; fruit slender, 1½ to 3 inches long.

PENNYCRESS or **WILD-CANDYTUFT** *(Thlaspi fendleri).* Stems 1 or several, 1 to 12 inches tall; leaf blades oval to ovate, petioled, sometimes purplish; raceme at first crowded; petals white or purple-tinged; fruits broadly elliptical, narrowly winged.

FRINGE POD *(Thysanocarpus laciniatus).* Stems 8 to 16 inches tall, branching above, smooth or nearly so; lower leaves linear, pinnately lobed or nearly entire, the upper ones narrowly linear, entire, about 1 inch long; flowers small, in long racemes, white or purplish.

CAPER FAMILY (CAPPARIDACEAE)

Mostly herbaceous plants with alternate, compound leaves with 3 or more leaflets; flowers perfect and regular, mostly in terminal racemes; sepals and petals 4; stamens 6 or more; fruit, in ours, a podlike capsule.

YELLOW BEEPLANT *(Cleome lutea).* Stems 1 to 2 feet tall, branched above; leaves with 3 to 7 leaflets, these 1 to 2 inches long, oblong to nearly linear; petals about ¼ inch long, yellow; stamens 6, about twice as long as the petals; capsule ½ to 1½ inches long, many-seeded.

ROCKY MOUNTAIN BEEPLANT *(Cleome serrulata).* Stems 20 to 36 inches tall or more, branched above; leaflets 3, lanceolate or oblong, smooth, entire or with very small teeth, 1 to 2 inches long; petals ½ inch long or less, reddish-purple, rarely pinkish or white; stamens 6; capsule slender, 1 to 2 inches long.

CLAMMYWEED *(Polanisia trachysperma)*. A branched, rather sticky plant with a disagreeable odor; stems 8 to 16 inches tall; leaflets 3, 1 to 2 inches long, oval or oblanceolate; petals yellowish-white, ½ inch long or less; stamens 12 or more, twice as long as the petals; fruits 1 to 2 inches long.

ORPINE FAMILY (CRASSULACEAE)

Low, somewhat fleshy herbs with simple, entire leaves and perfect, regular flowers. The fruit consists of 3 to 5 small pods.

STONECROP *(Sedum stenopetalum)*. Stems usually several, 2 to 8 inches tall; leaves alternate, lanceolate or linear, about ¼ inch long, flat; flowers in a compact cluster, petals usually 5, yellow; stamens usually 10.

SAXIFRAGE FAMILY (SAXIFRAGACEAE)

Herbs and shrubs with mostly simple leaves and perfect flowers, some with very showy flowers and some with edible fruits.

1. Woody plants (shrubs). 2.
Non-woody plants (herbs). 10.

2. Leaves opposite, entire or toothed but not lobed. 3.
Leaves alternate, mostly lobed; stamens 4 or 5. 5.

3. Sepals and petals 5; stamens 10; flowers not showy.

Sepals and petals 4; flowers showy, white. 4.

4. Stamens 8.

Stamens 20 or more.

5. Stems not spiny. 6.
Stems spiny. 7.

6. Leaves usually more than 2 inches wide, deeply lobed;
fruit black at maturity.

Leaves usually much less than 2 inches wide, shallowly lobed; fruit red at maturity.

7. Fruit easily separating from its stalk; flowers and fruits red, bristly.

Fruit not easily separating from its stalk; flowers white or pink. 8.

8. Styles hairy on the lower part; calyx not hairy.

Styles not hairy; calyx hairy. 9.

9. Berries yellow at maturity; leaves hairy.
   DESERT GOOSEBERRY *(Ribes velutinum)* 109
   Berries black or dark red at maturity; leaves smooth or
   nearly so.
   TRUMPET GOOSEBERRY *(Ribes leptanthum)* 109

10. Stamens 10; leaves mostly basal. 11.
    Stamens 5. 12.

11. Styles 2; capsule 2-celled and 2-beaked.
    DIAMONDLEAF SAXIFRAGE *(Saxifraga rhomboidea)* 110
    Styles 3; capsule 3-celled and 3-beaked.
    WOODLAND STAR *(Lithophragma tenella)* 109

12. Stamens longer than the sepals; flowers pink or pinkish. 13.
    Stamens shorter than the sepals; flowers greenish
    or yellowish. 14.

13. Lower ends of stamens noticeably widened and flattened.
    RED ALUMROOT *(Heuchera rubescens)* 108
    Lower ends of stamens not noticeably widened and flattened.
    ALUMROOT *(Heuchera versicolor)* 109

14. Sepals more or less spreading; petals longer than the sepals.
    LITTLELEAF ALUMROOT *(Heuchera parvifolia)* 108
    Sepals erect or incurved at the tip; petals shorter
    than the sepals.
    NEW MEXICO ALUMROOT *(Heuchera novomexicana)* 108

FENDLERBUSH *(Fendlera rupicola).* A branching shrub up to 7 feet tall; leaves less than 2 inches long but very variable in size, shape and hairyness; flowers solitary or 2 or 3 together, rather large, white, showy.

FENDLERELLA *(Fendlerella utahensis).* A low, much-branched shrub, 1 to 2 feet high; leaves opposite, oblong or elliptic, nearly sessile, ¼ to ½ inch long, hairy; flowers small, in small, dense, terminal clusters; petals white.

NEW MEXICO ALUMROOT *(Heuchera novomexicana).* Very similar to the following species but the petals shorter than the sepals.

LITTLELEAF ALUMROOT *(Heuchera parvifolia).* Flowering stems 9 to 25 inches tall, hairy; leaves all or nearly all basal, long-petioled, the blades nearly round in outline, 5- to 9-lobed, the lobes usually scalloped or toothed; flowers greenish or yellowish, the petals slightly longer than the sepals.

RED ALUMROOT *(Heuchera rubescens).* Flowering stems mostly 10 to 15 inches tall; leaves all basal, long-petioled, nearly round in outline, rather deeply lobed and sharply toothed; flowers in loose panicles; petals pink, nearly twice as long as the sepals; stamens longer than the petals; styles longer than the sepals.

ALUMROOT *(Heuchera versicolor)*. Very similar to the preceding and perhaps scarcely distinguishable from it. The stamens are about as long as the petals.

WOODLAND STAR *(Lithophragma tenella)*. A dainty and attractive little plant with a slender stem 4 to 7 inches tall; leaves mostly basal, usually with only 1 or 2 on the stem, the blades deeply cleft into 3 divisions, these each 3- or 4-lobed; flowers about 3 to 8, the petals pink and palmately 3- to 5-lobed.

MOCK-ORANGE *(Philadelphus microphyllus)*. A much-branched shrub, 2 to 7 feet high, with reddish-brown bark; leaves opposite, the blades ovate to lanceolate, 1½ inches long or less; flowers solitary or 2 or 3 together, showy; petals about ½ inch long, white to cream-colored.

WAX CURRANT *(Ribes cereum)*. A much-branched shrub 2 to 6 feet tall, without spines or prickles; leaves alternate, the blades nearly round, 3- to 5-lobed and scalloped, 1½ inches wide or less; flowers in few-flowered racemes, the petals about ½ as long as the calyx lobes; berries red, smooth or nearly so.

WHITESTEM GOOSEBERRY *(Ribes inerme)*. An erect shrub, usually 3 to 4 feet tall, usually without prickles but with 1 or 3 spines at each node; leaves 3- to 5-lobed, the lobes toothed; flowers 1 to 4 on short stalks; petals white or pink, much shorter than the sepals; berries wine-colored, smooth.

TRUMPET GOOSEBERRY *(Ribes leptanthum)*. An upright shrub, 2 to 7 feet tall, with spines at the nodes and with the branches sometimes bristly; leaves small, usually between ¼ and ½ inch wide, 3- to 5-cleft halfway to the middle and the divisions again 3-lobed or toothed; racemes 1 to 3-flowered, the petals white or pink and shorter than the calyx lobes; berries nearly black, smooth or somewhat bristly.

GOOSEBERRY CURRANT *(Ribes montigenum)*. A freely branching shrub usually 1 to 2 feet high, the stems more or less bristly and spiny at the nodes; leaf blades about 1 inch wide, more or less 5-lobed and the lobes again lobed and toothed, usually glandular-hairy, the petioles also hairy; racemes 4- to 8-flowered; flowers greenish-white to purple; petals about ½ as long as the calyx lobes; berries red, covered with gland-tipped hairs.

DESERT GOOSEBERRY *(Ribes velutinum)*. A stout, rigidly branched shrub, without prickles but with stout spines at the nodes; leaves less than 1 inch across, soft-hairy, deeply 5-lobed, the lobes again 3-lobed or toothed; flowers 1 to 4, yellowish to whitish, the petals slightly shorter than the sepals; berries dark, velvety-hairy.

STICKY CURRANT *(Ribes viscosissimum)*. A shrub, 2 to 5 feet tall, with neither prickles nor spines; leaf blades 1 to 3 inches across, shallowly lobed, the lobes scalloped or toothed; racemes few-flowered; flowers whitish or pink, the petals about ½ as long as the calyx lobes; berries black, glandular-hairy.

DIAMONDLEAF SAXIFRAGE *(Saxifraga rhomboidea)*. Flowering stems 4 to 12 inches tall, usually glandular-hairy; leaves all basal, 1 to 2½ inches long, with ovate blades and rather short petioles; flowers clustered near the end of the stem; petals white; fruit a capsule, often purplish.

CROSSOSOMA FAMILY (CROSSOSOMATACEAE)

Shrubs with alternate, entire, simple leaves and solitary, perfect, regular flowers at the ends or on the sides of branches.

CROSSOSOMA *(Crossosoma parviflorum)*. A much-branched shrub, 3 to 6 feet tall, with rigid, somewhat spiny-tipped branches; leaves elliptic to ovate, about 1 inch long or less, somewhat clustered, nearly sessile; flowers white or rose; stamens 15 or more; pistils about 3; petals 5, less than ½ inch long; fruit of 1 to 3 pods.

ROSE FAMILY (ROSACEAE)

A large and variable family with mostly alternate leaves, perfect, regular flowers and usually numerous stamens. The family contains many edible fruits and many beautiful flowers.

1. Woody plants (shrubs or small trees). 2.
   Non-woody plants (herbs). 19.

2. Ovary inferior or appearing so, the receptacle becoming fleshy and enclosing the pistils; fruit applelike. 3.
   Ovary evidently superior. 7.

3. Leaves simple. 4.
   Leaves compound. 5.

4. Top of ovary smooth; twigs and leaves smooth from the first.
   SERVICEBERRY *(Amelanchier polycarpa)* 113
   Top of ovary hairy; twigs and leaves at first hairy.
   UTAH SERVICEBERRY *(Amelanchier utahensis)* 113

5. Stems not prickly; flowers small, white.
   MOUNTAIN-ASH *(Sorbus dumosa)* 116
   Stems prickly; flowers large, showy, red. 6.

6. Leaflets wedge-shaped, less than ½ inch long, toothed only at the tip.
   DESERT ROSE *(Rosa stellata)* 115
   Leaflets not wedge-shaped, at least some of them more than ½ inch long, toothed well below the tip.
   ARIZONA ROSE *(Rosa arizonica)* 115

7. Pistil 1. 8.
   Pistils more than 1. 13.
8. Fruit cherrylike. 9.
   Fruit an akene. 10.
9. Leaves entire or nearly so, sessile or nearly so; fruit hairy, not juicy.
   DESERT PEACHBRUSH or **DESERT ALMOND** *(Prunus fasciculata)* 115
   Leaves regularly toothed, petioled; fruit smooth, juicy.
   CHOKE CHERRY *(Prunus virginiana)* 115
10. Leaves opposite; styles much twisted and bent, hairy only near the base.
   BLACKBRUSH *(Coleogyne ramosissima)* 113
   Leaves alternate; style not twisted and bent, hairy nearly to the tip. 11.
11. Leaves toothed, flat, usually less than twice as long as wide.
   TRUE MOUNTAIN-MAHOGANY *(Cercocarpus montanus)* 113
   Leaves entire, more or less rolled, more than twice as long as wide. 12.
12. Leaves elliptic, somewhat rolled but much of the lower surface exposed.
   CURL-LEAF MOUNTAIN-MAHOGANY *(Cercocarpus ledifolius)* 113
   Leaves narrowly linear, strongly rolled with little more than the midrib of the lower surface exposed.
   LITTLELEAF MOUNTAIN-MAHOGANY *(Cercocarpus intricatus)* 113
13. Leaves twice pinnately compound; stems not prickly.
   TANSYBUSH or **FERNBUSH** *(Chamaebatiaria millefolium)* 113
   Leaves once pinnately compound; stems prickly. 14.
   Leaves simple. 15.
14. Leaflets broadly oblong to nearly round; fruit black.
   HIMALAYA BERRY *(Rubus procerus)* 115
   Leaflets lanceolate to narrowly ovate; fruit red.
   RED RASPBERRY *(Rubus strigosus)* 116
15. Fruits fleshy, red.
   NEW MEXICO RASPBERRY *(Rubus neomexicanus)* 115
   Fruits not fleshy. 16.
16. Leaves entire; plants low.
   ROCKMAT *(Petrophytum caespitosum)* 114
   Leaves lobed or toothed; plants upright shrubs. 17.
17. Flowers in panicles, very small and numerous.

ROCK-SPIRAEA *(Holodiscus dumosus)* 114
Flowers solitary or in small clusters, medium-sized, showy. 18.

18. Flowers with 5 sepallike bracts alternating with the 5 sepals; akenes with purplish tails.
APACHE PLUME *(Fallugia paradoxa)* 114
Flowers without bracts between the sepals; akenes with white tails.
CLIFFROSE *(Cowania mexicana)* 113

19. Leaves simple and entire.
ROCKMAT *(Petrophytum caespitosum)* 114
Leaves compound. 20.

20. Akenes with feathery tails.
YELLOW AVENS *(Geum strictum)* 114
Akenes without tails. 21.

21. Calyx without bracts alternating with the sepals; petals yellow.
CINQUEFOIL *(Potentilla osterhoutii)* 115
Calyx with small bracts alternating with the sepals. 22.

22. Petals white. 23.
Petals yellow. 24.

23. Leaves palmately compound with 3 leaflets; plant spreading by runners.
STRAWBERRY *(Fragaria ovalis)* 114
Leaves pinnately compound with 7 or 9 leaflets; plant without runners.
CINQUEFOIL *(Potentilla arguta)* 114

24. Plant spreading by runners; petals much longer than the sepals.
SILVERWEED *(Potentilla anserina* var. *concolor)* 114
Plant not spreading by runners. 25.

25. Petals shorter than the sepals. 26.
Petals longer than the sepals. 27.

26. Petals not much shorter than the sepals; leaves with 3 or 5 leaflets.
NORWEGIAN CINQUEFOIL *(Potentilla norvegica)* 115
Petals much shorter than the sepals; leaves all with 3 leaflets.
BIENNIAL CINQUEFOIL *(Potentilla biennis)* 114

27. Basal leaves definitely pinnate.

HORSE CINQUEFOIL *(Potentilla hippiana* var. *diffusa)* 115
Basal leaves palmate or nearly so, the central axis, if
any, very short. 28.

28. Leaves dark green above, white-hairy beneath.

BEAUTY CINQUEFOIL *(Potentilla pulcherrima)* 115
Leaves about the same color on both sides, definitely
palmate.

VARILEAF CINQUEFOIL *(Potentilla diversifolia)* 114

SERVICEBERRY *(Amelanchier polycarpa* syn. *A. pumila).* A shrub, 3 to 9
feet tall; twigs and buds smooth; leaves 2 inches long or less, green above,
paler beneath, smooth from the start, oval to nearly round, coarsely toothed
to the middle or below; petals 5, white, ¼ to ½ inch long; fruit purple.

UTAH SERVICEBERRY *(Amelanchier utahensis).* A shrub or small tree, 9
to 12 feet tall; buds and twigs hairy; leaves at first hairy, ovate to nearly round,
toothed to the middle or below; flowers white; fruit purplish-black.

LITTLELEAF MOUNTAIN-MAHOGANY *(Cercocarpus intricatus).* A shrub,
1 to 5 feet high, with intricately branched, somewhat spiny twigs and gray bark;
leaves ½ inch long or less, linear, strongly rolled, green and smooth; flowers
small, without petals; tails of akenes 1 to 1½ inches long.

CURL-LEAF MOUNTAIN-MAHOGANY *(Cercocarpus ledifolius).* A large
shrub or small tree, usually 12 to 20 feet tall, with 1 or more trunks and reddish-
brown bark; leaves about 1 inch long or less, oblong to oblanceolate, somewhat
rolled, smooth above, white-hairy beneath; flowers very small, the calyx white-
hairy on the outside; tails of akenes 1½ to 3 inches long.

TRUE MOUNTAIN-MAHOGANY *(Cercocarpus montanus).* A shrub, 10 feet
tall or less, with grayish-brown bark; leaves 1 to 2 inches long and nearly as
wide, oval to obovate, coarsely toothed above the middle; flowers a little larger
than those of the other species with the calyx about ½ inch long; tails of akenes
2 to 4 inches long.

TANSYBUSH or **FERNBUSH** *(Chamaebatiaria millefolium).* A stout shrub,
2 to 6 feet tall, densely branched; leaves 1 to 1½ inches long, oblong in outline,
twice pinnately compound with numerous very small leaflets; flowers medium
small, white, in panicles, these 1 to 3 inches long. The fruits are small, few-
seeded pods.

BLACKBRUSH *(Coleogyne ramosissima).* A densely branched shrub, 1 to 6
feet tall, with ashy-gray, opposite, tangled branches; leaves ½ inch long or less,
linear or nearly so; flowers solitary on the ends of branches, small; sepals
greenish, yellowish or purplish; petals none; akenes with a short, twisted tail
which is hairy at the base.

CLIFFROSE *(Cowania mexicana).* A freely branched shrub, 1 to 10 feet tall, with reddish-brown twigs; leaves mostly ¼ to ½ inch long, obovate in outline, pinnately lobed into 3 to 5 lobes, these often again lobed or toothed; flowers solitary at the ends of small, leafy branches, about ½ inch across, showy, the petals white or whitish; akenes about 5, with feathery tails about 2 inches long.

APACHE PLUME *(Fallugia paradoxa)*. A shrub, 1 to 5 feet tall, the young twigs hairy, leaves similar to those of cliffrose; flowers also similar to those of cliffrose but the pistils and akenes are numerous.

STRAWBERRY *(Fragaria ovalis)*. Flowering stems shorter than the leaves; runners long and slender; leaves long-petioled, the 3 leaflets 1 to 2 inches long, coarsely toothed toward the tip; flowers mostly solitary; petals white, a little longer than the sepals; stamens and pistils many; akenes small, embedded in pits in the enlarged, fleshy receptacle.

YELLOW AVENS *(Geum strictum)*. Stems 1 to 2½ feet tall, hairy; lower leaves pinnate with 5 to 9 large leaflets alternating with small ones, variously toothed and lobed, upper stem leaves short-petioled with 3 leaflets; flowers few; petals yellow; tail of akenes only about as long as the body.

ROCK-SPIRAEA *(Holodiscus dumosus)*. A shrub, 2 to 10 feet tall, much-branched; leaf blades less than 2 inches long, elliptic to ovate, tapering to a short petiole, with 3 to 6 teeth on each side; flowers very small, in terminal panicles; petals white; akenes small, hairy.

ROCKMAT *(Petrophytum caespitosum)*. A low, prostrate, woody plant forming dense mats on rocks; leaves less than ½ inch long, oblanceolate to nearly linear, in clusters; flowers very small, in upright spikes; petals white; fruit of small, hairy pods.

SILVERWEED *(Potentilla anserina* var. *concolor)*. Main stems very short from a cluster of roots, producing runners up to 1 foot long or more; leaves in rosettes, 3 to 8 inches long, with 9 to 31 larger leaflets and smaller ones in between, the leaflets deeply toothed, silvery white on both sides; flowers solitary on rather long stalks from the axils of basal leaves or those of runners.

CINQUEFOIL *(Potentilla arguta)*. Stem rather coarse, 1 to 3 feet tall, hairy; basal leaves pinnate with 7 to 11 oval to ovate leaflets, these sharply cut and toothed; flowers in close clusters; petals white.

BIENNIAL CINQUEFOIL *(Potentilla biennis)*. Stems 8 to 20 inches tall, hairy, often tinged with dark red; leaves palmately compound with 3 leaflets, these coarsely scalloped, about 1 inch long; flowers in dense, leafy clusters; petals yellow, shorter than the sepals.

VARILEAF CINQUEFOIL *(Potentilla diversifolia)*. Stems 4 to 16 inches tall; leaves mostly basal, mostly palmate with 5 leaflets, sometimes with 7 leaflets and then appearing pinnate; leaflets 2 inches long or less with 3 to 7 teeth above the middle; flowers in small clusters; petals yellow.

HORSE CINQUEFOIL *(Potentilla hippiana* var. *diffusa).* Stems 4 to 20 inches tall, more or less hairy; leaves pinnate with 7 to 13 leaflets, these 2 inches long or less, coarsely toothed, white-silky beneath, green above; flowers usually few; petals ½ inch long or less, yellow.

NORWEGIAN CINQUEFOIL *(Potentilla norvegica).* Stems rather stout, 8 to 28 inches tall, often several from the same base; leaves palmate with 3 leaflets, these 1 to 2 inches long, coarsely toothed; flower cluster leafy; petals yellow, shorter than the sepals.

CINQUEFOIL *(Potentilla osterhoutii).* Stems 2 to 8 inches tall; leaves mostly basal, pinnate with 5 to 11 roundish or elliptical leaflets, these scalloped or palmately lobed; flowers in small clusters; petals yellow, sometimes pale or almost white, longer than the sepals; stamens 5.

BEAUTY CINQUEFOIL *(Potentilla pulcherrima).* Stems 8 to 24 inches tall; basal leaves long-petioled with 5 to 11 leaflets, usually 7, palmate or sometimes pinnate but with a very short axis, the leaflets conspicuously toothed, green above, conspicuously white-hairy beneath; flowers in dense, many-flowered clusters; petals yellow, much longer than the sepals; stamens about 20.

DESERT PEACHBRUSH or **DESERT ALMOND** *(Prunus fasciculata).* A shrub, usually 3 to 6 feet tall, with more or less spiny twigs; leaves in clusters on short, stubby branches, mostly entire, ¼ to ½ inch long; flowers small, less than ¼ inch across; petals white; fruit rather dry.

CHOKE CHERRY *(Prunus virginiana).* A shrub or small tree up to 10 feet tall; leaf blades 1½ to 4 inches long, broadly to narrowly elliptical, finely toothed, the petioles short; flowers nearly ½ inch across, in racemes, the petals white; fruit dark purple or black, juicy.

ARIZONA ROSE *(Rosa arizonica).* A very prickly shrub, usually 2 to 8 feet tall; leaves pinnate with mostly 5 or 7 leaflets, these 1 inch long or less, toothed; flowers 1 to 4 or more on lateral branches, mostly 1 to 2 inches across, showy, the petals red; fruits applelike, red or reddish, not prickly.

DESERT ROSE *(Rosa stellata).* A shrub, usually 2 feet tall or less, the stems densely covered with scalelike or starlike hairs, also prickly; leaves with 3 leaflets, these less than ¼ inch long, toothed near the tip; flowers solitary, large, showy, the petals 1 inch long or less, rose-purple.

NEW MEXICO RASPBERRY *(Rubus neomexicanus).* A shrub, 3 to 5 feet tall; without prickles; leaves simple, broadly ovate, toothed and more or less 3- to 5-lobed; flowers solitary on short, leafy branches, white, nearly 1 inch across, rather showy; berries red.

HIMALAYA BERRY *(Rubus procerus).* A prickly shrub, 3 to 5 feet tall; leaves with 3 to 5 leaflets, whitish on the lower side; flowers white, about

1 inch across; fruit black. An escape from cultivation and probably to be found in the park only at Indian Gardens.

RED RASPBERRY *(Rubus strigosus)*. A bristly shrub, 3 to 4½ feet tall; leaves with 3 or 5 leaflets, these doubly-toothed; flowers in small, terminal racemes, usually 3 or 4 together, rather small, the petals less than ½ inch long, white; fruit red.

MOUNTAIN-ASH *(Sorbus dumosa)*. A shrub, usually 7 or 8 feet tall; leaves pinnately compound with numerous, sharply toothed, lanceolate leaflets; flowers small, in terminal compound clusters; petals white; stamens many; pistil 1 with 3 styles; fruit small, berrylike, bright red.

PEA FAMILY (LEGUMINOSAE)

A large and important family of both woody and herbaceous plants. All but 2 of ours have compound leaves, all but 2 have more or less irregular flowers, and all but 8 have flowers of the sweetpea type. In the sweetpea type of flower the corolla usually has 5 petals and is very irregular. The large uppermost petal is called the standard, the 2 lateral ones are the wings, and the 2 lower ones are united along their edges to form the keel which usually encloses the stamens and pistil. In most of the sweetpea type of flowers there are 10 stamens, usually with 9 of them united and 1 free. The fruit is a pod.

1. Woody plants (shrubs). 2.
   Non-woody plants (herbs). 7.

2. Flowers regular or nearly so, yellow or yellowish; leaves twice pinnately compound. 3.
   Flowers more or less irregular, pink, purple or violet. 4.

3. Stamens numerous.
   CATCLAW *(Acacia greggii)* 120
   Stamens 10.
   HONEY MESQUITE *(Prosopis juliflora)* 142

4. Leaves simple. 5.
   Leaves pinnate. 6.

5. A low straggly shrub with small, linear leaves.
   RATANY *(Krameria parvifolia)* 139
   A large shrub or small tree with somewhat heart-shaped leaves.
   REDBUD *(Cercis occidentalis)* 139

6. Petal only 1; flowers rather small, in spikelike racemes.
   INDIGOBUSH *(Amorpha fruticosa)* 120
   Petals 5; flowers medium large and showy, in racemes.
   NEW MEXICO LOCUST *(Robinia neomexicana)* 142

7. Stamens 5; flowers in dense spikes, only slightly
irregular.   8.
Stamens mostly 10.   9.

8. Flowers white.
WHITE PRAIRIE-CLOVER (*Petalostemum candidum*) 142
Flowers rose or purple.
SEARLS PRAIRIE-CLOVER (*Petalostemum searlsiae*) 142

9. Stamens not united, often some of them sterile;
flowers yellow.
HAIRY SENNA (*Cassia covesii*) 139
Stamens, or 9 of them, united at least at the base.   10.

10. Leaves palmately compound.   11.
Leaves pinnately compound.   31.

11. Leaves with more than 3 leaflets.   12.
Leaves with only 3 leaflets.   18.

12. Flowers in heads, pink or whitish.
CLOVER (*Trifolium subcaulescens*) 143
Flowers in axillary clusters.   13.
Flowers in terminal racemes or panicles.   14.

13. Flowers yellow.
DEER-VETCH (*Lotus utahensis*) 140
Flowers purplish.
SCURFPEA (*Psoralea tenuiflora*) 142

14. Plants annual, usually much less than 1 foot tall; flowers in
rather small clusters, not very showy.   15.
Plants perennial, usually 1 foot tall or more;
flowers in rather large clusters, showy.   16.

15. Leaves mostly basal; stem, if any, much less than 1 inch long.
SHORTSTEM LUPINE (*Lupinus brevicaulis*) 140
Leaves not all basal; stem 1 inch long or more.
KINGS LUPINE (*Lupinus kingii*) 140

16. Banner petal hairy in the center of the back.
OSTERHOUT LUPINE (*Lupinus osterhoutianus*) 140
Banner petal smooth or nearly so.   17.

17. Flowers less than ¼ inch long, usually conspicuously
whorled in the raceme.
HILLS LUPINE (*Lupinus hillii*) 140
Flowers more than ¼ inch long, not whorled in the
raceme; stems and leaves densely hairy.

PALMER LUPINE (*Lupinus palmeri*) 140

18. Leaves thickly covered with black dots easily seen with a lens.

SCURFPEA (*Psoralea tenuifolia*) 142
Leaves not covered with black dots.   19.

19. Stems prostrate and trailing, sometimes twining.

WILDBEAN (*Phaseolus angustissimus*) 142
Stems erect or nearly so or, if prostrate, then short
and rooting at the nodes.   20.

20. Leaflets entire; flowers yellow.

DEER-VETCH (*Lotus utahensis*) 140
Leaflets toothed.   21.

21. Pods coiled.   22.
Pods straight or nearly so.   23.

22. Pods coiled in 1 plane; flowers purple.

ALFALFA (*Medicago sativa*) 140
Pods spirally coiled; flowers yellow.

BLACK MEDIC (*Medicago lupulina*) 140

23. Flowers in loose racemes.   24.
Flowers in heads or short, dense spikes.   26.

24. Flowers white.

WHITE SWEET-CLOVER (*Melilotus alba*) 142
Flowers yellow.   25.

25. Flowers often nearly ¼ inch long.

YELLOW SWEET-CLOVER (*Melilotus officinalis*) 142
Flowers much less than ¼ inch long.

ANNUAL SWEET-CLOVER or **SOUR-CLOVER** (*Melilotus indica*) 142

26. Heads subtended by involucres.   27.
Heads without involucres.   30.

27. Bracts of involucre often with blades of 3 small leaflets;
leaves mostly basal; flowers yellowish-white.

CLOVER (*Trifolium andinum*) 142
Bracts of involucre without blades.   28.

28. Bracts of involucre very short and sometimes not easily
seen; flowers pink or whitish.

CLOVER (*Trifolium subcaulescens*) 143
Involucre easily seen.   29.

29. Stipules entire or nearly so; flowers white or pinkish.

CLOVER (*Trifolium pinetorum*) 143
Stipules deeply and sharply toothed; flowers purplish.

30. Stems prostrate or partly so, often rooting at the nodes; flowers white.

Stems erect or nearly so, not rooting at the nodes; flowers pink.

31. Leaves ending in a tendril, this sometimes bristlelike. 32.
Leaves not ending in a tendril, usually ending in a leaflet. 35.

32. Tendrils bristlelike, not branching or coiling; flowers white.

Tendrils not bristlelike, sometimes branched or coiled. 33.

33. Flowers white.

Flowers purple or bluish. 34.

34. Corolla ¼ inch long or less.

Corolla ¾ to 1 inch long.

35. Leaves all basal or nearly so. 36.
Leaves not all basal. 44.

36. Keel of corolla with a prominent beak; leaves all basal; flowering stems erect or nearly so.

Keel of corolla not beaked or, if so, then the leaves not all basal and the stem prostrate or partly so. 37.

37. Flowers less than ¼ inch long.

Flowers about ¼ inch long or more. 38.

38. Flowers small, less than ½ inch long, solitary or in headlike or umbellike clusters of 2 to 5.

Flowers more than ½ inch long, in racemes. 39.

39. Leaflets of the largest leaves 21 to 35. 40.
Leaflets fewer than 21. 42.

40. Leaflets and pods silky-hairy with long white hairs.

Stems, leaflets and pods densely hairy with coarse hairs. 41.

41. Leaflets equally hairy on both sides.

MILKVETCH *(Astragalus amphioxys)* 122
Leaflets less hairy and thus greener on the upper surface.

MILKVETCH *(Astragalus tephrodes)* 139

42. Leaflets and pods smooth or nearly so; leaflets 11 or more.

MILKVETCH *(Astragalus zionis)* 139
Leaflets and pods more or less hairy; leaflets 3 to 13. 43.

43. Pods very woolly; leaflets silky, not silvery; flowers purple.

WOOLLYPOD *(Astragalus newberryi)* 122
Pods silvery-hairy, not woolly; leaflets silvery-hairy;
flowers white or pink-tipped, or the banner purple.

MILKVETCH *(Astragalus calycosus)* 122

44. Leaflets sharply spine-tipped.

MILKVETCH *(Astragalus kentrophyta)* 122
Leaflets not spine-tipped. 45.

45. Stems prostrate or nearly so.

MILKVETCH *(Astragalus humistratus)* 122
Stems erect or nearly so. 46.

46. Calyx teeth 2/3 as long as the tube or longer. 47.
Calyx teeth less than 2/3 as long as the tube. 49.

47. Leaflets densely hairy with coarse hairs; pods not inflated.

MILKVETCH *(Astragalus amphioxys)* 122
Leaflets smooth or somewhat hairy but not densely hairy
with coarse hairs; pods more or less inflated. 48.

48. Flowers cream-colored or yellowish; pods greatly inflated.

MILKVETCH *(Astragalus oophorus)* 139
Flowers purple or purplish; pods slightly or strongly inflated.

SPECKLEPOD LOCO *(Astragalus lentiginosus)* 122

49. Corolla whitish; pods 2 or 3 times as long as wide.

MILKVETCH *(Astragalus praelongus)* 139
Corolla violet; pods 5 to 8 times as long as wide.

BRYANT MILKVETCH *(Astragalus bryantii)* 122

CATCLAW *(Acacia greggii)*. A straggling shrub, 3 to 6 feet tall, the branches armed with short, stout, curved spines; leaves 1 to 2 inches long, twice pinnate, with small, entire leaflets; flowers yellow, in cylindrical spikes; stamens numerous; pods 1 to 5 inches long; more or less constricted between the seeds.

INDIGOBUSH *(Amorpha fruticosa)*. A shrub, 3 to 8 feet tall; leaves 4 to 8 inches long, pinnate; leaflets ovate to oblong, entire, 2 inches long or less; flowers purple, in dense, spikelike racemes; corolla of only 1 petal; stamens 9 or 10; pods very small with only 1 or 2 seeds.

GREENLEAF MANZANITA
(Arctostaphylos patula)

PHOTO MERKLE

PHOTO MERKLE

PINEDROPS
(Pterospora andromedea)

PHOTO MERKLE

DEERS-EARS
(Swertia radiata)

PHOTO MERKLE

POISON MILKWEED
(Asclepias subverticillata)

Families Of Plants 121

MILKVETCH *(Astragalus amphioxys).* Flowering stems 1 to 4 inches long, shorter to somewhat longer than the leaves; leaves all basal or nearly so, the leaflets varying from a few to more than 21, densely hairy on both sides; flowers purple, 1 inch long or more, in short, dense racemes; pods densely hairy, about 1 inch long or more, not inflated.

BRYANT MILKVETCH *(Astragalus bryantii).* Stems 6 to 18 inches tall; leaves up to 4 inches long; leaflets oval, less than ¼ inch long; flowers ¼ to ½ inch long, violet; pods smooth. Found within the Canyon. Known only from Grand Canyon. Very rare.

MILKVETCH *(Astragalus calycosus).* Flowering stems 1 to 10 inches tall; leaves all basal or nearly so, 1 to 3 inches long with 3 to 9 leaflets, silvery-hairy; flowers in rather loose, 3- to 10-flowered racemes, the petals whitish, but the banner often purple; pods about ½ inch long, silvery-hairy.

MILKVETCH *(Astragalus cremophylax).* A dwarf plant usually less than 1 inch high, forming a mat; leaves and leaflets very small; flowers very small, purple; pods very small, white-hairy. The type specimen was collected on the South Rim and the species is known only from that locality. We have not found it.

MILKVETCH *(Astragalus humistratus).* Stems prostrate, mostly 10 to 16 inches long; leaves mostly 1 to 2 inches long with 11 to 19 leaflets, sparsely to densely hairy, the stipules grown together around the stem; flowers in dense racemes; corolla between ¼ and ½ inch long, white to purple; pods ½ inch long or less, somewhat curved, hairy.

MILKVETCH *(Astragalus kentrophyta).* Stems 4 to 16 inches long, spreading or prostrate, often forming dense or loose mats; leaves less than 1 inch long with about 5 spine-tipped leaflets; flowers small, yellowish-white or purplish, usually in 2-flowered racemes among the leaves; pods elliptic, 1- to 3-seeded. Very different in appearance from any of our other species of *Astragalus.*

SPECKLEPOD LOCO *(Astragalus lentiginosus).* One of our most common and variable species of *Astragalus.* Stems 6 to 16 inches tall; leaves 2 to 16 inches long with mostly 13 to 21 leaflets; flowers mostly purple in loose or dense racemes; pods usually quite strongly inflated, several-seeded.

WOOLLYPOD *(Astragalus newberryi).* Flowering stems mostly 3 to 6 inches tall; leaves 1 to 5 inches long with 3 to 13 ovate or elliptic, silky leaflets; racemes short, 3- to 8-flowered, pink-purple; pods about ½ inch long, strongly curved, conspicuously white-woolly.

MILKVETCH *(Astragalus nuttallianus).* Stems rather slender, a few inches to 1 foot tall; leaves 1 to 2 inches long with about 9 to 13 oblong leaflets; flowers 1 to 5 in an umbellike cluster, small, purplish; pods about ½ inch long, linear and somewhat nerved.

PINYON PINE
(Pinus edulis)

PHOTO EVANS

UTAH JUNIPER
(Juniperus osteosperma)

PHOTO HAMILTON

PHOTO HAMILTON

LONGTONGUE MUTTON BLUEGRASS
(Poa longiligula)

SILVERTOP SEDGE
(Carex siccata)

PHOTO HAMILTON

Families Of Plants 123

WEAKSTEM MARIPOSA
(Calochortus flexuosus)

PHOTO HAMILTON

FRITILLARY
(Fritillaria atropurpurea)

PHOTO HAMILTON

FINELEAF YUCCA
(Yucca angustissima)

PHOTO HINCHLIFFE

ROCKY MOUNTAIN IRIS
(Iris missouriensis)

PHOTO BEAL

124 Grand Canyon Wild Flowers

QUAKING ASPEN
(Populus tremuloides)

PHOTO LUCCHITTA

GAMBEL OAK
(Quercus gambelii)

PHOTO HAMILTON

TRAILING ALLIONIA
(Allionia incarnata)

PHOTO EVANS

MINERS-LETTUCE
(Montia perfoliata)

PHOTO HAMILTON

COLORADO FOUR-O'CLOCK
(Mirabilis multiflora)
PHOTO HAMILTON

HORSE CINQUEFOIL
(Potentilla hippiana
var. *diffusa)*
PHOTO MERKLE

APACHE PLUME
(Fallugia paradoxa)
PHOTO HAMILTON

GOLDEN COLUMBINE
(Aquilegia chrysantha)

PHOTO BEAL

NELSON LARKSPUR
(Delphinium nelsoni)

PHOTO HAMILTON

BLADDERPOD
(Lesquerella arizonica)

PHOTO HAMILTON

TWISTFLOWER
(Streptanthus cordatus)

PHOTO HAMILTON

Families Of Plants 127

ROCKY MOUNTAIN BEEPLANT
(Cleome serrulata)
PHOTO BLACK

FENDLERBUSH
(Fendlera rupicola)
PHOTO HAMILTON

WOODLAND STAR
(Lithophragma tenella)
PHOTO HAMILTON

MILKVETCH
(Astragalus calycosus)
PHOTO EVANS

128   Grand Canyon Wild Flowers

NEW MEXICO LOCUST
(Robinia neomexicana)
PHOTO HAMILTON

DESERT-RUE
(Thamnosma montana)
PHOTO EVANS

SPURGE
(Euphorbia polycarpa)
PHOTO EVANS

Families Of Plants 129

GLOBE-MALLOW
(Sphaeralcea parvifolia)

WHITESTEM STICKLEAF
(Mentzelia albicaulis)

GOLDEN PRICKLY-PEAR
(Opuntia aurea)

REDBUD
(Cercis occidentalis)

PALMER LUPINE
(Lupinus palmeri)

MAMMILLARIA
(Mammillaria tetrancistra)

FIREWEED
(Epilobium angustifolium)

SHOOTING STAR
(Dodecatheon alpinum)

PHOTO STEVENS

PHOTO GRAND CANYON
NATURAL HISTORY ASSOCIATION

SINGLE LEAF ASH
(Fraxinus anomala)

PHOTO SCHULZ

SKYROCKET
(Gilia aggregata)

PHOTO WEBBER

SKYROCKET
(Gilia aggregata)

EATON BEARDTONGUE
(Penstemon eatoni)

PHOTO HAMILTON

PHOTO MERKLE

PAINTBRUSH
(Castilleja confusa)

PHOTO EVANS

BLUEBERRY ELDER
(Sambucus glauca)

PHOTO SCHULZ

CARDINAL FLOWER
(Lobelia cardinalis)

Families Of Plants 133

TUFTED EVENING-PRIMROSE
(Oenothera caespitosa)
PHOTO WEBBER

**HOOKER
EVENING-PRIMROSE**
(Oenothera hookeri)
PHOTO WEBBER

OCOTILLO
(Fouquieria splendens)
PHOTO WEBBER

RUBBER RABBITBRUSH
(Chrysothamnus nauseosus)

PHOTO WEBBER

DOGWEED
(Dyssodia pentachaeta)

PHOTO HAMILTON

WHITE BRITTLEBUSH
(Encelia farinosa)

PHOTO EVANS

BUSH ENCELIA
(Encelia frutescens)

PHOTO HAMILTON

Families Of Plants 135

PORELEAF
(Porophyllum gracile)

PHOTO EVANS

TOWNSENDIA
(Townsendia exscapa)

PHOTO HAMILTON

HEARTLEAF ARNICA
(Arnica cordifolia)

PHOTO CONDON

GOATSBEARD
(Tragopogon dubius)

PHOTO SCHULZ

136   Grand Canyon Wild Flowers

DESERT PHLOX
(Phlox austromontana)
PHOTO HAMILTON

PHACELIA
(Phacelia crenulata)
PHOTO WEBBER

COYOTE TOBACCO
(Nicotiana attenuata)
PHOTO WEBBER

Families Of Plants 137

COMMON MONKEYFLOWER
(Mimulus guttatus)
PHOTO WEBBER

MOHAVE ASTER
(Aster abatus)
PHOTO EVANS

SPREADING FLEABANE
(Erigeron divergens)
PHOTO HAMILTON

138 *Grand Canyon Wild Flowers*

MILKVETCH *(Astragalus oophorus)*. Stems 2 to 12 inches tall, the entire plant smooth or nearly so; leaves 2 to 6 inches long with 9 to 23 ovate leaflets; racemes loosely 5- to 12-flowered; petals about ½ inch long, whitish or yellowish, sometimes with pink or purple tips; pods about 1 inch long, somewhat inflated, usually streaked with red.

MILKVETCH *(Astragalus praelongus)*. Stems mostly 1 to 2 feet tall, smooth; leaflets about 13 to 21, linear to oblong or oval, ½ to 1 inch long; racemes 1 to 4 inches long, rather densely flowered; flowers ½ inch long, white, the keel purple-tipped; pods ½ inch long, inflated, smooth.

MILKVETCH *(Astragalus tephrodes)*. This species is very similar to *Astragalus amphioxys* and often difficult to distinguish from it but the leaflets are usually less hairy, especially above, and the pods are relatively broader and more densely hairy.

THOMPSON LOCO *(Astragalus thompsonae)*. The entire plant is conspicuously white-hairy. Flowering stems 2 to 12 inches tall; leaves all basal with 9 to 21 oval leaflets; racemes 1 to 23 inches long, densely flowered; corollas about ½ inch long, purple; pods about ½ inch long, strongly curved, silky-hairy.

MILKVETCH *(Astragalus zionis)*. This species is reported from the park but we have not found it. It has oval or ovate leaflets which are nearly ½ inch long, light purple flowers, and spotted pods 1 inch long or more.

HAIRY SENNA *(Cassia covesii)*. Stems 12 to 20 inches tall, often somewhat woody at the base, densely whitish-hairy throughout; leaves 1 to 3 inches long with 3 pairs of oblong leaflets, these about 1 inch long; racemes few-flowered; petals nearly ½ inch long, yellow, veiny; pods brownish, 1 to 2 inches long.

REDBUD *(Cercis occidentalis)*. A shrub or small tree, 6 to 30 feet tall; leaves simple, nearly round with a heart-shaped base, entire, 1 to 3½ inches across, with petioles 1 inch long or less; flowers appearing before the leaves in small clusters on the old wood, purplish-red; stamens 10, not united; pods oblong, flat, 2 to 3½ inches long and ½ inch wide, several-seeded.

RATANY *(Krameria parvifolia)*. A low, much-branched shrub, usually 1 to 2 feet tall; leaves simple, very narrowly linear, usually less than ½ inch long; flowers purple, numerous, mostly axillary; pods about the size of gooseberries with long, slender prickles; stems, leaves, flower stalks and calyx often beset with stalked glands.

ARIZONA PEAVINE *(Lathyrus arizonicus)*. Stems 4 to 16 inches tall; leaves with 2 to 6 leaflets, these 1 to 3 inches long; tendrils bristlelike, unbranched, not coiling; flowers white, nearly ½ inch long; pods somewhat flattened, several-seeded.

GRASSLEAF PEAVINE *(Lathyrus graminifolius)*. Stems 4 to 24 inches tall;

leaflets 4 to 10, linear, at least 10 times as long as wide; tendril well developed; flowers about ½ inch long, bluish to purple.

BUSH PEAVINE (*Lathyrus eucosmus*). Stems 6 to 20 inches tall; leaves with 6 or 8 leaflets, these 1 to 2½ inches long, narrowly oblong to elliptic; tendrils simple or branched, sometimes coiling; flowers nearly 1 inch long, rose to purple; pods about 1½ inches long, several-seeded.

ASPEN PEAVINE (*Lathyrus leucanthus* var. *laetivirens*). Stems 6 to 20 inches tall; leaves with 4 to 10 leaflets, these 1 to 2 inches long, narrowly elliptic to ovate; at least some of the tendrils branched and coiling; flowers about ½ inch long or more, white.

DEER-VETCH (*Lotus utahensis*). Stems 4 to 16 inches tall, branched from the base; leaves with 3 to 6 leaflets, nearly sessile and appearing palmate; flowers yellow, axillary, 2 to 4 on a stalk, this ½ inch long or more; pods linear, about 1 inch long.

SHORTSTEM LUPINE (*Lupinus brevicaulis*). A low plant, seldom over 4 inches tall, the leafy stem less than ½ inch long, densely hairy; leaves crowded on the short stem; leaflets 5 to 9, palmately arranged, smooth or nearly so above, somewhat hairy beneath; racemes somewhat headlike, less than 1 inch long, dense; flowers about ½ inch long, blue or purple.

HILLS LUPINE (*Lupinus hillii*). Stems 8 to 20 inches tall; leaflets 5 to 9, narrowly oblong, 1½ inches long or less; racemes 4 inches long or less, rather crowded; the flowers more or less conspicuously whorled, purple, ¼ inch long or less; pods narrowly oblong, 1½ inches long or less.

KINGS LUPINE (*Lupinus kingii*). Stem 1 to 6 inches tall, branched near the base and often wide-spreading, silky-hairy; leaflets silky-hairy on both sides, oblong to lanceolate; racemes dense and rather headlike, usually less than 1 inch long; flowers purplish or blue.

OSTERHOUT LUPINE (*Lupinus osterhoutianus*). Stems 8 to 20 inches tall, hairy; leaflets 5 to 7, about ½ inch long, hairy, the hairs not spreading; flowers purple or white or sometimes pink; pods ½ inch long, hairy. North Rim.

PALMER LUPINE (*Lupinus palmeri*). Stems 1 to 2 feet tall; petioles 2 to 4 inches long; leaflets 6 to 9, oblanceolate to elliptic, densely soft-hairy on both sides; racemes 4 to 12 inches long; flowers blue.

BLACK MEDIC (*Medicago lupulina*). Stems 1 to 2 feet long, branched from the base and prostrate or partly so; leaflets 3, obovate or nearly round; flowers very small, yellow, in short, headlike or spikelike racemes.

ALFALFA (*Medicago sativa*). Stems 1 to 3 feet tall; leaflets 1 inch long or less; racemes dense, 2 inches long or less; flowers purple; pods coiled in 2 or 3 spirals.

SPREADING PHLOX
(Phlox diffusa)

CRYPTANTHA
(Cryptantha setosissima)

BLUEBELLS
(Mertensia franciscana)

TALL VERBENA
(Verbena macdougalii)

Families Of Plants 141

WHITE SWEET-CLOVER *(Melilotus alba)*. Stems 1 to 6 feet tall; leaflets 1 inch long or less; flowers in racemes, small, about 1/5 inch long, numerous, white; pods very small, 1- or 2-seeded. Usually starting to bloom in July.

ANNUAL SWEET-CLOVER or **SOUR-CLOVER** *(Melilotus indica)*. Very similar to the preceding but usually not more than 3 feet tall and the flowers yellow and only about ½ as large.

YELLOW SWEET-CLOVER *(Melilotus officinalis)*. Very similar to white sweet-clover in all ways except in flower color, but it usually starts blooming about a month earlier.

CRAZYWEED or **LOCO** *(Oxytropis lambertii)*. Flowering stems 4 to 12 inches tall; leaves all basal with 7 to 17 oblong to linear leaflets; racemes many-flowered; flowers ½ to 1 inch long, rose-purple, very showy. Plant poisonous to livestock when eaten.

WHITE PRAIRIE-CLOVER *(Petalostemum candidum)*. Stems mostly 1 to 2 feet tall; leaves with 3 to 7 leaflets; flowers white, in dense spikes, only slightly irregular, the wings and keel attached to the stamen tube; stamens 5; pods very small, smooth.

SEARLS PRAIRIE-CLOVER *(Petalostemum searlsiae)*. Very similar to the preceding except that the flowers are rose or purple and the pods are hairy.

WILDBEAN *(Phaseolus angustissimus)*. Stems from a few inches to 3 feet long or more, trailing or climbing; leaves with 3 linear to triangular ovate, mostly entire leaflets; flowers purple, in axillary clusters; pods similar to those of a cultivated bean.

HONEY MESQUITE *(Prosopis juliflora)*. A large shrub or small tree, the wide-spreading branches armed with axillary spines; leaves with 2 branches at the end of the petiole, each branch with 16 to 24 leaflets, these ½ inch long or less; spikes axillary, 2 or 3 inches long, densely flowered; flowers small, greenish-yellow, fragrant; pods 4 to 6 inches long, ¼ to ½ inch wide.

SCURFPEA *(Psoralea tenuiflora)*. Stems 1 to 2 feet tall, slender, branched; leaflets mostly 3 to 5, oblong or obovate, about ½ inch long; flowers small, purplish, in slender, axillary racemes.

NEW MEXICO LOCUST *(Robinia neomexicana)*. A shrub or small tree up to 25 feet tall, armed with stout, spiny stipules; leaves mostly 3 to 8 inches long with 9 to 19 oblong leaflets, these 1 inch long or less; racemes 2 to 4 inches long; flowers about ¾ inch long, rose-purple, very showy; pods 2 to 4 inches long, 4- to 8-seeded.

CLOVER *(Trifolium andinum)*. Flowering stems 2 inches tall or less; leaves all basal or nearly so; stems and leaves densely silky-hairy; heads subtended by 2 or 3 leaflike bracts, these often with 3 small leaflets; heads many-flowered, the corollas yellowish-white.

FENDLER CLOVER *(Trifolium fendleri).* Stems 3 to 10 inches tall, leafy; leaflets 1 inch long or less, obovate to lanceolate, the margins rather sharply toothed; stipules rather broad and toothed; heads long-stalked, borne above the leaves, each subtended by an involucre; flowers purple or sometimes white.

ALSIKE CLOVER *(Trifolium hybridum).* Stems 6 to 20 inches tall; leaflets ½ to 1½ inches long, obovate to elliptic, more or less toothed; heads spherical, about 1 inch across, long-stalked, involucre absent or very small; corolla about ¼ inch long, pink to nearly white, turned downward after blooming.

CLOVER *(Trifolium pinetorum).* Very similar to *Trifolium fendleri* but usually a much smaller plant throughout and the stipules are narrower and entire or nearly so.

WHITE CLOVER *(Trifolium repens).* Stems 2 to 12 inches long, branching from the base, trailing and often rooting at the nodes; leaflets less than 1 inch long, obovate, more or less toothed, with a white blotch near the base; heads long-stalked, ½ to 1 inch across, involucre absent or nearly so; corolla white or nearly so, turned downward in age.

CLOVER *(Trifolium subcaulescens).* Stems 1 to 4 inches tall, the base covered with brown stipules of fallen leaves; leaflets less than 1 inch long, oval or oblong, sharply toothed, sometimes 5 in number, smooth above but coarsely hairy below; heads 5- to 12-flowered, the flowers less than ½ inch long, yellowish-white or tinged with pink; involucre very small or none.

GERANIUM FAMILY (GERANIACEAE)

Herbs with opposite leaves with stipules and perfect, regular flowers with 5 sepals, 5 petals, 5 or 10 stamens, and a compound pistil which separates into 5 parts at maturity.

1. Stamens with anthers 5. 2.
   Stamens with anthers 10. 3.
2. Leaves pinnately compound.

   Leaves pinnately lobed but not compound.

3. Flowers purple.

   Flowers white.

ALFILARIA or **FILAREE** *(Erodium cicutarium).* Stems 4 to 20 inches long, prostrate and wide-spreading; leaves pinnate, the leaves much lobed and cut; flowers purple, the petals less than ¼ inch long, soon falling off; fruit with a long tail, twisted when dry but untwisted when wet. The twisting and untwisting serves to "plant" the seed in the soil by a corkscrew action.

HERONBILL *(Erodium texanum).* Similar to the preceding except that the leaves are simple, broadly ovate, usually heart-shaped at the base, about as broad as long, and 3- to 5-lobed, and the petals are usually more than ¼ inch long.

CRANESBILL *(Geranium caespitosum).* Stems 4 to 24 inches tall, usually much-branched; leaves 1 to 2 inches across, deeply 5 lobed and the lobes again 3-lobed; flowers purple, about 1 inch across; style column in fruit about 1 inch long, the styles not becoming coiled after separation.

CRANESBILL *(Geranium richardsonii).* Similar to the preceding but the leaves more sharply cut and the flowers white.

WOOD-SORREL FAMILY (OXALIDACEAE)

Mostly low herbs with palmately compound leaves with wedge-shaped leaflets; flowers perfect, regular; 5 sepals, 5 petals, 10 stamens; pistil with 5 distinct styles; fruit a capsule.

WOOD-SORREL *(Oxalis pilosa).* Stems 4 to 16 inches long, partly prostrate; leaflets 3, notched at the end; stems and leaves hairy; flowers yellow, 1 to 3 on axillary stalks that are as long as or longer than the petioles.

FLAX FAMILY (LINACEAE)

Herbaceous plants with slender stems, simple leaves, and perfect, regular flowers with 5 sepals, 5 petals, 5 stamens and 1 pistil with several styles. The fruit is a capsule.

BLUE FLAX *(Linum lewisii).* Stems 1 to 2 feet tall; leaves linear, sessile, numerous, less than 1 inch long; flowers blue to white, about 1 inch across, blooming early in the morning and falling apart before night; styles 5.

YELLOW FLAX *(Linum puberulum).* Stems 4 to 20 inches tall, finely short-hairy; leaves linear, sessile, ½ inch long or less; flowers yellow, about ¾ inch across; styles 4 or 5.

CALTROP FAMILY (ZYGOPHYLLACEAE)

Herbs or shrubs with compound leaves and perfect, regular flowers, the stamens more numerous than the petals. In all of ours the flowers are yellow.

CALTROP *(Kallstroemia californica).* A herb with stems 4 to 15 inches long, branching from the base and wide-spreading; leaves 1 to 2 inches long with 5 to 7 pairs of leaflets, these about ¼ inch long, white-hairy; petals about ⅛ inch long; fruit angled and rough but not spiny.

CREOSOTE-BUSH *(Larrea tridentata).* A much-branched shrub, usually 1 to 6 feet high; leaves evergreen, strong-scented, with 2 resinous leaflets, these averaging about ¼ inch long; flowers solitary in the leaf axils; sepals and petals 5; stamens 10; fruit densely white-hairy, breaking up into 5 1-seeded nutlets.

PUNCTURE VINE *(Tribulus terrestris).* Very similar to the caltrop except that the fruits are spiny and the leaflets are less hairy and therefore brighter green.

RUE FAMILY (RUTACEAE)

Our members of this family are shrubs or small trees with alternate leaves and regular flowers.

HOPTREE *(Ptelea angustifolia).* A large shrub or small tree up to 20 feet tall with dark brown or purple twigs; leaves compound with 3 lanceolate or ovate leaflets, these bright green, the terminal one 3 or more times as long as wide; flowers small, in paniclelike clusters, both perfect and imperfect flowers on the same plant, greenish-white; fruit 2-seeded and winged all around, making a nearly flat disk.

HOPTREE *(Ptelea pallida).* Very similar to the preceding but the twigs straw-colored or light olive and the leaflets yellowish-green, the terminal one less than 3 times as long as wide.

DESERT-RUE or **TURPENTINE BROOM** *(Thamnosma montana).* A strongly scented shrub, 1 to 2 feet high, with broomlike, yellowish-green, often spiny branches; leaves simple, linear or nearly so, ½ inch long or less; flowers dark blue; petals 4, between ¼ and ½ inch long; stamens 8 in 2 lengths; fruit a 2-lobed capsule.

MALPIGHIA FAMILY (MALPIGHIACEAE)

Plants with trailing or twining, somewhat woody stems and opposite leaves. The flowers are perfect, slightly irregular, with 5 petals, 5 or 6 stamens, and 1 pistil with a 3-lobed ovary.

SLENDER JANUSIA *(Janusia gracilis).* Stems slender, twining, often tangled; leaves linear or nearly so, ¼ to 1 inch long; flowers small, yellow.

MILKWORT FAMILY (POLYGALACEAE)

Herbaceous or somewhat woody, mostly rather low plants with simple, entire leaves and very irregular flowers; sepals 5, the inner 2 more or less petal-like; petals usually 3, the upper 2 partly united with the stamen tube; stamens 6 or 8, united to form a tube; fruit a flat capsule.

WHITE MILKWORT *(Polygala alba).* Stems 4 to 12 inches tall, several or many from the same root, smooth, angled; leaves mostly alternate, linear or nearly so, mostly less than 1 inch long; flowers small, in dense, spikelike racemes, white with a green center.

SPURGE FAMILY (EUPHORBIACEAE)

Many members of this family have a milky juice. The flowers are imperfect and usually not conspicuous. The fruits are mostly 3-angled and 3-seeded.

1. Woody plants (shrubs).

BERNARDIA *(Bernardia incana)* 146
Non-woody plants (herbs). 2.

2. Sepals and petals present; male and female flowers
separated, either solitary or in different parts of the
same axillary raceme.

DITAXIS *(Ditaxis neomexicana)* 146
Sepals and petals lacking; male and female flowers
clustered together in a calyxlike involucre with 1
female flower at the center surrounded by several
male flowers, the whole resembling a perfect flower. 3.

3. Glands on the margins of the involucre without petallike
appendages. 4.
Glands on the margins of the involucres with petallike
appendages. 6.

4. Stem leaves pointed at the tip.
SPURGE *(Euphorbia incisa)* 147
Stem leaves rounded at the tip. 5.

5. Stem leaves oblong to nearly round, not wider above the
middle; leaves subtending flowers wider than long.
PALMER SPURGE *(Euphorbia palmeri)* 147
At least some of the stem leaves wider above the middle;
leaves subtending flowers not wider than long.
SPURGE *(Euphorbia lurida)* 147

6. Stems, leaves, ovary and fruit somewhat hairy.
SPURGE *(Euphorbia polycarpa)* 147
Stems, leaves, ovary and fruit not hairy. 7.

7. Leaves narrowly linear.
SPURGE *(Euphorbia revoluta)* 147
Leaves not linear. 8.

8. Plant perennial with a stout root; leaves broadly ovate.
SPURGE *(Euphorbia fendleri)* 147
Plant annual with a slender or fibrous root; leaves
narrowly ovate or oblong.
SPURGE *(Euphorbia serpyllifolia)* 147

BERNARDIA *(Bernardia incana)*. A much-branched shrub, 3 to 6 feet high;
leaves oblong, ¼ to ½ inch long, scalloped; flowers very small, 1 to 2 in the axils
of bracts of small, axillary racemes.

DITAXIS *(Ditaxis neomexicana)*. Stems 3 to 12 inches tall; leaves lanceolate
to oblanceolate, 1 inch long or less, entire or nearly so, sparsely hairy; sepals
of the female flowers conspicuously margined; petals inconspicuous.

SPURGE *(Euphorbia fendleri)*. Stems several from a deep taproot, 2 to 6 inches long, erect or nearly prostrate, smooth; leaves ovate, less than ½ inch long, entire; glands of involucre reddish, 2 to 4 times as long as wide; appendages white, about as wide as the glands.

SPURGE *(Euphorbia incisa)*. Stems 4 to 12 inches tall; erect or nearly so, mostly unbranched except for the umbellike cluster of flowering branches at the top; leaves ¼ to ½ inch long, ovate or elliptic, conspicuously pointed; glands reddish, irregularly toothed but without appendages.

SPURGE *(Euphorbia lurida)*. Very similar to the preceding but the leaves rounded at the tip, those subtending the flowers about as wide as long, those near the base of the stem often reddish.

PALMER SPURGE *(Euphorbia palmeri)*. Very similar to the preceding but the leaves subtending the flowers mostly wider than long.

SPURGE *(Euphorbia polycarpa)*. Stems 2 to 8 inches long, prostrate or nearly so, smooth or hairy; leaves round or oblong, entire, less than ¼ inch long, often much less; involucres solitary at the nodes; glands oblong, the appendages wider than the glands.

SPURGE *(Euphorbia revoluta)*. Stems 2 to 8 inches tall, very profusely branched, purplish; leaves narrowly linear and rolled, 1 inch long or less; involucres very small; glands and their appendages so small that they are difficult to see without a lens.

SPURGE *(Euphorbia serpyllifolia)*. Stems 2 to 12 inches long, prostrate or erect, smooth; leaves ovate to oblong, usually less than ½ inch long and with very small teeth around the tip; glands oblong with narrow, white appendages.

WATER STARWORT FAMILY (CALLITRICHACEAE)

Aquatic plants with opposite, entire leaves and imperfect flowers.

WATER STARWORT *(Callitriche heterophylla* syn. *C. palustris)*. Stems very slender, 1 to 10 inches long; submerged leaves linear, 1 inch long or less, those at the end of the stem broader, crowded, forming a floating rosette; flowers very small, a male flower consisting of a single stamen, a female of a single pistil, both borne in leaf axils; fruit of 4 nutlets.

SUMAC FAMILY (ANACARDIACEAE)

Shrubs or trees with alternate leaves and small, regular, mostly perfect flowers. The fruit is small, 1-seeded, cherrylike but dry.

SKUNKBUSH *(Rhus trilobata)*. A shrub, 1 to 7 feet high; leaves compound with 3 leaflets, these about 1 inch long or less and about as wide, scalloped, sessile or nearly so; flowers appearing before the leaves in dense, spikelike clusters, the petals yellowish; fruits red, hairy, sticky.

SKUNKBUSH (*Rhus trilobata* var. *simplicifolia*). Like the preceding but most of the leaves with a single leaflet.

BITTERSWEET FAMILY (CELASTRACEAE)

Woody plants with simple leaves or none, small, mostly perfect flowers and dry fruits.

1. Leaves none.

   CANOTIA (*Canotia holacantha*) 148
   Leaves present. 2.

2. Leaves opposite; some of the stems partly trailing; flowers reddish-brown.

   MOUNTAIN-LOVER (*Pachystima myrsinites*) 148
   Leaves alternate; stems all upright, much-branched; flowers white. 3.

3. Leaves thick, evergreen, crowded; stamens 5.

   MORTONIA (*Mortonia utahensis*) 148
   Leaves neither thick nor evergreen, not crowded; stamens 10.

   GREASEBUSH (*Glossopetalon nevadense*) 148

CANOTIA (*Canotia holacantha*). A shrub or small tree up to 15 feet tall with yellowish-green, spine-tipped branches and no leaves; flowers small and inconspicuous in small clusters on the stems; fruit a somewhat woody capsule.

GREASEBUSH (*Glossopetalon nevadense*). A much-branched shrub, 1 to 6 feet high; leaves oblong to oblanceolate, ¼ to ½ inch long with a very short petiole, entire; flowers very small, solitary in the axils of leaves; petals white.

MORTONIA (*Mortonia utahensis* syn. *M. scabrella* var. *u.*). A low, much-branched shrub, 30 to 40 inches high; leaves broadly oval to nearly round, ¼ to ½ inch long; flowers in terminal panicles; petals white.

MOUNTAIN-LOVER (*Pachystima myrsinites*). A low, much-branched shrub, 1 to 3 feet high; leaves mostly oblong, 1 inch long or less, more or less toothed; flowers 1 to 3 in the leaf axils, very small; petals reddish-brown.

MAPLE FAMILY (ACERACEAE)

Trees or shrubs with opposite, simple or compound leaves and small flowers, mostly in axillary clusters. The fruit is very characteristic. It consists of 2 akenes united at the base, each with a long, narrow wing.

MOUNTAIN MAPLE (*Acer glabrum*). A shrub or small tree, 6 to 30 feet tall; leaves simple, the blades 3- to 5-lobed and with numerous sharp teeth, 1 to 3 inches long and about as broad, with slender petioles; flowers in small clusters; wings of fruit less than 1 inch long.

BIGTOOTH MAPLE (*Acer grandidentatum*). A shrub or tree up to 30 feet tall; leaves simple, the blades 3- to 5-lobed and with a few blunt teeth, 2 to 4 inches long, usually hairy beneath; flowers in small axillary clusters; wings of fruit up to 1 inch long.

BOX-ELDER *(Acer negundo).* A tree, 15 to 60 feet tall; leaves with 3 to 5 leaflets, these 2 to 4 inches long, entire to coarsely toothed and often 3-lobed; flowers imperfect, the male and female flowers on different trees; each half of the fruit, including the wing, 1 to 2 inches long.

BUCKTHORN FAMILY (RHAMNACEAE)

Shrubs or small trees with simple leaves and small, mostly perfect flowers.

1. Ovary wholly superior; fruit cherrylike.   2.
   Ovary partly inferior; fruit a capsule.   3.

2. Branches spiny; fruit with a single seed.

   GRAY THORN *(Condalia lycioides)* 149
   Branches not spiny; fruit with 2 to 4 seeds.

   BUCKTHORN *(Rhamnus betulaefolia* var. *obovata)* 149

3. Leaves opposite, pinnately veined.

   DESERT CEANOTHUS *(Ceanothus greggii)* 149
   Leaves alternate, palmately 3-nerved.   4.

4. Branches usually spiny; leaves elliptic, at least twice
   as long as wide, pointed at the tip.

   BUCKBRUSH *(Ceanothus fendleri)* 149
   Branches not spiny; leaves oval to nearly round, less
   than twice as long as wide, broadly rounded at the tip.

   MARTIN CEANOTHUS *(Ceanothus martini)* 149

BUCKBRUSH *(Ceanothus fendleri).* Low shrubs 1 to 2½ feet high; leaves less than 1 inch long, narrowly elliptic, densely hairy beneath; flowers white, in umbellike clusters arranged in terminal racemes.

DESERT CEANOTHUS *(Ceanothus greggii).* A rigidly branched, evergreen shrub, 3 to 6 feet high; leaves opposite, elliptic to ovate, ¼ to ½ inch long, entire or toothed; flowers creamy-white, in umbellike clusters on short, axillary stalks.

MARTIN CEANOTHUS *(Ceanothus martini).* A shrub, mostly 1 to 3 feet high, the branches not spiny; leaves alternate, oval or nearly round, less than ½ inch long; flowers white, in small axillary racemes.

GRAY THORN *(Condalia lycioides).* A rigid, much-branched shrub, 3 to 8 feet tall, with spiny branches; leaves elliptic to ovate, ¼ to ½ inch long, entire; flowers very small, axillary, whitish; fruit dark blue.

BUCKTHORN *(Rhamnus betulaefolia* var. *obovata).* A shrub, 8 feet high or less; leaves broadly oval to obovate, 1 to 4 inches long, toothed or nearly entire; flowers greenish-white, in axillary clusters; fruits usually 3-seeded.

GRAPE FAMILY (VITACEAE)

A small family of woody vines with alternate leaves, small greenish-white flowers and berrylike fruits.

THICKET CREEPER (*Parthenocissus inserta*). A woody vine, climbing by means of tendrils which are opposite the leaves; leaves palmately compound with 5 to 7 leaflets, these 1½ to 4 inches long, lanceolate, toothed; flowers in axillary clusters; fruits blue-black when mature.

CANYON GRAPE (*Vitis arizonica*). A trailing or climbing woody vine; leaves simple, rounded or heart-shaped, often shallowly lobed, 1 to 4 inches long and about as wide; tendrils, when present, opposite the leaves; flowers in panicles opposite the leaves; berry juicy, few-seeded.

MALLOW FAMILY (MALVACEAE)

Flowers belonging to this family are usually readily recognized by the numerous stamens which are united to form a column around the styles. Our members of the family are all herbs with alternate, simple leaves with petioles, and perfect, regular flowers.

conspicuously scalloped margins.

GLOBE-MALLOW *(Sphaeralcea angustifolia)* 151
Leaves never almost linear, the margins not
conspicuously scalloped. 9.

9. Larger leaves more than 1 inch long, more or less lobed. 10.
Larger leaves mostly less than 1 inch long, usually with a
single lobe on either side near the base. 11.

10. Leaves conspicuously hairy.

GLOBE-MALLOW *(Sphaeralcea incana* var. *cuneata)* 152
Leaves conspicuously green.

GLOBE-MALLOW *(Sphaeralcea fendleri)* 151

11. Flowers usually more than 3 at each node.

GLOBE-MALLOW *(Sphaeralcea emoryi)* 151
Flowers 1 to 3 at each node.

GLOBE-MALLOW *(Sphaeralcea subhastata)* 152

WILD-HOLLYHOCK *(Iliamna grandiflora)*. Stems 2 to 6 feet tall; leaves 2
to 6 inches wide, deeply 5- to 7-lobed, resembling maple leaves, the lobes
toothed; flowers large and showy, the petals about 1 inch long, lavender.

MALLOW *(Malva neglecta)*. Stems 4 to 12 inches long, branching at the
base and spreading; leaves 1 to 2½ inches wide, rounded or kidney-shaped, with
5 to 9 shallow lobes or sometimes merely scalloped; petals about twice as long
as the calyx, pale blue or nearly white.

MALLOW *(Malva parviflora)*. Similar to the preceding but the stems more
erect, the leaves often larger, and the pink or lilac petals scarcely longer than the
calyx.

CHECKER-MALLOW *(Sidalcea neomexicana)*. Stems 8 to 30 inches tall, 1 or
several; basal leaves shallowly 5- to 9-lobed or scalloped, those on the stem very
deeply lobed and the lobes again lobed; flowers in an open raceme; petals 5,
about ½ inch long, rose-purple.

GLOBE-MALLOW *(Sphaeralcea angustifolia)*. Stems 1 to 5 feet tall; leaf
blades 2 to 4 inches long, narrowly lanceolate, scalloped; stems and leaves
rather densely hairy with star-shaped hairs; raceme long and narrow; petals
¼ to ½ inch long, red or pink.

GLOBE-MALLOW *(Sphaeralcea emoryi)*. Stems several, 12 to 40 inches tall,
gray-hairy; leaves ovate, 1 to 3½ inches long, shallowly scalloped or toothed,
usually with a broad, short lobe on each side at the base; flowers in a narrow,
open panicle; petals red, pink or lavender.

GLOBE-MALLOW *(Sphaeralcea fendleri)*. Stems 2 to 5 feet tall; leaf blades
1 to 2½ inches long, ovate, more or less 3-lobed and scalloped; petals red or pink.

GLOBE-MALLOW *(Sphaeralcea grossulariaefolia)*. Plant densely white-hairy, the few stems 25 to 40 inches tall; leaves ¼ to 1½ inches long and about as wide, deeply 5-lobed and again lobed and toothed; flowers in dense clusters in a narrow panicle; petals red, ¼ to ¾ inch long.

GLOBE-MALLOW *(Sphaeralcea incana* var. *cuneata)*. This plant is quite similar to *Sphaeralcea fendleri* but can be distinguished from it by the gray-green or yellowish-green color of the leaves. It is characteristically found in open places whereas S. *fendleri* is more often found in forested areas.

GLOBE-MALLOW *(Sphaeralcea parvifolia)*. Stems 24 to 40 inches tall, white-hairy; leaves ½ to 1½ inches long and about as wide, broadly ovate or nearly round, prominently veined beneath; flowers in a narrow panicle; calyx densely hairy; petals red.

GLOBE-MALLOW *(Sphaeralcea rusbyi)*. Plant green and only sparsely hairy; stems 1 to 2 feet tall; leaves less than 1 inch long and about as wide, deeply 3- to 5-lobed, the lobes again lobed and toothed; flowers few in a loose panicle; calyx woolly; petals apricot-colored, about ½ inch long.

GLOBE-MALLOW *(Sphaeralcea subhastata)*. A low plant with stems less than 20 inches tall; leaves mostly 1 to 2 inches long, narrowly lanceolate, usually with a single, short lobe on either side at the base; flowers few in a raceme; petals pink.

CACAO FAMILY (STERCULIACEAE)

Shrubs or herbs with star-shaped hairs, alternate leaves, and small, perfect, regular flowers with a 5-lobed calyx, 5 petals, 5 fertile stamens, and a compound pistil. The fruit is a capsule.

AYENIA *(Ayenia californica* syn. *A. pusilla)*. A low shrub with several slender stems 4 to 12 inches tall, woody below, herbaceous above; leaf blades ovate, toothed, about ¼ inch long on petioles ½ as long; flowers very small, brownish; capsule hairy, dotted with black glands.

ST. JOHNSWORT FAMILY (GUTTIFERAE)

Herbs with opposite, entire, sessile leaves and perfect, regular flowers with usually 5 petals, numerous stamens and a single pistil with 3 styles. The fruit is a capsule.

TRAILING ST. JOHNSWORT *(Hypericum anagalloides)*. Stems 2 to 6 inches long, partly prostrate, rooting at the nodes, often forming mats; leaves elliptic to ovate or nearly round, less than ½ inch long; flowers small, salmon color, the petals only slightly longer than the sepals.

ST. JOHNSWORT *(Hypericum formosum)*. Stems erect, 8 to 28 inches tall, not rooting at the nodes; leaves oblong to ovate, ½ to 1 inch long; flowers yellow, the petals between ¼ and ½ inch long, much longer than the sepals.

WATERWORT FAMILY (ELATINACEAE)

Very small, smooth, herbaceous plants growing in shallow water or creeping on mud; stems 2 inches long or less, rooting at the nodes; leaves opposite, linear or nearly so; flowers very small, in leaf axils, ours usually with 2 sepals, 2 petals, and 2 stamens; fruit a capsule. Our 2 species are distinguished by their seeds.

AMERICAN WATERWORT *(Elatine americana)*. Seeds with 16 to 35 pits in each row.

SHORTSEED WATERWORT *(Elatine brachysperma)*. Seeds with 9 to 15 pits in each row.

TAMARIX FAMILY (TAMARICACEAE)

Shrubs with slender branches, scalelike leaves, and small but numerous, perfect flowers.

TAMARIX *(Tamarix pentandra)*. A shrub or small tree, usually 6 to 20 feet tall, with smooth, often purplish branches; leaves alternate, scalelike, lanceolate, pale green; flowers pink, in densely flowered racemes which are arranged in large panicles.

VIOLET FAMILY (VIOLACEAE)

Low herbaceous plants with simple leaves and irregular flowers. There are 5 petals, the lower one with a short spur at the base. The 5 stamens are very short, the anthers close together around the style. The fruit is a capsule.

CANADA VIOLET *(Viola canadensis)*. Stems 6 to 12 inches tall, short-hairy; leaves ovate with a heart-shaped base, 2 inches wide or less and about as long, toothed; petals ¼ to ½ inch long, white, usually with purple veins and purple-tinged on the back, the 2 lateral ones bearded.

WANDERER VIOLET *(Viola nephrophylla)*. Flowering stems 2 to 8 inches tall; leaves all basal, the blades broadly ovate with a heart-shaped base, 1 to 3 inches broad, the petioles 2 to 6 inches long; petals violet, lighter and purple-veined toward the base, the spurred one bearded.

LOASA FAMILY (LOASACEAE)

Mostly herbaceous, rough-hairy plants with pale bark, simple but often deeply lobed leaves, and perfect, regular flowers with few to many stamens and 1 pistil with an inferior ovary. The fruit is a capsule.

1. Woody plants; flowers with 5 stamens.
   SANDPAPER PLANT *(Petalonyx parryi)* 154
   Herbs; flowers with more than 5 stamens. 2.

2. Stamens inserted on the petals; leaves more or less heart-shaped at the base.

3. Petals less than ¼ inch long; capsule more than 5 times
   as long as wide.

4. Petals pale yellow when fresh.

5. Stems erect, not branched from the base.

STINGPLANT *(Eucnide urens).* Plant armed with long, sharp-pointed stinging hairs and shorter barbed ones; stems 1 to 2 feet tall forming a rounded bush
often much broader than high; leaf blades ovate, 1 to 2½ inches long, on somewhat shorter petioles; flowers large, the cream-colored petals 1 to 1½ inches long.

WHITESTEM STICKLEAF *(Mentzelia albicaulis).* Stems 4 to 10 inches tall,
slender, white and shining, smooth or nearly so; leaf blades sessile, mostly
pinnately lobed, sometimes merely toothed or nearly entire, 1 to 3 inches long;
flowers quite numerous, small, about ¼ inch across; petals 5, yellow; capsule
linear, cylindric, about ½ inch long.

STICKLEAF *(Mentzelia pumila).* Stems 8 to 20 inches tall, mostly branched
toward the top; leaves lanceolate or oblong, toothed or pinnately lobed; flowers
terminal, solitary or in clusters of 2 or 3; petals about ½ inch long, yellow;
stamens 60 or more, the outer ones with petallike stalks.

STICKLEAF *(Mentzelia puberula).* Stems 4 to 12 inches tall, openly branched,
white; leaf blades lanceolate to oblong, coarsely toothed, the upper ones sessile
but not clasping; flowers terminal on the numerous branches; petals 5, yellow,
nearly ½ inch long.

STICKLEAF *(Mentzelia rusbyi).* This is a coarser and larger plant than any
of our other species of stickleaf; stems 2 to 4 feet tall, branched near the top;
leaves narrowly lanceolate, coarsely toothed, 2 to 8 inches long; flowers terminal
on the branches, the petals about ¾ inch long, pale yellow.

SANDPAPER PLANT *(Petalonyx parryi).* A round shrub about 3 feet high;
leaf blades lanceolate to ovate, finely scalloped, short-petioled, very rough with
short, barbed hairs; flowers whitish, in short spikes, the 5 petals between ¼ and
½ inch long.

CACTUS FAMILY (CACTACEAE)

Plants with thick, fleshy, very prickly stems and usually no leaves. The flowers are usually large and beautiful with many sepals, petals and stamens, and a single pistil with an inferior ovary which matures into a berrylike, many-seeded fruit.

1. Stems armed with spines but not with barbed bristles, not divided into joints. 2.
   Stems armed with barbed bristles and often also with spines, divided into joints. 9.

2. Stems not ribbed but with distinct tubercles arranged in spiral rows. 3.
   Stems with longitudinal ribs. 4.

4. Flowers borne laterally on the stem; outer covering of ovary and fruit spiny. 5.
   Flowers terminal on the stem; fruit not spiny. 7.

10. Stems only moderately flattened, the joints short,
    narrow, easily breaking apart.
    BRITTLE PRICKLY-PEAR *(Opuntia fragilis)* 158
    Stems definitely flattened, the joints broad, not easily
    breaking apart. 11.

11. Stems without spines.
    GOLDEN PRICKLY-PEAR *(Opuntia aurea)* 157
    Stems with spines. 12.

12. Plants large, often more than 2 feet high, the joints
    of the stems often more than 8 inches long. 13.
    Plants small or medium-sized, mostly less than 1½ feet
    high, the joints of the stems mostly less than 6 inches long. 14.

13. Spines about 2 inches long, not pointed downward; stems
    partly prostrate and rooting where they touch the soil.
    PRICKLY-PEAR *(Opuntia phaeacantha)* 158
    Stems upright, often 6 feet tall; principal spines about
    1 inch long. 15.

14. Principal spines all pointed downward, yellow.
    DOLLARPOINT PRICKLY-PEAR *(Opuntia chlorotica)* 157
    Only the lowermost principal spines pointed downward,
    whitish.
    ENGELMANN PRICKLY-PEAR *(Opuntia engelmannii)* 157

15. Joints of stem with spines all over or nearly so. 16.
    Joints of stem with spines only near the upper end or
    on the upper half. 17.

16. Spines along the margins of the joints longer than the others.
    PLAINS PRICKLY-PEAR *(Opuntia polyacantha)* 158
    Spines along the margins of the joints not longer than
    the others.
    GRIZZLY BEAR PRICKLY-PEAR *(Opuntia erinacea)* 158

17. Flowers red or pink.
    PRICKLY-PEAR *(Opuntia rhodantha)* 158
    Flowers yellow.
    PRICKLY-PEAR *(Opuntia compressa* var. *macrorhiza)* 157

COTTONTOP CACTUS *(Echinocactus polycephalus).* Stems 8 to 24 inches
tall and 8 to 12 inches in diameter, in clusters of 30 or fewer; ribs 10 to 20;
central spines 3 or 4, spreading, curved, 2 or 3 inches long, the surrounding 6
to 8 spines similar but shorter; flowers 3 inches across when fully open, yellow;
fruits egg-shaped, densely woolly.

ECHINOCACTUS *(Echinocactus xeranthemoides).* Very similar to the preceding but the spines are straight, the flowers are smaller, and often there are fewer stems in a cluster.

HEDGEHOG CACTUS *(Echinocereus engelmannii)*. Stems 1 to 25, not crowded, cylindrical, 6 to 12 inches high and 2 to 3 inches in diameter; ribs 10 to 13; central spines 2 to 6, all large and well developed, 1½ to 3½ inches long, the surrounding spines 6 to 12; flowers 2 to 3 inches across, purple; fruit red, spiny, nearly spherical.

HEDGEHOG CACTUS *(Echinocereus fendleri)*. Stems solitary or in small clusters, not crowded, 3 to 6 inches tall and 3 to 4 inches in diameter; central spine solitary, 2 to 3 inches long, turned upward, the 9 to 11 surrounding spines shorter; flowers 2 to 3 inches across, purplish; fruit egg-shaped, spiny, about 1 inch long.

HEDGEHOG CACTUS *(Echinocereus triglochidiatus* var. *melanocanthus)*. Stems in clusters of a few up to 500 or more, 3 to 6 inches tall and 1½ to 2½ inches in diameter; ribs 8 to 10; central spine usually solitary ½ to 1½ inches long, straight, the surrounding spines 5 to 10; flowers 1 to 2 inches long, red.

MAMMILLARIA *(Mammillaria arizonica)*. Stems nearly spherical, 2 inches in diameter or more, single or several together; spines several, brownish; flowers pink, 1½ inches across, at tip of stem; fruit not spiny.

MAMMILLARIA *(Mammillaria tetrancistra)*. Stems 4 to 10 inches tall and 2 to 5 inches in diameter; tubercles cylindrical, about ½ inch long; central spines 1 to 4, ½ inch long, 1 or more of them hooked at the end, the surrounding spines bristlelike, very numerous; flowers 1 inch across, the petals lavender with white margins; fruit red, about ½ to 1 inch long.

GOLDEN PRICKLY-PEAR *(Opuntia aurea)*. Stems prostrate, branching near the middle of the edge of each joint but usually only 1 joint high; joints nearly circular or oval, about 4½ inches across, armed with barbed bristles but without spines; flowers usually yellow but sometimes pink or red, about 2½ inches across when wide open.

DOLLARPOINT PRICKLY-PEAR *(Opuntia chlorotica)*. Stems erect forming a bushy plant, sometimes with a definite trunk, 3 to 6 feet tall, the branches nearly erect; joints nearly circular, 6 to 8 inches long and 5 to 7 inches wide; spines 1 to 6, the longest about 1 inch long, yellow; flowers light yellow; about 2½ inches across.

PRICKLY-PEAR *(Opuntia compressa* var. *macrorhiza* syn. *O. plumbea)*. Stems mostly prostrate, usually less than 18 inches long, the joints 3 to 5 inches long and about as wide; long spines 1 to 3 in each cushion near the upper end of the joint, not in the lower ones, the long spines accompanied by barbed prickles and often by shorter spines; flowers about 2 inches across, yellow.

ENGELMANN PRICKLY-PEAR *(Opuntia engelmannii)*. A large prickly-pear sometimes as much as 6 feet high and 15 feet in diameter, the joints ovate to nearly round, 7 to 11 inches long and 6 to 9 inches wide; spine cushions about 1½ inches apart, bearing prominent barbed hairs and all but the lower ones with 1 to 5 stout spines, these 1 to 2 inches long, many of them turned downward; flowers greenish-yellow to apricot color.

GRIZZLY BEAR PRICKLY-PEAR *(Opuntia erinacea* syn. *O. hystricina).* A low plant forming clumps up to 3 feet across and about 6 inches high, the stems usually with 2 to 4 joints, these round or elliptic; spine cushions close together and all bearing both spines and barbed prickles; spines 4 to 9 on each cushion, up to 4 inches long; flowers 2 to 3 inches across, yellow, white, pink or red.

BRITTLE PRICKLY-PEAR *(Opuntia fragilis).* Stems prostrate or largely so, forming very dense clumps up to 1 foot across and 4 to 6 inches high; joints usually 2 to 5, these obovate or nearly cylindric, 1 to 2 inches long and 1 inch wide often causing the plant to resemble a cholla; spines 5 to 7, long and slender, brown, the cushions filled with brown wool and yellowish barbed bristles; flowers about 2 inches across, pale yellow.

PRICKLY-PEAR *(Opuntia phaeacantha).* Stems largely prostrate, forming clumps up to 10 feet across, with chains of joints lying on their edges along the ground and rooting where they touch the soil; joints 4 to 9 inches long and 3 to 6 inches broad; spines 1 to 4, usually 1 much longer than the others; flowers 2 to 3 inches across, yellow.

PLAINS PRICKLY-PEAR *(Opuntia polyacantha).* Stems largely prostrate, forming clumps up to 1 foot in diameter; joints circular, 2 to 4 inches across; spine cushions rather close together; spines 7 to 10, those on the margins of the joints 1 to 2 inches long, the others shorter; flowers 2 inches across, yellow.

PRICKLY-PEAR *(Opuntia rhodantha).* Very similar to the grizzly bear prickly-pear but the joints lead-colored instead of green and spiny only on the upper half; spines usually 1 to 4, mostly turned downward, 1 to 1½ inches long; flowers usually red but sometimes yellow.

CHOLLA *(Opuntia whipplei).* Stems usually less than 18 inches high, forming mats of low, erect stems with short lateral branches, but in rich bottomlands this plant may become 6 or 7 feet tall; stems cylindric, about ¾ inch in diameter, bearing many narrow nipples; spines 4 to 12 in each cluster, some very short, others up to ¾ inch long; barbed prickles very small; flowers 1 inch across or less, pale yellow; fruit nearly spherical, yellow.

PINEAPPLE CACTUS *(Sclerocactus parviflorus).* Stems 4 to 7 inches high and 2½ to 3 inches in diameter; ribs 13 to 15, often spiraled, more or less nippled; spines borne on the nipples; longer spines 1 to 4, 1 of them strongly hooked; surrounding spines 8 to 10; flowers 1 to 2 inches across, green, yellow, pink or purple, fruit red, covered with fringed scales with tufts of short hairs in their axils.

OLEASTER FAMILY (ELAEAGNACEAE)

Our only member of this family is a shrub with opposite leaves and imperfect flowers, the male and female flowers on separate plants.

BUFFALOBERRY *(Shepherdia rotundifolia).* A compact, evergreen shrub, usually about 3 feet high; leaves silvery above, densely yellowish- or whitish-hairy beneath, oval or nearly round, 1 inch long or less; flowers small and inconspicuous; male flowers with 8 stamens; female flowers with a single pistil, the ovary maturing into a cherrylike, 1-seeded fruit.

EVENING-PRIMROSE FAMILY (ONAGRACEAE)

The flowers in our members of this family have 4 sepals, 4 petals, 8 stamens and 1 pistil. The ovary is inferior and in a few cases may be several inches below the other parts of the flower.

1. Fruits nutlike, not opening at maturity; flowers white or
   pinkish. 2.
   Fruit a capsule, opening at maturity. 4.

2. Capsule sessile or nearly so; flowers very small, the petals
   less than 1/10 inch long.
   SMALL-FLOWERED GAURA *(Gaura parviflora)* 162
   Capsule narrowed into a stalklike base; flowers larger,
   the petals about ¼ inch long. 3.

3. Fruits widest at, or near, the middle; winged only above
   this point.
   SCARLET GAURA *(Gaura coccinea)* 162
   Fruits widest near the base, winged almost the entire length.
   GAURA *(Gaura gracilis)* 162

4. Seeds with a tuft of hairs at one end. 5.
   Seeds without tufts of hairs. 12.

5. Flowers large and conspicuous, the petals more than ¼
   inch long, not notched at the tip.
   FIREWEED *(Epilobium angustifolium)* 161
   Flowers small, the petals less than ¼ inch long, notched
   at the tip. 6.

6. Plants growing in dry places; bark of stem peeling off in
   thin layers; plants annual. 7.
   Plants usually growing in moist places; bark of stem not
   peeling; plants perennial. 8.

7. Stems smooth except in the upper parts, usually more than
   1 foot high; leaves mostly alternate.
   AUTUMN WILLOW-WEED *(Epilobium paniculatum)* 162

Stems short-hairy throughout, usually less than 1 foot
high; leaves mostly opposite.

LITTLE WILLOW-WEED *(Epilobium minutum)* 162

8. Underground stem bearing winter buds with overlapping,
fleshy scales. 9.
Underground stems without winter buds with fleshy scales. 10.

9. Leaves lanceolate, sharply toothed.

HALL WILLOW-WEED *(Epilobium halleanum)* 162
Leaves ovate, nearly entire or slightly toothed.

MOUNTAIN WILLOW-WEED *(Epilobium saximontanum)* 162

10. Plant nearly smooth throughout, pale green.

SMOOTH WILLOW-WEED *(Epilobium glaberrimum* var.
fastigiatum) 162
Plant more or less hairy, especially above. 11.

11. Stems usually less than 1 foot tall; upper leaves few, opposite.

ALPINE WILLOW-WEED *(Epilobium alpinum)* 161
Stems usually 1 to 3 feet tall; upper leaves more
numerous, alternate.

STICKY WILLOW-WEED *(Epilobium adenocaulon)* 161

12. Stigma disk-shaped, somewhat shallowly 4-lobed. 13.
Stigma headlike, not lobed. 14.
Stigma with 4 linear lobes. 16.

13. Stems and leaves densely hairy; stems 2 to 8 inches tall.

EVENING-PRIMROSE *(Oenothera lavandulaefolia)* 163
Stems and leaves smooth or nearly so; stems 4 to 16
inches tall.

EVENING-PRIMROSE *(Oenothera hartwegii)* 163

14. Stems leafy throughout; flowers borne in the leaf axils.

EVENING-PRIMROSE *(Oenothera micrantha* var. *exfoliata)* 163
Leaves mostly basal or near the base of the stem; flowers
in terminal racemes. 15.

15. Stems unbranched or branched from the base; flowers
medium large, the petals about ½ inch long, bright yellow.

GOLDEN EVENING-PRIMROSE *(Oenothera brevipes)* 162
Stems branched near the top; flowers relatively small,
the petals about ¼ inch long or less.

EVENING-PRIMROSE *(Oenothera multijuga)* 164

16. Leaves all basal or nearly so. 17.
Leaves not all basal. 19.

STICKY WILLOW-WEED *(Epilobium adenocaulon* syn. *E. californicum).* Stem 1 to 3 feet tall, smooth except near the upper end, freely branched above; leaves 1 to 2½ inches long, ovate to lanceolate, small-toothed, the petioles very short; flowers small, the petals white to reddish; capsule 1½ to 2½ inches long, slender.

ALPINE WILLOW-WEED *(Epilobium alpinum).* Stems many, slender, densely crowded, 2 to 6 inches tall; leaves mostly opposite, oblong to lanceolate, ½ to 1 inch long; petals lilac to purple; capsules 1 to 1½ inches long, somewhat hairy.

FIREWEED *(Epilobium angustifolium).* Stems 2 to 8 feet tall, mostly unbranched, rather densely leafy; leaves alternate, lanceolate, entire or nearly so, sessile or nearly so, 3 to 8 inches long; flowers many in a long, terminal raceme; petals purple, about ½ inch long.

SMOOTH WILLOW-WEED (*Epilobium glaberrimum* var. *fastigiatum*). Stems mostly 4 to 12 inches tall, smooth or nearly so, slender, mostly unbranched; leaves ovate, ½ to 1 inch long, sessile; petals much less than ¼ inch long, purplish to nearly white.

HALL WILLOW-WEED (*Epilobium halleanum*). Stems 4 to 16 inches tall, mostly unbranched, with lines of hairs on the ridges extending down from the leaf bases; leaves linear, sessile, sometimes clasping the stem, 1½ to 2½ inches long, mostly opposite.

LITTLE WILLOW-WEED (*Epilobium minutum*). Stems 2 to 12 inches tall, from unbranched to much-branched, the branches more or less reddish; leaves mostly opposite, lanceolate, less than 1 inch long; flowers in the axils of the upper leaves, very small; the petals lavender to white; capsule 1 inch long or less.

AUTUMN WILLOW-WEED (*Epilobium paniculatum*). Stems 1 to 7 feet tall, branched above, smooth or nearly so; leaves narrowly lanceolate or linear, 1 to 2 inches long, few-toothed, mostly alternate; flowers on slender branches of a panicle; petals less than ¼ inch long, pink to almost white, deeply 2-lobed; capsule about 1 inch long, 4-angled.

MOUNTAIN WILLOW-WEED (*Epilobium saximontanum*). Stems 4 to 16 inches tall, with lines of hairs extending down from the leaf bases; leaves ovate to elliptical, sessile to short-petioled, entire or nearly so; petals less than ¼ inch long, white, pink or purple; capsule 1½ to 2½ inches long, somewhat hairy.

SCARLET GAURA (*Gaura coccinea*). Stems several or many, 4 to 20 inches tall, branched to form a bushy plant; leaves many, sessile, lanceolate to linear, entire or toothed; flowers in short spikes, the petals about ¼ inch long, whitish, pink or red; fruit 4-angled in the upper half.

GAURA (*Gaura gracilis*). Very similar to the preceding but the fruit angled or narrowly winged nearly the entire length.

SMALL-FLOWERED GAURA (*Gaura parviflora*). Stems 20 to 80 inches tall, widely branched above, soft-hairy throughout; basal leaves broadly oblanceolate, 2 to 6 inches long, those on the stems mostly lanceolate and smaller; spikes slender, nodding at the tip; flowers very small, pink or reddish.

WHITESTEM EVENING-PRIMROSE (*Oenothera albicaulis*). Stems 18 inches tall or less; leaves mostly lanceolate, variously scalloped, toothed or lobed, 2 inches long or less; flowers solitary in the leaf axils; petals ½ to 1½ inches long and about as wide, white, often pinkish in age; capsule 1 to 1½ inches long, sessile.

GOLDEN EVENING-PRIMROSE (*Oenothera brevipes*). Usually a single stem, 4 to 16 inches tall, nodding at the tip, unbranched or branched above; leaves mostly in a basal rosette with only a few smaller ones on the stem, often partly red beneath; flowers in a terminal raceme; petals bright yellow, ¼ to ½ inch long; capsule slender, linear, 2 to 3½ inches long.

EVENING-PRIMROSE *(Oenothera cavernae).* A low plant with no visible stem; leaves in a basal rosette, 1 to 5 inches long, with a large terminal lobe and much smaller lobes below; flowers with the ovary sessile among the leaves; petals between ¼ and ½ inch long, white becoming pink in age; sepals often with purple dots; capsule ½ to 1 inch long, rather woody.

TUFTED EVENING-PRIMROSE *(Oenothera caespitosa).* Usually with no visible stem but occasionally with a stem up to 8 inches long; plant usually hairy throughout; leaf blades mostly 1 to 4 inches long on winged petioles about as long, narrowly lanceolate, pinnately lobed; petals 1 to 1½ inches long, white, aging pink; capsule about 1½ inches long, stalked.

EVENING-PRIMROSE *(Oenothera coronopifolia).* Stems 2 to 10 inches tall, often branched from the base as well as above; leaves ½ to 1½ inches long, oblong in outline but deeply lobed with linear lobes; flowers in the upper leaf axils; petals ¼ to ½ inch long, white, aging pink; entire plant including the capsules densely short-hairy.

EVENING-PRIMROSE *(Oenothera hartwegii).* Stems several from the same base, 4 to 16 inches tall, mostly unbranched; leaves numerous, linear or nearly so, 1 inch long or less; flowers in the upper leaf axils, white aging pink, the petals about ¾ inch long.

HOOKER EVENING-PRIMROSE *(Oenothera hookeri).* Stems 1 to 5 feet tall, often reddish; leaves 2 to 6 inches long, the lower petioled, more or less hairy, usually with small teeth; flowers in the upper leaf axils; petals 1 to 1½ inches long, yellow, turning reddish with age; capsules 1 to 2 inches long, angled.

EVENING-PRIMROSE *(Oenothera lavanduleafolia).* Stems 2 to 8 inches tall, clustered, somewhat woody at the base; leaves ½ inch long or less, linear to oblanceolate, crowded; flowers in the upper leaf axils; petals ½ to ¾ inch long, yellow, reddish in age.

EVENING-PRIMROSE *(Oenothera longissima).* Stems 3 to 9 feet tall; basal leaves oblanceolate, 4 to 8 inches long and ½ to 1 inch wide, those higher up on the stem narrowly lanceolate and shorter; flowers sessile in the upper leaf axils; petals yellow, reddish in age, about 1½ inches long; capsule somewhat 4-angled.

EVENING-PRIMROSE *(Oenothera micrantha* var. *exfoliata).* Stems several from the same base, 2 to 10 inches long, spreading and partly prostrate, densely white-hairy, the bark easily peeling off; leaves narrowly oval or almost linear, ½ to 2 inches long; flowers solitary in the leaf axils; petals less than ¼ inch long, yellow, becoming pink in age; capsules 4-angled, often curved.

EVENING-PRIMROSE *(Oenothera multijuga).* Stem 8 to 32 inches tall, rather slender; leaves pinnately compound, all basal or on the lower part of the stem, 10 inches long or less, the veins on the lower surface conspicuously reddish; flowers small, in racemes, these often arranged in a panicle; petals yellow, ¼ inch long or less; capsule linear, ½ to 1 inch long.

PALE EVENING-PRIMROSE *(Oenothera pallida).* Stems 8 to 20 inches tall, white, smooth or nearly so; leaves lanceolate to linear, toothed or nearly entire, usually smooth; flowers in the upper leaf axils; petals ½ to 1 inch long, white, turning pink in age; capsule nearly cylindrical, often curved.

DESERT EVENING-PRIMROSE *(Oenothera primiveris).* Plant without visible stem, hairy throughout; leaves all basal, the blades oblanceolate in outline, usually deeply pinnately lobed, ½ to 5 inches long, the petioles shorter than the blades; flowers yellow; petals about 1 inch long, deeply notched at the end; capsule 1 to 1½ inches long and ¼ inch thick, 4-angled with a heavy rib down the middle of each side.

EVENING-PRIMROSE *(Oenothera runcinata).* Very similar to the pale evening-primrose except that the entire plant is conspicuously hairy and the leaves are deeply, pinnately lobed.

PARSLEY FAMILY (UMBELLIFERAE)

Herbaceous plants with alternate or basal leaves and small, perfect flowers with 5 petals, 5 stamens, and an inferior ovary. The calyx lobes are very small, or lacking entirely, and the flowers are borne in umbels. The fruit consists of two 1-seeded parts united by their flat faces, each part having 5 ribs, 1 on each edge and 3 on the back. It is often necessary to have fruits as well as flowers in order to identify members of this family.

1. Flowers purple. 2.
   Flowers yellow. 4.
   Flowers white, greenish-white or pinkish. 8.

2. Leaves usually not all basal.
   PSEUDOCYMOPTERUS *(Pseudocymopterus montanus)* 167
   Leaves all basal or nearly so. 3.

3. Only the lateral ribs of the fruit winged.
   CYMOPTERUS *(Cymopterus purpurascens)* 167
   All of the ribs of the fruit winged.
   LOMATIUM *(Lomatium mohavense)* 167

4. Leaves all basal or nearly so. 5.
   Leaves usually not all basal. 6.

5. Leaf blades once or twice pinnately compound.
   ALETES *(Aletes macdougali)* 166

SACRED DATURA
(Datura meteloides)

TOADFLAX BEARDTONGUE
(Penstemon linarioides)

WANDBLOOM BEARDTONGUE
(Penstemon virgatus)

BEARDLIP BEARDTONGUE
(Penstemon barbatus)

Families Of Plants 165

Leaf blades divided into 3 parts, each part 3 times pinnately compound.

LOMATIUM *(Lomatium macdougali)* 167

6. Leaves more than 3 times pinnately compound.

BISCUITROOT *(Lomatium leptocarpum)* 167
Leaves 1 to 3 times pinnately compound. 7.

7. Calyx teeth narrowly lanceolate, often unequal.

PSEUDOCYMOPTERUS *(Pseudocymopterus montanus)* 167
Calyx teeth triangular to ovate.

PTERYXIA *(Pteryxia petraea)* 168

8. Fruits armed with hooked prickles.

FALSE-CARROT *(Caucalis microcarpa)* 167
Fruits not armed with prickles. 9.

9. Fruits club-shaped, about 10 times as long as wide.

SWEETROOT *(Osmorhiza depauperata)* 167
Fruits oblong, about 3 times as long as wide.

LOVAGE *(Ligusticum porteri)* 167
Fruits oblong, about twice as long as wide.

PERIDERIDIA *(Perideridia parishii)* 167
Fruits about as long as wide, nearly round. 10.

10. Fruits narrowly winged.

WILD CELERY *(Apium graveolens)* 166
Fruit not winged, the ribs inconspicuous. 11.

11. Leaves once pinnate, the leaflets linear and entire.

YAMPA *(Perideridia gairdneri)* 167
Leaves once or twice pinnate, the leaflets toothed or lobed or both.

BERULA *(Berula erecta)* 166

ALETES *(Aletes macdougali)*. Flowering stems 2 to 10 inches tall, smooth; leaves all basal, 1 to 3 inches long, once or twice pinnately compound, the leaflets narrowly oblong and entire or wider and lobed; flowers yellow; fruits mostly less than ¼ inch long, the ribs corky-winged.

WILD CELERY *(Apium graveolens)*. Stems 6 to 60 inches tall, branched; leaves pinnately compound with 3 to 5 leaflets, lower ones 4 to 24 inches long and petioled, upper ones much smaller and sessile; flowers white; fruits very small.

BERULA *(Berula erecta)*. Stems 8 to 32 inches tall; leaves 4 to 12 inches long with few or many leaflets, these much lobed and toothed; flowers white; fruits very small, somewhat flattened, ribs obscure.

FALSE-CARROT *(Caucalis microcarpa)*. Stems 4 to 14 inches tall, slender; leaves several times compound and very much dissected into very small segments; flowers white; fruits with 5 regular ribs and 4 secondary ones all armed with barbed or hooked bristles.

CYMOPTERUS *(Cymopterus purpurascens)*. Flowering stems 1 to 6 inches tall; leaves all basal or nearly so, the blades 1 to 2 inches long, once or twice pinnately compound, the petioles nearly as long; umbels very compact; bracts subtending the umbels white, often with green veins; flowers purple; fruit ¼ to ½ inch long and about as broad, the wings thin, 2 or 3 times as broad as the body.

LOVAGE *(Ligusticum porteri)*. Stem 20 to 40 inches tall, stout, freely branched, nearly smooth; leaf blades 1 to 3 times pinnately compound; leaflets 1 to 2 inches long, sharply lobed; flowers white; fruit oblong, slightly flattened, about ¼ inch long, the wings thin and narrow.

BISCUITROOT *(Lomatium leptocarpum)*. Flowering stems 6 to 20 inches tall from tuberous roots; leaves near the base, the blades several times pinnately compound, 3 to 6 inches long; flowers yellow; fruit narrowly oblong, about ½ inch long, the wings thin and narrow.

LOMATIUM *(Lomatium macdougali)*. Flowering stems 4 to 12 inches tall from a long, slender taproot; leaves all basal, the blades 1 to 5 inches long, several times pinnately compound, the ultimate segments very small, crowded; flowers yellow, often purple-tinged; fruit oval or nearly round, the wings narrower than the body; entire plant, including the fruit, short-hairy.

LOMATIUM *(Lomatium mohavense)*. Flowering stems 4 to 12 inches tall; leaves all basal, the blades 1 to 4 inches long, oblong in outline, 3 or 4 times pinnate, the petioles longer than the blades; flowers purple; fruits nearly round, the wings nearly as wide as the body.

SWEETROOT *(Osmorhiza depauperata* syn. *O. obtusa)*. Stems 6 to 28 inches tall; leaves pinnately compound with 5 or more leaflets, on long petioles, the leaflets 1 to 2 inches long, broadly lanceolate or ovate, coarsely toothed or lobed; flowers greenish-white; fruit about ½ inch long, club-shaped.

YAMPA *(Perideridia gairdneri)*. Stems slender, 1 to 4 feet tall; leaves few, once or twice pinnately compound, the few leaflets linear, entire, 1 to 5 inches long; flowers white; fruit very small, about as broad as long.

PERIDERIDIA *(Perideridia parishii)*. Very similar to the preceding but usually not as tall, the leaflets somewhat smaller and the fruits about twice as long as broad.

PSEUDOCYMOPTERUS *(Pseudocymopterus montanus)*. Plant very variable; stem 8 to 30 inches tall; leaves mostly near the base, once or twice pinnately compound, the ultimate divisions narrowly linear to lanceolate; umbels loose, compound; flowers either yellow or purple; fruits oblong, the lateral ribs broadly winged.

PTERYXIA *(Pteryxia petraea).* Stems 6 to 16 inches tall, slender; leaf blades pale green, 1 to 6 inches long, 1 to 3 times pinnately compound, the ultimate divisions linear, mostly less than ¼ inch long; flowers yellow; fruits oblong, the lateral wings as wide as the body or narrower.

DOGWOOD FAMILY (CORNACEAE)

Shrubs or small trees with opposite, simple, entire or nearly entire leaves and small flowers and cherrylike or berrylike fruits.

1. Flowers in flat-topped clusters, perfect, with petals and 1 style.
   RED-OSIER DOGWOOD *(Cornus stolonifera)* 168
   Flowers in catkins, imperfect, without petals; styles 2;
   male and female flowers on separate plants. 2.

2. Catkins dense; bracts subtending flowers triangular,
   not leaflike.
   YELLOWLEAF SILKTASSEL *(Garrya flavescens)* 168
   Catkins loose; bracts subtending flowers leaflike, not triangular.
   WRIGHTS SILKTASSEL *(Garrya wrightii)* 168

RED-OSIER DOGWOOD *(Cornus stolonifera).* A shrub, usually 6 to 12 feet high, the twigs bright purple-red; leaf blades lanceolate to elliptic or ovate, 2 to 3½ inches long, the petioles ¼ to ½ inch long; flowers small, with 4 stamens and 1 style, the petals white; fruit cherrylike, white.

YELLOWLEAF SILKTASSEL *(Garrya flavescens).* A shrub, 4 to 12 feet tall; leaf blades elliptic to oval, densely silky beneath, 1½ to 2½ inches long; bracts of fruiting catkins densely silky; fruits densely silky.

WRIGHTS SILKTASSEL *(Garrya wrightii).* Very similar to the preceding but differs in the characters given in the key and the leaves and fruits are smooth or nearly so instead of silky.

HEATH FAMILY (ERICACEAE)

Shrubs and herbs, often with evergreen leaves; flowers perfect, regular or nearly so; petals more or less united; stamens mostly 8 to 12; style 1.

1. Woody plants (shrubs). 2.
   Non-woody plants (herbs). 4.

2. Low shrubs with crowded, linear leaves.
   MOUNTAIN-HEATH *(Phyllodoce empetriformis)* 169
   Large shrubs with broad leaves. 3.

3. Twigs short-hairy, not glandular; stems not rooting
   where they touch the soil.

GREENLEAF MANZANITA *(Arctostaphylos patula).* A shrub; our specimens usually not more than 3 feet high, the stems spreading, often rooting where they touch the soil and forming dense thickets; leaves evergreen, 1 to 1½ inches long, ovate to nearly round, usually rounded at the tip; flowers in panicles, the corolla white, tinged with pink.

POINTLEAF MANZANITA *(Arctostaphylos pungens).* Very similar to the preceding but more upright and often taller and the leaves more pointed at the tip.

MOUNTAIN-HEATH *(Phyllodoce empetriformis).* A low much-branched, mat-forming shrub with upright shoots 4 to 20 inches tall; leaves linear, crowded, ¼ to ½ inch long; flowers rose-pink, in umbellike clusters at the ends of branches; corolla 5-lobed; stamens 10.

PINEDROPS *(Pterospora andromedea).* Stems stout, unbranched, 1 to 3 feet tall, purplish-brown, densely covered with sticky hairs; leaves reduced to brown scales; flowers drooping, the sepals brown, the corolla white. Parasitic on the roots of pine trees and probably also on a fungus.

WAXFLOWER WINTERGREEN *(Pyrola elliptica).* Flowering stem 4 to 12 inches tall; leaves all basal or nearly so, elliptic to obovate, about 1 inch long or less, usually sharp-pointed, finely toothed; flowers white or creamy, sometimes pink-tinged.

ONE-SIDED WINTERGREEN *(Pyrola secunda).* Flowering stems 8 to 12 inches tall; leaves all basal or near the base, elliptic to ovate, finely toothed, blunt at the tip; corolla greenish-white; ovary with 10 small tuberlike bodies at the base.

WINTERGREEN *(Pyrola virens).* Flowering stems 3 to 12 inches tall; leaves all basal, the blades ovate to nearly round, the largest 1 to 2½ inches broad, obscurely scalloped, rounded at the base and tip; panicle slender; corolla greenish-white.

PRIMROSE FAMILY (PRIMULACEAE)

Herbaceous plants with simple leaves and perfect, regular flowers, sepals, petals and stamens 4 or 5, the petals more or less united; pistil 1; fruit a capsule.

1. Ovary partly inferior.
   WATER PIMPERNEL (*Samolus floribundus*) 171
   Ovary wholly superior; leaves all basal or nearly so. 2.

2. Corolla with the lobes turned downward; stamens extending beyond the corolla tube, the anthers close together around the style.
   SHOOTING STAR (*Dodecatheon alpinum*) 170
   Corolla with the lobes upright or merely spreading; stamens included within the corolla tube. 3.

3. Flowers relatively large and showy. 4.
   Flowers small and inconspicuous, in umbels. 5.

4. Petioles shorter than the leaf blades; calyx longer than the capsule.
   PRIMROSE (*Primula specuicola*) 171
   Petioles about as long as the leaf blades; calyx shorter than the capsule.
   PRIMROSE (*Primula hunnewellii*) 171

5. Bracts subtending umbels ovate or obovate; plants of low altitudes, blooming in early spring.
   WESTERN ROCK-JASMINE (*Androsace occidentalis*) 170
   Bracts subtending umbels lanceolate or awl-shaped; plants of high altitudes, blooming in summer.
   ROCK-JASMINE (*Androsace septentrionalis*) 170

WESTERN ROCK-JASMINE (*Androsace occidentalis*). Flowering stems, 1 or several, 1 to 4 inches tall; leaves lanceolate to linear, entire or nearly so; calyx tube whitish, the lobes green; corolla very small, shorter than the calyx, white.

ROCK-JASMINE (*Androsace septentrionalis*). Flowering stems 1 to 12 inches tall, often profusely branched and spreading; leaves linear to oblanceolate, entire to somewhat toothed; calyx tube 5-ridged, greenish; corolla about as long as the calyx, white or pinkish.

SHOOTING STAR (*Dodecatheon alpinum*). Flowering stems 6 to 16 inches tall, smooth; leaves 2 to 8 inches long, narrowly oblanceolate or elliptic, entire or scalloped; flowers solitary or as many as 20 in an umbel; sepals, petals and stamens 4; corolla ½ to ¾ inch long, purple with a dark, wavy line in the throat and yellow in the tube.

PRIMROSE *(Primula hunnewellii)*. This plant differs from the following species only in the characters given in the key and may not be specifically distinct from it. North Rim.

PRIMROSE *(Primula specuicola)*. Flowering stems 3 to 6 inches tall; leaves all basal, oblanceolate, whitish on the underside, green on the upper side, toothed, petioled, 6 inches long or less; flowers in umbellike clusters, purple with yellow tube, ½ inch long or less, showy.

WATER PIMPERNEL *(Samolus floribundus)*. Stems usually solitary, 6 to 16 inches tall; our only member of the family with a leafy stem; leaves alternate on the stem and in a basal rosette, the blades 1 to 2 inches long, nearly round or oblong and narrowed to a short, winged petiole; flowers small, white, in short, often panicled racemes.

OCOTILLO FAMILY (FOUQUIERIACEAE)

Spiny shrubs which drop their leaves as soon as the soil dries but quickly produce a new crop when the rains come. Very showy when in bloom.

OCOTILLO *(Fouquieria splendens)*. Stems several in a cluster, mostly unbranched and canelike, 6 to 20 feet tall, gray with darker furrows and spreading spines; leaves somewhat fleshy, in clusters in the axils of the spines, 1 inch long or less, oblong or obovate; flowers in a dense panicle, 4 to 10 inches long, the corolla tubular, about 1 inch long, bright scarlet; stamens 10 or more, longer than the corolla.

OLIVE FAMILY (OLEACEAE)

Mostly woody plants with very diverse characters and habit.

1. Plant woody only near the base; leaves mostly alternate;
   flowers perfect; fruit a capsule.
   MENODORA *(Menodora scabra)* 172
   Plant woody throughout; leaves opposite; flowers
   imperfect; fruit a winged akene.   2.

2. Twigs 4-sided.
   SINGLE LEAF ASH *(Fraxinus anomala)* 172
   Twigs not 4-sided.   3.

3. Leaflets not more than 1½ inches long; flowers with corolla.
   FRAGRANT ASH *(Fraxinus cuspidata var. macropetala)* 172
   Leaflets mostly more than 1½ inches long; flowers
   without corolla.
   VELVET ASH *(Fraxinus velutina)* 172

Families Of Plants *171*

SINGLE LEAF ASH (*Fraxinus anomala*). A shrub or small tree, 6 to 36 feet tall, bushy; leaves often simple but sometimes with 3 or more leaflets, the leaf blades, or the terminal leaflets of compound leaves, nearly round, 1 to 2 inches across, entire or scalloped; flowers very small, in panicles, appearing before the leaves, mostly imperfect, the male and female flowers on separate plants; fruits ½ to 1 inch long, the wing extending nearly to the base of the body.

FRAGRANT ASH (*Fraxinus cuspidata* var. *macropetala*). A large shrub or small tree; leaves mostly with 3 or 5 leaflets, these less than 1¼ inches long, pointed at both ends; flowers with 4 petals, fragrant.

VELVET ASH (*Fraxinus velutina* syn. *F. pennsylvanica* var. *velutina*). Usually a tree up to 30 feet tall, the twigs varying from densely short-hairy to nearly smooth; leaflets 3 to 7, lanceolate or obovate, mostly 1½ to 3½ inches long, more or less hairy; male and female flowers on separate plants, without petals; fruits with the wing extending to about the middle of the body.

MENODORA (*Menodora scabra*). Stems 2 to 12 inches tall, woody toward the base; leaves 1 inch long or less, narrowly oblong or linear; flowers several near the ends of the branches, bright yellow, the corolla about ¼ inch long; fruit a capsule.

GENTIAN FAMILY (GENTIANACEAE)

Herbaceous, mostly smooth, plants with simple, entire, sessile leaves and perfect, regular or nearly regular flowers, the petals united, the ovary superior.

1. Flowers pink.

Flowers blue, purplish or yellowish-white; corolla 5-lobed. 2.
Flowers greenish-white; corolla 4-lobed. 3.

2. Corolla about 1 inch long or more, dark blue.

Corolla ½ inch long or less, pale blue to nearly white.

3. Leaves not white-margined; 2 fringed gland pits on each corolla lobe.

Leaves white-margined; 1 fringed gland pit on each corolla lobe. 4.

4. Stem leaves, except the uppermost, whorled; gland pit broadened and notched at the top.

Stem leaves opposite; gland pit not notched at the top, 2-lobed at the base.

CENTAURIUM *(Centaurium calycosum)*. Stems 4 to 24 inches tall, often much-branched; leaves opposite, linear to narrowly oblong, ½ to 1½ inches long; flowers on long stalks in the axils of upper leaves; corolla 5-lobed, the lobes pink, the tube yellow; stamens 5, the anthers becoming twisted spirally. Flowers very showy.

GENTIAN *(Gentiana heterosepala)*. Stems 3 to 10 inches tall, usually unbranched; leaves opposite, ½ to 1½ inches long, lanceolate to oblanceolate; flowers 1 to 3 on slender stalks in the axils of upper leaves; corolla ½ inch long or less, pale blue to nearly white, without pleats in the sinuses between the lobes.

GENTIAN *(Gentiana parryi)*. Leaves opposite, ovate to lanceolate, about 1½ inches long or less; flowers 1 to 6 in a terminal cluster subtended by leaflike bracts which often conceal the calyx; corolla about 1½ inches long, blue with bands of green outside, the 5 lobes short and with pleats in the sinuses forming 5 additional lobes.

DESERT SWERTIA *(Swertia albomarginata)*. Stem 8 to 24 inches tall, usually much-branched; leaves mostly in whorls of 3 or 4, linear to oblanceolate, often folded; corolla lobes greenish-white dotted with purple.

DEERS-EARS *(Swertia radiata* syn. *Frasera speciosa)*. Stem stout, 1 to 5 feet tall; basal leaves 4 to 12 inches long, narrowly oblong; those on the stem in whorls of 3 to 7, lanceolate to linear; corolla lobes ½ to 1 inch long, greenish-white dotted with purple.

GREEN-GENTIAN *(Swertia utahensis)*. Stems 3½ feet tall or less, few-branched near the top; leaves largely basal, narrowly lanceolate, 2 inches long or less, those on the stem much smaller, linear; corolla 4-lobed, the lobes greenish-white usually spotted with purple.

DOGBANE FAMILY (APOCYNACEAE)

Herbaceous plants with milky juice, simple, entire leaves, and perfect regular flowers with 5 united petals, 5 stamens and 2 pistils. The fruit is a pair of pods.

1. Leaves alternate; flowers blue; seeds without a tuft of hairs.
   AMSONIA *(Amsonia eastwoodiana)* 174
   Leaves opposite; flowers not blue; seeds with a tuft
   of hairs. 2.

2. Corolla white, less than ⅛ inch long, not much longer
   than the calyx.
   HEMP DOGBANE *(Apocynum cannabinum)* 174
   Corolla pinkish or striped with pink, more than ⅛
   inch long. 3.

3. Corolla lobes conspicuously spreading and often curved
   downward at the tip, at least 3 times as long as the calyx.

SPREADING DOGBANE *(Apocynum androsaemifolium)* 174
Corolla lobes only moderately spreading, not much
curved at the tip, about twice as long as the calyx.

DOGBANE *(Apocynum medium)* 174

AMSONIA *(Amsonia eastwoodiana).* Stems usually 20 inches tall or less,
usually branched; leaves linear to narrowly lanceolate, ½ to 2½ inches long, rather
numerous; flowers 1 to several near the ends of the branches; corolla tube about
½ inch long, blue, the lobes spreading, ¼ inch long, pale blue or whitish; pods
slender, 1 to 3 inches long.

SPREADING DOGBANE *(Apocynum androsaemifolium).* Stems 8 to 20
inches tall; leaves ovate to lanceolate, 1 to 4 inches long, white with pink veins;
pods 2 to 5 inches long.

HEMP DOGBANE *(Apocynum cannabinum).* Stems 12 to 20 inches tall;
leaves mostly ovate, mostly short-petioled, 1 to 4 inches long; corolla white or
pinkish; pods 3 to 5 inches long.

DOGBANE *(Apocynum medium).* Stems 8 to 20 inches tall; leaves mostly
ovate, sessile or nearly so, 2 to 4 inches long; flowers white or greenish-white;
pods 3 to 5 inches long.

MILKWEED FAMILY (ASCLEPIADACEAE)

Mostly herbs with simple leaves, milky juice, and regular, perfect flowers
which are borne in umbels and are highly specialized for insect pollination. The
stamens and pistils are united in a column and there is a sort of crown between
the corolla and the column with hoodlike or hornlike appendages. The sepals
and often the corolla lobes are turned back when the flower is in bloom. The
fruit is a pod containing many seeds each provided with a tuft of hairs.

1. Stems climbing; leaves opposite.   2.
   Stems erect or nearly so, not climbing.   3.

2. Flowers white or whitish.
   CLIMBING-MILKWEED *(Funastrum cynanchoides)* 175
   Flowers purplish.
   CLIMBING-MILKWEED *(Funastrum heterophyllum)* 175

3. Leaves mostly in whorls of 3 or 4.
   POISON MILKWEED *(Asclepias subverticillata)* 175
   Leaves all opposite.
   BROADLEAF MILKWEED *(Asclepias latifolia)* 175
   Leaves mostly alternate.   4.

4. Flowers greenish with maroon or purple hood; plant with
   milky juice.
   ANTELOPE HORNS *(Asclepias capricornu)* 175

Flowers orange-red; plant without milky juice.
BUTTERFLY MILKWEED (*Asclepias tuberosa*) 175

ANTELOPE HORNS (*Asclepias capricornu*). Stems 8 to 24 inches tall, often several from the same base; leaves lanceolate to broadly linear, 1 to 3 inches long; umbel large, terminal; flowers greenish with maroon or purple hood, the corolla lobes not turned back; pods 2 to 4 inches long.

BROADLEAF MILKWEED (*Asclepias latifolia*). Stems 1 to 2½ feet tall, stout, unbranched; leaves 3 to 6 inches long, sessile or nearly so, broadly oval to nearly round, thick; umbels in the upper leaf axils, many-flowered; pods egg-shaped, 2 to 3 inches long.

POISON MILKWEED (*Asclepias subverticillata*). Stems 6 to 40 inches tall, branched or unbranched; leaves 1 to 5 inches long, linear; flowers small, in medium-sized umbels in the upper leaf axils; pods narrowly spindle-shaped, 2 to 4 inches long. Plant poisonous to livestock when eaten; not poisonous to touch.

BUTTERFLY MILKWEED (*Asclepias tuberosa*). Stems 1 to 2½ feet tall, hairy, very leafy; leaves mostly lanceolate, sessile or nearly so, 1 to 3 inches long; umbels several at the end of the stem; flowers varying from orange to yellow, very showy; pods 3 to 4 inches long, hairy.

CLIMBING-MILKWEED (*Funastrum cynanchoides* syn. *Sarcostemma cynanchoides*). Stems twining, several feet long; leaves ovate to lanceolate, heart-shaped or arrow-shaped at the base, mostly 1 inch long or less; flowers, white or whitish, in axillary umbels; pods spindle-shaped, 2 to 3 inches long, about ¼ inch wide in greatest width.

CLIMBING-MILKWEED (*Funastrum heterophyllum* syn. *Sarcostemma cynanchoides* ssp. *hegwegii*). Very similar to the preceding but the leaves are linear or nearly so, often 2 or 3 inches long, and not heart-shaped or arrow-shaped at the base. The flowers are purplish also, especially on the backs of the corolla lobes.

MORNING GLORY FAMILY (CONVOLVULACEAE)
Herbaceous plants mostly with trailing or twining stems, simple leaves and perfect, regular flowers, usually very showy; sepals nearly separate but the petals united; stamens 5; styles 1 or 2; fruit a capsule.

1. Plants without green leaves.
DODDER (*Cuscuta campestris*) 176
Plants with green leaves. 2.

2. Flowers bright red, the corolla with a narrow tube.
SCARLET STARGLORY (*Ipomoea coccinea* var. *hederifolia*) 176
Flowers white or pinkish, the corolla bell-shaped.

FIELD BINDWEED or **GLORYBIND** (*Convolvulus arvensis*) 176

FIELD BINDWEED or **GLORYBIND** *(Convolvulus arvensis)*. Stems usually trailing, often covering the ground over a considerable area; leaves variable but usually more or less ovate with an arrow-shaped base; flowers white or pink, similar to those of a cultivated morning glory but smaller.

DODDER *(Cuscuta campestris)*. Stems yellow, twining on a variety of herbaceous plants and parasitic on them; leaves reduced to alternate scales; flowers very small, whitish.

SCARLET STARGLORY *(Ipomoea coccinea* var. *hederifolia)*. Stems sometimes trailing but often twining and climbing high on other plants; leaves broadly heart-shaped, about 2 inches long or less, entire or 3-lobed; flowers 1 to 3 at the ends of short branches; corolla trumpet-shaped, about 1 inch long.

PHLOX FAMILY (POLEMONIACEAE)

Our members of this family are all herbaceous or somewhat woody only toward the base and all have simple leaves. The flowers are perfect and regular or nearly so; the petals are united; stamens 5; the pistil usually 3-lobed at the end of the style. The fruit is a capsule. In many species the flowers are very showy.

1. Leaves in alternate clusters; plant somewhat woody
   toward the base.
   Leaves mostly alternate or basal, not in alternate clusters.   2.
   Leaves mostly opposite.   11.

2. Teeth or lobes of leaves tipped with long, white bristles.
   Leaves without long, white bristles.   3.

3. Leaves entire.   4.
   Leaves toothed or lobed or both.   5.

4. Corolla about ½ inch long or less, about twice as long
   as the calyx or less, purplish-pink or white.
   Corolla ½ to 1 inch long, about 3 times as long as the
   calyx, salmon-pink or apricot.

5. Flowers bright red or bright pink.
   Flowers blue, violet, purple, pale pink or whitish.   6.

6. Stems with a cluster of leaves at the base, the upper
   leaves few and small.   7.
   Stems rather equally leafy throughout, without a definite
   cluster of leaves at the base.   8.

   COLLOMIA *(Collomia grandiflora)*. Stems 6 to 36 inches tall; leaves linear to lanceolate, 1 to 3 inches long; flowers in dense clusters at the end of the stem or its branches.

COLLOMIA *(Collomia linearis)*. Similar to the preceding but smaller throughout, usually 2 to 10 inches tall, the lower leaves often purplish.

SKYROCKET *(Gilia aggregata)*. Stems mostly 1 to 2½ feet tall; leaves pinnately dissected into many linear lobes, mostly ½ to 2 inches long; corolla mostly 1 to 1¼ inches long, bright red or pink, sometimes spotted with yellow, the tube rather narrow, the lobes spreading.

GILIA *(Gilia longiflora)*. Stems mostly 6 to 12 inches tall, much-branched; leaves mostly less than 1 inch long, some linear and entire but mostly with a few linear lobes; flowers in an open panicle, the corolla between 1 and 2 inches long with a narrow tube and spreading lobes, pale blue, very attractive.

GILIA *(Gilia multiflora)*. Stems 3 to 16 inches tall, usually branched from the base, the larger plants somewhat woody at the base; leaves less than 1 inch long, linear and entire or with 2 linear lobes; flowers in small, headlike clusters; corolla between ¼ and ½ inch long, pale blue to nearly white.

GILIA *(Gilia polyantha* var. *whitingi)*. Very similar to the preceding but the flowers are smaller, the leaves often have 5 linear lobes, and the plant is entirely herbaceous.

GILIA *(Gilia sinuata)*. Stems mostly 4 to 12 inches tall, branched; leaves mostly basal, 1 to 2 times pinnately lobed; flowers in a rather loose panicle and quite numerous; corolla very variable in color, pinkish or purplish varying to nearly white, or the tube yellowish, sometimes with light or dark spots at the upper end of the tube.

GILIA *(Gilia tenuiflora)*. Very similar to the preceding but the flowers larger and fewer. Both species are very variable and some specimens seem intermediate between the two.

LANGLOISIA *(Langloisia setosissima)*. Stems clustered, 1 to 3 inches tall, sometimes with prostrate branches up to 4 inches long; leaves crowded near the ends of the branches; flowers light violet, about ¼ inch long, resembling the flowers of a gilia. The plant was formerly classified as a gilia but is readily distinguished from the gilias by the conspicuous white bristles mentioned in the key.

LEPTODACTYLON *(Leptodactylon pungens)*. Stems usually less than 1 foot high, very leafy, woody toward the base; leaves mostly alternate, about ¼ inch long with several linear lobes; flowers solitary or in small clusters, the corolla ½ to ¾ inch long, white or yellowish.

LINANTHUS *(Linanthus bigelovii)*. Stems 4 to 12 inches high, usually repeatedly forked to form a bushy plant; leaves opposite, 1 inch long or less, linear, usually with 2 or 3 linear lobes; flowers sessile in the forks of the stem, the corolla 1 inch long or less, white or pale yellow with brownish-purple on the backs of the lobes.

DESERT LINANTHUS *(Linanthus demissus)*. Very similar to the preceding but seldom more than 4 inches tall, most of the leaves alternate, and the corolla tube very short.

MICROSTERIS *(Microsteris gracilis)*. Stems 1 to 6 inches tall, the larger plants branched above; leaves broadly linear to oblong, the lower ones often purplish, mostly less than 1 inch long; flowers in rather dense clusters, mostly about ¼ inch long; corolla with yellowish tube and pink or purplish lobes.

DESERT PHLOX *(Phlox austromontana)*. Stems clustered, 2 to 4 inches tall, the leafy branches with short, spreading hairs; leaves mostly ½ inch long or less, needle-shaped; flowers mostly solitary at the ends of the branches; corolla white or purplish, the tube nearly ½ inch long, the lobes ½ as long as the tube.

SPREADING PHLOX *(Phlox diffusa)*. Stems clustered, 2 to 10 inches long, usually spreading or even prostrate; leaves very abundant, about ½ inch long, needle-shaped but not very stiff nor sharp-pointed; flowers usually abundant, less than ½ inch long, the corolla pink, lilac or white.

GRAY PHLOX *(Phlox grayi)*. Stems 4 to 8 inches tall; leaves narrowly lanceolate, 2 inches long or less; flowers few in rather loose clusters, nearly 1 inch long, the corolla lobes about ¼ inch long, pink to white.

LONGLEAF PHLOX *(Phlox longifolia)*. Stems 3 to 12 inches tall, varying from nearly prostrate to erect; leaves narrowly linear, 1 to 3 inches long; flowers few or many; corolla white to pink, the tube about ½ inch long, the lobes ½ as long as the tube.

WATERLEAF FAMILY (HYDROPHYLLACEAE)

Our members of this family are herbs with perfect, regular flowers, 5 united petals, 5 stamens and 1 pistil with 1 or 2 styles.

1. Leaves all basal.

Leaves not all basal. 2.

2. Stems, leaves and capsules prickly.

Stems, leaves and capsules not prickly. 3.

3. Leaves entire. 4.
Leaves more or less toothed or lobed. 5.

4. Leaves linear or nearly so; flowers purple.

Leaves mostly oblanceolate or ovate; flowers bluish with a white tube.

5. Ovary 1-celled; flowers very small.
EUCRYPTA *(Eucrypta micrantha)* 180
Ovary more or less completely 2-celled; flowers larger
and more conspicuous. 6.

6. Leaves toothed or scalloped, not pinnately lobed
or pinnate. 7.
Leaves pinnately lobed or 1 or more times pinnate. 9.

7. Flowers white.
PHACELIA *(Phacelia laxiflora)* 182
Flowers lilac or purple, often with a whitish tube. 8.

8. Lower flower stalks much longer than the calyx.
PHACELIA *(Phacelia glechomaefolia)* 182
Lower flower stalks as long as or shorter than the calyx.
PHACELIA *(Phacelia rotundifolia)* 182

9. Leaves mostly pinnate with few entire leaflets.
PHACELIA *(Phacelia magellanica)* 182
Leaves pinnate or pinnately lobed, the leaflets or lobes
not entire. 10.

10. Leaves definitely pinnate with the leaflets distinct
and well separated. 11.
Basal portion of leaves usually pinnate with the leaflets
close together, the upper portion merely pinnately lobed. 12.

11. Plant very bristly with stiff hairs, especially in the flower
cluster, not very sticky nor ill-scented; leaflets oblong.
PHACELIA *(Phacelia cryptantha)* 182
Plant more or less hairy but not bristly with stiff hairs,
very sticky and ill-scented; leaflets nearly round.
PHACELIA *(Phacelia pedicellata)* 182

12. Leaves pinnately lobed not more than halfway to the midrib.
PHACELIA *(Phacelia corrugata)* 182
Leaves pinnately lobed more than halfway to the midrib.
PHACELIA *(Phacelia crenulata)* 182

EUCRYPTA *(Eucrypta micrantha).* Stems 2 to 10 inches tall, rather weak
and widely branched; lower leaves mostly 1 to 2 inches long, pinnately lobed
into 7 or 8 oblong, entire or few-toothed lobes, the upper ones shorter and somewhat clasping at the base of the petiole; flowers 4 to 12 on each branch, very
small; corolla white to bluish.

HESPEROCHIRON *(Hesperochiron pumilus).* Flowering stems 1 to 2 inches
tall, often shorter than the leaves; leaves all in a basal rosette, the blades oblong

PAINTBRUSH
(Castilleja confusa)

PHOTO SCHULZ

PAINTBRUSH
(Castilleja linariaefolia)

PHOTO MERKLE

MOUNTAIN SNOWBERRY
(Symphoricarpos oreophilus)

PHOTO MERKLE

ROCKY MOUNTAIN PUSSYTOES
(Antennaria aprica)

PHOTO MERKLE

or oblanceolate, 1 to 2 inches long, entire, the petioles about 1 inch long or less; flowers solitary on each stalk, about ½ inch across, lilac-purple to nearly white.

NAMA *(Nama dichotomum)*. This species is said to have been collected on the South Rim several years ago but we have not found it. It is a low, annual plant with narrow leaves and small, purple flowers.

PHACELIA *(Phacelia corrugata)*. Stem 6 to 20 inches tall, moderately hairy and glandular; leaves 1 to 4 inches long, scalloped or pinnately lobed; raceme 6 inches long or less, coiled at the tip; corolla ¼ to nearly ½ inch long, about twice as long as the calyx, deep blue or violet; stamens longer than the corolla.

PHACELIA *(Phacelia crenulata)*. Very similar to the preceding but more densely glandular and strongly scented, and the leaves more deeply lobed or divided.

PHACELIA *(Phacelia cryptantha)*. Stems 4 to 20 inches tall; leaves 1½ to 4 inches long with rather few leaflets, these toothed or lobed; flowers numerous in short racemes coiled at the tip; corolla lavender, ¼ inch long or less, about as long as the calyx; stamens included within the corolla tube.

PHACELIA *(Phacelia glechomaefolia)* (*P. filiformis* which was described as a new species from the park is probably synonymous with *P. glechomaefolia)*. Stems 4 to 15 inches tall, unbranched; leaf blades nearly round, ¼ to 1 inch across, the petioles about as long; racemes 1 to 5 inches long, loosely 1-flowered, not coiled at the tip; corolla ¼ to ½ inch long; stamens included within the corolla tube.

PHACELIA *(Phacelia laxiflora)*. Very similar to the preceding but the plant more leafy, the racemes more densely flowered and the corollas white.

PHACELIA *(Phacelia magellanica)*. Stems several, mostly unbranched except for the short flower branches, mostly 4 to 30 inches tall; leaves 1 to 8 inches long with 1 to 3 pairs of lateral leaflets; racemes short and dense; corolla blue or purplish to almost white; stamens and styles nearly twice as long as the corolla.

PHACELIA *(Phacelia pedicellata)*. Stems rather stout, openly branched, 5 to 20 inches tall, the entire plant densely glandular-hairy and very ill-scented; leaves 1 to 5 inches long with 3 to 7 rounded, lobed or toothed leaflets; flowers many in a rather dense panicle; corolla lilac to nearly white.

PHACELIA *(Phacelia rotundifolia)*. Stems 2 to 10 inches tall, branched from the base, more or less glandular-hairy throughout; leaf blades broadly ovate to round, less than 1 inch long, coarsely toothed or lobed, the petiole longer than the blade; flowers in loose racemes, these coiled at the tip; corolla less than ¼ inch long, pale violet to white, often yellowish at the base; stamens included within the corolla tube.

PHACELIA *(Phacelia saxicola)*. A low annual herb 2 to 6 inches tall, widely branched; leaf blades oblanceolate, less than ¼ inch long, the petiole about as long; racemes 2 or 3 inches long, rather few-flowered, coiled at the tip; flowers very small; corolla bluish with a white tube.

FIESTA FLOWER (*Pholistoma auritum* var. *arizonicum*). A straggling, rather coarse, loosely branched plant with stems 1 to 3 feet long, the entire plant armed with prickles; leaf blades 2 to 6 inches long, deeply lobed with the lobes projecting backward somewhat, the petioles broadly winged, clasping the stem at the base; flowers in terminal clusters of 2 to 6 or solitary in the leaf axils; corolla pale blue with darker markings, ½ to 1 inch across; stamens included within the corolla tube.

BORAGE FAMILY (BORAGINACEAE)

Herbaceous plants and a few woody species with simple, alternate leaves and perfect, regular flowers with a 5-lobed calyx, a 5-lobed corolla, 5 stamens, and 1 pistil. The ovary is often 5-lobed and breaks up into 4 nutlets at maturity. Many members of the family are quite difficult to identify. In fact identification of some species is impossible unless mature fruits are present.

1. Stems more or less woody, especially toward the base. 2.
   Stems not woody; style not lobed; stigma 1. 4.

2. Style not lobed; stigma 1.
   Style 2-lobed; stigmas 2. 3.

3. Leaf blades nearly as wide as long, densely hairy with white hairs.
   Leaf blades linear or nearly so, much longer than wide, armed with scattered, white bristles.

4. Nutlets wide-spreading, armed with hooked prickles; plants prostrate or partly so. 5.
   Nutlets erect or nearly so, not wide-spreading. 7.

5. Nutlets of 2 sorts, 2 of them conspicuously winged, the other 2 not winged or very narrowly so.
   Nutlets all alike or nearly so. 6.

6. Nutlets with a very conspicuous, broad, toothed margin, the body of the nutlet straight or nearly so.
   Nutlets with a very inconspicuous margin, the body of the nutlet becoming conspicuously curved.

7. Nutlets armed with barbed prickles. 8.
   Nutlets not armed with prickles. 9.

8. Margin of 2 or more of the nutlets conspicuously swollen.
   TEXAS STICKSEED *(Lappula texana)* 188
   None of the nutlets with swollen margins.
   WESTERN STICKSEED *(Lappula redowskii)* 188

9. Corolla blue. 10.
   Corolla white or yellow. 11.

10. Flower stalks hairy; calyx lobed to the base or nearly
    so; leaves more or less hairy above, smooth below.
    BLUEBELLS *(Mertensia franciscana)* 188
    Flower stalks not hairy; calyx lobed only to the middle
    or less; leaves smooth on both sides.
    BLUEBELLS *(Mertensia macdougalii)* 188

11. Nutlets with a ridge along the inner face. 12.
    Nutlets with a groove along the inner face. 17.

12. Flowers white. 13.
    Flowers yellow. 14.

13. Roots and lower parts of the stem purplish and containing
    a purple dye.
    POPCORN PLANT or **BLOODWEED** *(Plagiobothrys arizonicus)* 189
    Roots and stems without a purple dye.
    POPCORN PLANT *(Plagiobothrys jonesii)* 189

14. Plants very bristly with spreading white hairs. 15.
    Plants hairy but not bristly, the hairs not conspicuously
    spreading. 16.

15. Calyx 5-lobed; corolla 10-nerved below the stamens.
    FIDDLENECK *(Amsinckia intermedia)* 186
    Calyx 2- to 4-lobed, the broader lobes toothed at the
    end; corolla 20-nerved below the stamens.
    FIDDLENECK *(Amsinckia tessellata)* 186

16. Corolla about 1 inch long, the lobes fringed or
    irregularly toothed.
    GROMWELL or **PUCCOON** *(Lithospermum incisum)* 188
    Corolla about ½ inch long, the lobes entire.
    GROMWELL or **PUCCOON** *(Lithospermum multiflorum)* 188

17. Plants coarse, rather stout, mostly perennial. 18.
    Plants slender, mostly annual. 24.

18. Corolla tube distinctly longer than the calyx. 19.

Corolla tube scarcely if any longer than the calyx. 21.

19. Corolla white.

CRYPTANTHA *(Cryptantha capitata)* 187
Corolla yellow. 20.

20. Flowers in a rather dense, narrow panicle; corolla
bright yellow.

CRYPTANTHA *(Cryptantha flava)* 187
Flowers in terminal, headlike clusters with a few
similar but smaller clusters in the leaf axils; corolla
pale yellow.

CRYPTANTHA *(Cryptantha confertiflora)* 187

21. Nutlets smooth and shiny, not flattened.

CRYPTANTHA *(Cryptantha jamesii)* 187
Nutlets rough, strongly flattened. 22.

22. Margin of nutlets with a conspicuous, papery wing;
plant usually more than 16 inches tall.

CRYPTANTHA *(Cryptantha setosissima)* 188
Margin of nutlets not winged; plants usually less than
16 inches tall. 23.

23. Flower-bearing branches 6- to 10-flowered, 1 to 3
inches long or more.

CRYPTANTHA *(Cryptantha virginensis)* 188
Flower-bearing branches 2- to 6-flowered, 1 inch long or less.

CRYPTANTHA *(Cryptantha abata)* 186

24. Nutlets all smooth and shining. 25.
Nutlets all or some of them roughened. 26.

25. Plant not conspicuously bristly, the hairs rather short;
nutlets 1 to 3.

CRYPTANTHA *(Cryptantha gracilis)* 187
Plant conspicuously bristly with white, spreading
hairs; nutlets 4.

CRYPTANTHA *(Cryptantha fendleri)* 187

26. Calyx conspicuously curved.

CRYPTANTHA *(Cryptantha recurvata)* 188
Calyx not conspicuously curved. 27.

27. One nutlet distinctly differing from the others in size. 28.
Nutlets all alike or nearly so. 30.

28. Odd nutlets on the side away from the axis of the flower
cluster; nutlets dark.

CRYPTANTHA *(Cryptantha inaequata)* 187
Odd nutlet on the side toward the axis of the flower
cluster; nutlets usually pale.   29.

29. The similar nutlets winged.
    CRYPTANTHA *(Cryptantha pterocarya)* 188
    The similar nutlets not winged.
    CRYPTANTHA *(Cryptantha crassisepala)* 187

30. Style distinctly surpassing the nutlets.   31.
    Style not surpassing the nutlets or barely so.   32.

31. Nutlets more or less winged, the wings entire; plant
    usually 1 to 2 feet tall.
    CRYPTANTHA *(Cryptantha holoptera)* 187
    Nutlets winged, the wings scalloped or lobed; plants
    usually less than 1 foot tall.
    CRYPTANTHA *(Cryptantha pterocarya)* 188

32. Nutlets wing-margined.
    CRYPTANTHA *(Cryptantha pterocarya)* 188
    Nutlets not wing-margined.   33.

33. Plants bristly with spreading hairs.
    CRYPTANTHA *(Cryptantha barbigera)* 187
    Plant hairy but not bristly, most of the hairs not spreading.
    CRYPTANTHA *(Cryptantha nevadensis)* 187

FIDDLENECK *(Amsinckia intermedia)*. Stems 8 to 32 inches tall, somewhat
bristly, especially in the flower cluster; leaves linear to lanceolate, 2 to 6 inches
long, alternate; flowers in racemes that are coiled at the tip; corolla yellow,
between ¼ and ½ inch long.

FIDDLENECK *(Amsinckia tessellata)*. Very similar to the preceding except
in the characters given in the key.

SPREADING COLDENIA *(Coldenia canescens)*. A low-spreading plant, often
forming mats, the older stems woody, white-hairy throughout; stems 2 to 10
inches long; leaf blades ovate to oblong, about ¼ inch long with shorter petioles;
flowers mostly solitary, often partly hidden by the numerous leaves; corolla
white, less than ¼ inch long.

HISPID COLDENIA *(Coldenia hispidissima)*. Stems mostly 3 to 6 inches
long, prostrate or partly so or at least wide-spreading, woody at least below,
with white, bristlelike hairs; leaves narrowly oblanceolate to linear, rolled; flowers
small, white, solitary in the leaf axils.

CRYPTANTHA *(Cryptantha abata)*. Several stems from a branched base,
usually less than 1 foot tall; leaves crowded at the base, scattered on the stem,

1 to 3 inches long, linear to oblanceolate; flowers white, crowded in a short, dense spike.

CRYPTANTHA *(Cryptantha barbigera)*. Stems 3 to 15 inches tall, much-branched from the base, very bristly; leaves linear to narrowly oblong, bristly like the stems; corolla white, very small and inconspicuous.

CRYPTANTHA *(Cryptantha capitata)*. Known only from the Grand Canyon this plant is very similar to the following species except that the corolla is white instead of yellow and the plant is smaller, somewhat greener, and the small lateral flower clusters are very small or lacking entirely.

CRYPTANTHA *(Cryptantha confertiflora)*. Stems 6 to 20 inches tall, the bases white-hairy, the upper parts somewhat less hairy and bristly; leaves linear to narrowly oblanceolate; flowers pale yellow and quite conspicuous, nearly ½ inch long and about ¼ inch across the corolla.

CRYPTANTHA *(Cryptantha crassisepala)*. Stems 2 to 6 inches tall, erect or wide-spreading, hairy, leaves oblanceolate, about 1 inch long or less, hairy; corolla white, very small; odd nutlet larger than the other 3.

CRYPTANTHA *(Cryptantha fendleri)*. Stems 4 to 20 inches tall, branched near the top, more or less bristly; leaves 1 to 2 inches long, bristly, narrowly oblanceolate; corolla very small and inconspicuous; nutlets usually 4, all alike.

CRYPTANTHA *(Cryptantha flava)*. Very similar to *Cryptantha confertiflora* except for the characters given in the key.

CRYPTANTHA *(Cryptantha gracilis)*. Stems 4 to 8 inches tall, the branches not spreading, hairy; leaves about 1 inch long or less, linear to narrowly oblanceolate, rather few; corolla very small and inconspicuous; nutlets 1 to 3, all alike.

CRYPTANTHA *(Cryptantha holoptera)*. Stems 4 to 24 inches tall, usually much-branched, bristly; leaves linear to narrowly lanceolate, the upper sessile, the lower short-petioled; corolla very small and inconspicuous; nutlets 4, all alike.

CRYPTANTHA *(Cryptantha inaequata)*. Stems 12 to 16 inches tall, branched throughout, hairy and bristly; leaves mostly linear, ½ to 1½ inches long; corolla very small and inconspicuous; nutlets 4, the odd one a little longer.

CRYPTANTHA *(Cryptantha jamesii)*. Stems 4 to 12 inches tall, branched from the base and usually above also, hairy; leaves linear to narrowly lanceolate, 1 to 4 inches long, hairy; corolla white, less than ¼ inch long, not longer than the calyx; nutlets 1 to 4.

CRYPTANTHA *(Cryptantha nevadensis)*. Stems slender, 4 to 20 inches tall, rather short-hairy; leaves linear to oblanceolate, ½ to 1½ inches long; racemes up to 6 inches long; corolla white, very small; nutlets 4.

CRYPTANTHA *(Cryptantha pterocarya)*. Stems 4 to 20 inches tall, branched throughout, the branches not spreading; leaves ½ to 1 inch long, linear to lanceolate, hairy; corolla very small and inconspicuous, white; nutlets 4, all alike and winged.

CRYPTANTHA *(Cryptantha racemosa)*. A bush plant, 1 to 2½ feet high, woody below, upper branches slender, hairy; leaves awl-shaped to narrowly oblanceolate, from less than ½ inch to 1½ inches long; corolla white, very small and inconspicuous; nutlets 4, 1 a little larger.

CRYPTANTHA *(Cryptantha recurvata)*. Stems slender, 4 to 12 inches tall; branched from the base; lower leaves oblanceolate, ½ to 1 inch long, those on the stem few and smaller; corolla white, very small and inconspicuous; ovary 2-parted, producing 2 nutlets but only 1 matures a seed.

CRYPTANTHA *(Cryptantha setosissima)*. Stem stout, 15 to 30 inches tall, mostly unbranched except near the top, very bristly; basal leaves 2 to 6 inches long, oblanceolate, narrowed to a petiole, those on the stem smaller; racemes in a narrow panicle; flowers numerous; corolla white.

CRYPTANTHA *(Cryptantha virginensis)*. Stems clustered, 4 to 16 inches tall, bristly; leaves oblanceolate, 2 to 4 inches long, the lower ones crowded, bristly; corolla white, about ¼ inch long.

WESTERN STICKSEED *(Lappula redowskii)*. Stems 4 to 24 inches tall, usually branched only near the top but sometimes with several branches from the base, hairy; leaves 1½ inches long or less, linear to lanceolate, hairy; flowers very numerous in terminal racemes on all branches; corolla whitish to pale blue.

TEXAS STICKSEED *(Lappula texana)*. Distinguished from the preceding primarily by the fruit characters given in the key.

GROMWELL or **PUCCOON** *(Lithospermum incisum)*. Stems 4 to 20 inches tall, usually several together, hairy; leaves ½ to 2 inches long, linear or oblong, hairy; flowers in terminal, leafy racemes; corolla ½ to 1 inch long with narrow tube, yellow.

GROMWELL or **PUCCOON** *(Lithospermum multiflorum)*. Stems 1 to 2 feet tall, often clustered, hairy; leaves linear to narrowly lanceolate, 1 to 2½ inches long, smaller near the flowers; flowers in racemes; corolla yellow, ¼ to ½ inch long.

BLUEBELLS *(Mertensia franciscana)*. Stems 4 to 40 inches tall; leaves 4 inches long or less, elliptical, the lower petioled, the upper sessile, all entire; corolla about ¼ inch long, blue all over.

BLUEBELLS *(Mertensia macdougalii)*. Very similar to the preceding but the flowers are nearly twice as large and the lower part of the corolla tube is yellowish or whitish.

CHUCKWALLA COMBSEED *(Pectocarya heterocarpa)*. Stems 1 to 6 inches long, branched from the base and often wide-spreading; leaves narrowly linear, 1 inch long or less; flowers solitary in the leaf axils, very small and inconspicuous, the corolla white, shorter than the calyx; the wide-spreading nutlets unlike, 2 narrower, the 2 wider ones with prominent wings which are bristly at the tip.

BROAD-FRUITED COMBSEED *(Pectocarya platycarpa)*. Very similar to the preceding except that all the nutlets are nearly alike and broadly winged, the hooked prickles prominent.

RECURVED COMBSEED *(Pectocarya recurvata)*. Very similar to the 2 preceding species but the nutlets strongly curved back and the hooked prickles more or less awl-shaped.

POPCORN PLANT or **BLOODWEED** *(Plagiobothrys arizonicus)*. Stems branched from the base, 4 to 16 inches tall, bristly with stiff, white hairs; leaves linear to narrowly lanceolate, ½ to 2 inches long; racemes several inches long, the flowers loosely arranged; corolla small, white.

POPCORN PLANT *(Plagiobothrys jonesii)*. Stems erect, 1 or several from the same base, 4 to 12 inches tall, very bristly; leaves linear to lanceolate, ½ to 1 inch long, bristly; racemes terminating the branches, ½ to 1 inch long, some flowers also solitary or few in leaf axils; corolla very small, white.

VERBENA FAMILY (VERBENACEAE)

Members of this family resemble mints, often having 4-sided stems and irregular flowers, but they differ from both mints and borages in having unlobed ovaries, although the fruit usually consists of 2 or 4 nutlets; stamens 4; style 1; leaves simple and mostly opposite.

1. Aromatic shrubs.

LIPPIA *(Aloysia wrightii)* 189
Herbs. 2.

2. Corolla tube more than ¼ inch long; flowers very showy.

WRIGHTS VERBENA *(Verbena wrightii)* 190
Corolla tube less than ¼ inch long; flowers not very showy. 3.

3. Stem branched from the base; leaves lobed and toothed.

BIGBRACT VERBENA *(Verbena bracteata)* 190
Stem usually branched only near the top; leaves toothed but not lobed.

TALL VERBENA *(Verbena macdougalii)* 190

LIPPIA *(Aloysia wrightii)*. A shrub, 2 to 6 feet high, with slender, opposite, somewhat hairy branches; leaves opposite, less than ½ inch long, broadly ovate to nearly round, the margin finely and deeply scalloped; flowers very small, white, in slender axillary spikes.

BIGBRACT VERBENA *(Verbena bracteata)*. Stems 4 to 20 inches long, wide-spreading and partly prostrate; leaves 1½ inches long or less, pinnately lobed, hairy; spikes mostly 1 to 2½ inches long, the bracts conspicuous, much longer than the calyx; corolla blue or purple.

TALL VERBENA *(Verbena macdougalii)*. Stems 1 to 2½ feet tall, branched near the top, hairy; leaves 1 to 3 inches long, elliptic to lanceolate, coarsely toothed; spikes ½ to 5 inches long; flowers blue or purple.

WRIGHTS VERBENA *(Verbena wrightii)*. Stems 8 to 24 inches tall, usually several from the same base, hairy, branched, spreading; leaves twice pinnately lobed, the lobes cut and toothed, hairy; spikes short and broad when in flower, becoming longer in fruit; bracts shorter than the calyx and not conspicuous; corolla pink to purple.

MINT FAMILY (LABIATAE)

Herbs or shrubs with usually 4-sided stems, opposite leaves, irregular flowers with united petals, 2 or 4 stamens, a 4-lobed ovary, and often a characteristic odor. The fruit consists of 4 nutlets.

1. Woody plants (shrubs).
Non-woody plants (herbs). 2.

2. Stamens 2. 3.
Stamens 4. 7.

3. Flowers red.
Flowers yellow.
Flowers neither red nor yellow. 4.

4. Flowers in several dense whorls, these subtended by an involucre of conspicuous bracts.
Flowers solitary or in small clusters in the leaf axils, without conspicuous bracts. 5.

5. Leaves more than ½ inch long, mostly toothed; flowers blue.
Leaves less than ½ inch long, mostly entire; flowers purple. 6.

6. Calyx teeth at maturity bent inward thus closing the calyx tube, the calyx tapering from the middle to the tip.
Calyx teeth spreading, the upper 2 turned downward, the tube thus open and the calyx clearly 2-lipped.

7. Calyx teeth 10, hooked at the tip.
   HOREHOUND *(Marrubium vulgare)* 191
   Calyx teeth 5.   8.

8. Lobes of the calyx very unequal; flowers in dense
   spikes with prominent bracts.   9.
   Lobes of the calyx somewhat unequal in length but
   otherwise much alike.   10.

9. Leaves coarsely and sharply toothed; stamens included
   within the corolla tube.
   DRAGONHEAD *(Dracocephalum parviflorum)* 191
   Leaves entire or with a few small teeth; stamens longer
   than the corolla tube, lying beneath its upper lip.
   SELFHEAL *(Prunella vulgaris)* 192

10. Flowers in a dense, terminal spike.
    GIANT HYSSOP *(Agastache pallidiflora)* 191
    Flowers in dense clusters in the axils of the upper leaves.
    FIELD MINT *(Mentha arvensis)* 191
    Flowers in a solitary, terminal, headlike cluster.
    MONARDELLA *(Monardella odoratissima)* 192

   GIANT HYSSOP *(Agastache pallidiflora)*. Stems 1 to 2 feet tall or more; leaf blades 1 to 2 inches long, broadly ovate or more or less heart-shaped, petioled; flowers in a thick, terminal spike; corolla strongly 2-lipped, white or lavender-tinged; stamens longer than the corolla tube.

   DRAGONHEAD *(Dracocephalum parviflorum* syn. *Moldavica parviflora)*. Stems 8 to 30 inches tall, rather few-branched; leaf blades lanceolate to oblong, coarsely toothed, narrowed to a slender petiole; flowers in a dense, terminal spike, the bracts prominent and spine-tipped; corolla 2-lipped, light blue, the lower lip 3-lobed.

   FALSE-PENNYROYAL *(Hedeoma drummondii)*. Stems 3 to 10 inches tall, usually rather widely branched; leaves linear to oval, mostly less than ½ inch long; corolla about ¼ inch long, purple.

   DWARF FALSE-PENNYROYAL *(Hedeoma nanum)*. A low, usually much-branched herb with slender, short-hairy stems, 4 to 8 inches tall; leaves entire, short-petioled, about ¼ inch long or less, sparsely hairy and glandular-dotted beneath; flowers pale purple, crowded in clusters in the upper leaf axils.

   FIELD MINT *(Mentha arvensis)*. Stems 4 to 16 inches tall; leaves oblong to lanceolate, toothed, 2 inches long or less; flowers pink or purplish, small, in dense axillary clusters. Very aromatic.

   HOREHOUND *(Marrubium vulgare)*. Stems rather stout, branches 1 to 3 feet tall, white-woolly; leaves oval to broadly ovate, the blades 1 to 2 inches long, white-woolly beneath, white-hairy above, the petiole about ½ inch long; flowers small, white, in dense, axillary whorls.

BEEBALM *(Monarda pectinata).* Stems mostly 6 to 15 inches high, branched from the base; leaves oblong, entire or nearly so, mostly less than 1 inch long; flowers light rose, pink or whitish, in several dense clusters with conspicuous, subtending bracts, these with stiff bristles on the margins.

MONARDELLA *(Monardella odoratissima).* Stems usually 8 to 12 inches tall from an often prostrate base, branched or unbranched; leaves lanceolate to oblong, entire or nearly so, mostly less than 1 inch long; flowers in a single, headlike, terminal cluster subtended by purplish bracts; corolla white or rose often dotted with purple.

SELFHEAL *(Prunella vulgaris).* Stems 3 to 12 inches tall; leaves 1 to 3 inches long, ovate to lanceolate, entire or nearly so; spike 1 to 2 inches long or more, dense, the bracts leaflike; corolla ¼ to ½ inch long, strongly 2-lipped, violet.

MEDITERRANEAN SAGE *(Salvia aethiopis).* Stems 1 to 2 feet tall, rather bushy, hairy; lower leaf blades ovate to nearly round, sharply cut and toothed, 1 to 2 inches long on petioles about as long, the upper leaves much smaller; flowers pale yellow, in whorls on the branches of a wide-spreading panicle; calyx white-woolly; corolla ½ inch long or more, about twice as long as the calyx.

DESERT SAGE *(Salvia carnosa).* A low, much-branched shrub, 1 to 2 feet high and often as wide, the branches and leaves densely covered with whitish scales; leaf blades oval to oblong, less than ½ inch long, on petioles about as long; flowers in 1 to 3 headlike whorls on each branch with conspicuous purple or greenish bracts, these hairy or nearly smooth; corolla blue, between ¼ and ½ inch long.

RED SAGE *(Salvia davidsonii).* Stems up to 30 inches tall, sparsely branched and sparsely leafy, hairy; leaves highly variable, some of the lower ones pinnately compound, up to 4 inches long, with some very small, entire leaflets and some larger, coarsely toothed ones, while some of the upper leaves are simple, entire and only ½ inch long or less; flowers solitary in the axils of upper leaves; corolla about 1 inch long, bright red.

ROCKY MOUNTAIN SAGE *(Salvia reflexa).* Stems 4 to 12 inches tall, usually unbranched; leaves narrowly linear, 1 to 2 inches long, entire or sharply toothed; corolla between ¼ and ½ inch long, light purple.

NIGHTSHADE FAMILY (SOLANACEAE)

Herbs and shrubs with perfect, regular flowers, the petals united. Stamens usually distinct but the anthers often close together around the style producing a characteristic cone-shaped structure. The fruit is a capsule or a berry.

1. Woody plants (shrubs), producing red berries.   2.

Non-woody plants (herbs).   4.

2. Corolla greenish.
PALE WOLFBERRY *(Lycium pallidum)* 194
Corolla tube yellowish, the lobes pale lavender or pink.   3.

3. Largest leaves 1 to 2 inches long.
TORREY WOLFBERRY *(Lycium torreyi)* 194
Largest leaves ½ inch long or less, very narrow.
ANDERSON WOLFBERRY or **DESERT THORN** *(Lycium andersonii)* 194

4. Corolla 4 to 8 inches long, white.
SACRED DATURA or **JIMSONWEED** *(Datura meteloides)* 194
Corolla less than 2 inches long.   5.

5. Corolla long-tubular, more than ½ inch long.   6.
Corolla open, bell-shaped or flatter; less than ½ inch long.   7.

6. Leaves with slender petioles, not clasping at the base.
COYOTE TOBACCO *(Nicotiana attenuata)* 194
Leaves sessile or with short, broad petioles, more or less
clasping at the base.
DESERT TOBACCO *(Nicotiana trigonophylla)* 194

7. Flowers in terminal, or more often lateral, clusters,
not in the axils of leaves.   8.
Flowers solitary or few in the axils of leaves.   10.

8. Stems prickly; flowers purple.
SILVERLEAF NIGHTSHADE *(Solanum elaeagnifolium)* 196
Stems not prickly; flowers white.   9.

9. Corolla with greenish spots near the base.
DOUGLAS NIGHTSHADE *(Solanum douglasii)* 196
Corolla without greenish spots, sometimes purple-tinged.
AMERICAN NIGHTSHADE *(Solanum americanum)* 196

10. Calyx not bladdery in fruit, its lobes not closed over the top
of the berry; corolla with hairy pads between the stamens.
CHAMAESARACHA *(Chamaesaracha coronopus)* 194
Calyx bladdery in fruit, its lobes closed over the top of the
berry; corolla without hairy pads.   11.

11. Leaves entire or slightly scalloped; plant usually sticky.
GROUND-CHERRY *(Physalis crassifolia)* 194
Leaves coarsely few-toothed; plants usually not sticky.   12.

12. Calyx in fruit 10-angled.
GROUND-CHERRY *(Physalis hederaefolia)* 194
Calyx in fruit obscurely angled.

Families Of Plants   193

GROUND-CHERRY *(Physalis fendleri)* 194

CHAMAESARACHA *(Chamaesaracha coronopus).* Stems 4 to 8 inches long, much-branched and often partly prostrate; leaves oblong to linear, ½ to 2 inches long, often coarsely toothed; flowers solitary or 2 or 3 together on slender stalks; corolla between ¼ and ½ inch across, greenish-white often tinged with purple.

SACRED DATURA or **JIMSONWEED** *(Datura meteloides).* Stems 1 to 3 feet tall, branched; leaves 4 to 6 inches long, petioled, entire or few-toothed, ovate; flowers solitary in the leaf axils or in forks of the stem, large and showy; corolla white, 6 to 8 inches long; capsule about 1 inch long, oblong or nearly spherical, very spiny.

ANDERSON WOLFBERRY or **DESERT THORN** *(Lycium andersonii).* A shrub up to 9 feet high, but usually lower; leaves linear or nearly so, ½ inch long or less, somewhat fleshy; corolla about ½ inch long, slender, usually yellowish-white with lavender lobes; stamens longer than the corolla tube; berry bright red.

PALE WOLFBERRY *(Lycium pallidum).* A much-branched shrub, 3 to 6 feet high, spiny; leaves ½ to 1½ inches long, pale green, mostly oblong or oblanceolate; corolla about ½ inch long or more, greenish or tinged with purple; stamens usually slightly longer than the corolla tube; berries red or reddish-blue.

TORREY WOLFBERRY *(Lycium torreyi).* A much-branched shrub, 3 to 10 feet high, with heavy spines and dense foliage; leaves narrowly oblong or oblanceolate, 2 inches long or less, gradually narrowing to a short petiole; corolla about ½ inch long with a narrow tube; stamens slightly longer than the corolla tube; berries bright red.

COYOTE TOBACCO *(Nicotiana attenuata).* Stems 1 to 3 feet tall, often branched, glandular-hairy; leaves narrowly ovate or lanceolate to nearly linear, pointed at both ends, petioled, 2 to 3 inches long; flowers mostly in few-flowered racemes; corolla about 1 inch long, white or greenish.

DESERT TOBACCO *(Nicotiana trigonophylla).* This tobacco differs from the preceding in being more conspicuously glandular-hairy and in having shorter, broader, sessile leaves which clasp the stem at the base.

GROUND-CHERRY *(Physalis crassifolia).* Stems 1 to 2 feet tall, the branches wide-spreading and forming a bushy plant often wider than high; leaf blades broadly ovate, ½ to 1½ inches long, on slender petioles about as long; corolla dull yellow with 5 hairy bands extending from the base to the tips of the lobes; fruiting calyx 1 to 2 inches long; berry greenish.

GROUND-CHERRY *(Physalis fendleri).* Stems usually 8 to 16 inches tall; leaves heart-shaped to lanceolate, shallowly scalloped or toothed, mostly 1 to 2 inches long; corolla about ½ inch across, dull yellow with a brown center; fruiting calyx about 1 inch long; berry yellow.

GROUND-CHERRY *(Physalis hederaefolia).* Stems usually erect, 4 to 10

HOARY ASTER
(Aster canescens)

LEAFYBRACT ASTER
(Aster foliaceus)

RAGLEAF
(Bahia dissecta)

HAIRY GOLD-ASTER
(Chrysopsis villosa)

Families Of Plants 195

inches tall; leaf blades broadly ovate to somewhat heart-shaped, ½ to 1½ inches long on petioles about as long, coarsely scalloped or toothed; corolla about ½ inch across, yellow; fruiting calyx about 1 inch long, 10-angled; berry yellow.

AMERICAN NIGHTSHADE *(Solanum americanum)*. Stems 18 to 30 inches tall; leaf blades ovate to lanceolate, the larger ones 1 to 4 inches long, on slender petioles; flowers in clusters of 2 to 4, with slender stalks; corolla white or purple-tinged; berry black.

DOUGLAS NIGHTSHADE *(Solanum douglasii)*. Stems 1 to 5 feet tall; leaf blades ovate, petioled, pointed at both ends, 1 to 3 inches long, white with greenish spots near the base; berry black.

SILVERLEAF NIGHTSHADE *(Solanum elaeagnifolium)*. Stems 3 feet high or less, silvery-hairy, usually prickly; leaves oblong or lanceolate, 1 to 3 inches long, petioled; corolla blue or violet, about 1 inch across, showy; berry yellow.

FIGWORT FAMILY (SCROPHULARIACEAE)

Herbs and a few shrubs with more or less irregular flowers; calyx with 4 or 5 teeth or lobes; stamens 2, 4, or 5, most often 4; ovary superior, 2-celled, not lobed; style 1; fruit a capsule.

1. Stems woody, at least toward the base. 2.
   Stems not woody. 4.
2. Flowers red.
   BRIDGES BEARDTONGUE *(Penstemon bridgesii)* 201
   Flowers blue or purple. 3.
3. Corolla rounded below and not 2-ridged within; stems often more than 6 inches long.
   TOADFLAX BEARDTONGUE *(Penstemon linarioides)* 202
   Corolla flattened below and 2-ridged within; stems usually less than 6 inches long, forming mats.
   MAT BEARDTONGUE *(Penstemon caespitosus)* 201
4. Anther-bearing stamens 5; corolla only slightly irregular.
   FLANNEL MULLEIN *(Verbascum thapsus)* 203
   Anther-bearing stamens 4. 5.
   Anther-bearing stamens 2. 30.
5. Leaves all basal or nearly so. 6.
   Leaves all alternate. 7.
   Leaves opposite. 15.
6. Flowers white or pink-tinged; petioles much longer than the leaf blades.
   MUDWORT *(Limosella aquatica)* 200
   Flowers purple; petioles as long as, or shorter than the leaf blades.

LOUSEWORT or **WOOD BETONY** *(Pedicularis centranthera)* 201
Flowers yellow; leaves sessile or the petioles very short.

PRIMROSE MONKEYFLOWER *(Mimulus primuloides)* 200

7. Leaves all basal or near the base; plants low.

LOUSEWORT or **WOOD BETONY** *(Pedicularis centranthera)* 201
Plants with upright leafy stems. 8.

8. Calyx lobed; bracts and calyx not brightly colored. 9.
Calyx with 2 or more lobes; bracts and calyx brightly
colored. 10.
Flowers in terminal heads or short spikes.

BIRDBEAK *(Cordylanthus tenuifolius)* 200
Flowers scattered along the stems.

BIRDBEAK *(Cordylanthus parviflorus)* 200

10. Upper lip of corolla not much, if any, longer than the
somewhat flattened lower lip. 11.
Upper lip of corolla much longer than the small, usually
3-toothed lower lip. 12.

11. Flowers yellow.

YELLOW OWL-CLOVER *(Orthocarpus luteus)* 201
Flowers purple and white.

PURPLE-WHITE OWL-CLOVER *(Orthocarpus purpureo-albus)* 201

12. Bracts subtending flowers entire or 3-toothed at the tip;
leaves all entire or nearly so.

WHOLELEAF PAINTEDCUP or **PAINTBRUSH** *(Castilleja integra)* 199
Bracts subtending flowers, or some of them, deeply cut
or lobed. 13.

13. Leaves mostly pinnately lobed.

PAINTEDCUP or **PAINTBRUSH** *(Castilleja chromosa)* 199
Leaves mostly entire. 14.

14. Calyx cut much deeper on the upper side than on the
lower; bracts deeply divided into linear lobes, red.

WYOMING PAINTEDCUP or **PAINTBRUSH** *(Castilleja linariaefolia)* 199
Calyx cut about equally deep on both sides; bracts more or
less lobed but broad and conspicuous, red or yellow.

PAINTEDCUP or **PAINTBRUSH** *(Castilleja confusa)* 199

15. Stems climbing by twining.

TWINING-SNAPDRAGON *(Maurandya antirrhiniflora)* 200
Stems erect or prostrate, not twining. 16.

16. Flowers with a fifth sterile stamen. 17.
Flowers without a sterile stamen. 26.

17. Flowers white, tinged with pink at the top.

PALMER BEARDTONGUE *(Penstemon palmeri)* 202
Flowers some shade of red or pink. 18.
Flowers some shade of purple or blue. 21.

18. Leaves finely and sharply toothed, the bases of the upper ones grown together around the stem.

DESERT BEARDTONGUE *(Penstemon pseudospectabilis)* 202
Leaves entire or nearly so. 19.

19. Leaves broad, sessile and somewhat clasping at the base.

EATON BEARDTONGUE *(Penstemon eatoni)* 201
Leaves narrow at the base, not at all clasping. 20.

20. Corolla strongly 2-lipped, the lower lip turned back.

BEARDLIP BEARDTONGUE *(Penstemon barbatus)* 201
Corolla not strongly 2-lipped, the lips about equally erect or spreading.

UTAH BEARDTONGUE *(Penstemon utahensis)* 202

21. Stems prostrate or partly so, forming mats 1 to 2 inches high and 4 to 10 inches across.

THOMPSON BEARDTONGUE *(Penstemon thompsonae)* 202
Stems erect or nearly so, not forming mats. 22.

22. Calyx densely glandular-hairy.

JAMES BEARDTONGUE *(Penstemon jamesii)* 201
Calyx smooth or nearly so. 23.

23. Leaves linear or nearly so, narrow at the base, not clasping.

WANDBLOOM BEARDTONGUE *(Penstemon virgatus)* 202
At least some of the leaves with broad, more or less clasping bases. 24.

24. Sterile stamen bearded almost its entire length.

THICKLEAF BEARDTONGUE *(Penstemon pachyphyllus)* 202
Sterile stamen bearded only at or near the tip. 25.

25. Corolla dark purple.

RYDBERG BEARDTONGUE *(Penstemon rydbergii)* 202
Corolla skyblue to lavender.

NARROWLEAF BEARDTONGUE *(Penstemon angustifolius)* 201

26. Corolla blue and white, swollen at one side of the base.

COLLINSIA *(Collinsia parviflora)* 200
Corolla red.

CRIMSON MONKEYFLOWER *(Mimulus cardinalis)* 200
Corolla yellow, sometimes with red spots or pink lobes. 27.

27. Upper calyx tooth much longer than the others; corolla strongly 2-lipped.

COMMON MONKEYFLOWER *(Mimulus guttatus)* 200
Upper calyx tooth not much, if any, longer than the others; corolla only slightly 2-lipped. 28.

28. Leaves all basal or crowded toward the base of the stem.

PRIMROSE MONKEYFLOWER *(Mimulus primuloides)* 200
Leaves not all basal or crowded toward the base of the stem; stem usually much-branched from the base. 29.

29. Leaves about as long as the distance between nodes, appearing crowded; calyx lobes fringed with hairs.

MONKEYFLOWER *(Mimulus suksdorfii)* 201
Leaves much shorter than the distance between nodes, not appearing crowded; calyx lobes not fringed with hairs.

MONKEYFLOWER *(Mimulus rubellus)* 200

30. Flowers solitary in the axils of most of the leaves; corolla white.

PURSLANE SPEEDWELL *(Veronica peregrina)* 203
Flowers in racemes. 31.

31. Racemes terminal; corolla pale blue or white.

THYMELEAF SPEEDWELL *(Veronica serpyllifolia)* 203
Racemes axillary; corollas blue.

AMERICAN SPEEDWELL *(Veronica americana)* 203

PAINTEDCUP or **PAINTBRUSH** *(Castilleja chromosa)*. Stems 10 to 20 inches tall, several from the same base; leaves 1 to 3 inches long, mostly cleft into narrow lobes; spikes 1 to 2 inches long, becoming longer as the fruits develop; bracts tipped with red, cleft like the upper leaves; calyx reddish or yellowish; corolla greenish-yellow.

PAINTEDCUP or **PAINTBRUSH** *(Castilleja confusa)*. Stem 1 to 2 feet tall; leaves 1 to 2 inches long, narrowly lanceolate to ovate, mostly entire; bracts red or yellow, mostly lobed or toothed; calyx about equally cleft above and below; corolla about 1 inch long, often tipped with red.

WHOLELEAF PAINTEDCUP or **PAINTBRUSH** *(Castilleja integra)*. Stems 4 to 16 inches tall, more or less white-hairy; leaves 1½ to 2½ inches long, narrowly lanceolate to linear, mostly entire; bracts conspicuous, entire or toothed at the tip, red; calyx 1 to 1½ inches long, red at the tip; corolla greenish or the margins red.

WYOMING PAINTEDCUP or **PAINTBRUSH** *(Castilleja linariaefolia)*. Very similar to the preceding but the stem is often taller and not white-hairy, the leaves are often narrower, and the bracts are usually lobed.

COLLINSIA *(Collinsia parviflora).* Stems 2 to 16 inches tall; leaf blades 1 to 1½ inches long, oblong or elliptic, narrowed to a sessile base, the lower ones much smaller and petioled, the upper ones whorled; flowers mostly solitary in the axils of leaves on slender stalks; corolla strongly 2-lipped, the upper lip white or whitish, the lower lip blue.

BIRDBEAK *(Cordylanthus parviflorus).* Stem 5 to 20 inches tall, much-branched; leaves linear, about ½ inch long or less; flowering bracts purplish; corolla about ½ inch long, purplish or lavender with a yellow tip.

BIRDBEAK *(Cordylanthus tenuifolius).* This species is reported to have been found in the park but we have not seen it.

MUDWORT *(Limosella aquatica).* This little plant, usually less than 3 inches high, grows in wet soil and each flowering plant is usually surrounded by a group of smaller plants each at the end of a small runner; leaf blades 1 inch long or less, the petioles several times as long as the blades and the flower stalks about ½ as long as the petioles; flowers very small; corolla white or purplish.

TWINING-SNAPDRAGON *(Maurandya antirrhiniflora).* Stems much-branched and extensively climbing over other vegetation; leaf blades triangular in outline, shaped like an arrowhead but with 2 spreading basal lobes, ½ to 1 inch long and about as wide at the base; flowers solitary in the leaf axils, violet or purple, resembling snapdragon flowers.

CRIMSON MONKEYFLOWER *(Mimulus cardinalis).* Stems 5 to 40 inches tall, hairy; leaf blades oval to elliptic, toothed, sessile and more or less clasping at the base, the larger ones 3 to 4 inches long; flowers solitary on long stalks in the leaf axils; corolla 1½ to 2 inches long, the lobes red, the throat yellowish, strongly 2-lipped.

COMMON MONKEYFLOWER *(Mimulus guttatus).* Stems 16 to 40 inches tall; leaf blades oval, irregularly toothed, 3 to 4 inches long, the petiole often as long as the blade on the lower leaves but the upper leaves sessile; corolla about 1 inch long, yellow, usually spotted with red, the palate nearly closing the throat of the tube.

PRIMROSE MONKEYFLOWER *(Mimulus primuloides).* Stem usually less than 2 inches long, hairy; leaves crowded at or near the base, oblong or obovate, mostly less than 1 inch long; entire or finely toothed; flowers on slender stalks, these ½ to 1½ inches long; corolla about ½ inch long, yellow, the palate darker yellow and densely hairy.

MONKEYFLOWER *(Mimulus rubellus).* Stems 1 to 6 inches tall, simple or branched from the base; leaves ovate to lanceolate or linear, sessile or nearly so, the margins entire or irregularly toothed; corolla usually about ¼ inch long, yellow, sometimes pink near the tip.

MONKEYFLOWER *(Mimulus suksdorfii).* Very similar to the preceding with the exception of the differences given in the key.

YELLOW OWL-CLOVER *(Orthocarpus luteus).* Stems 4 to 15 inches tall, unbranched or branched only near the top; leaves linear or nearly so, less than ½ inch long; flowers in a terminal spike; corolla about ½ inch long, golden yellow.

PURPLE-WHITE OWL-CLOVER *(Orthocarpus purpureo-albus).* Stems 4 to 16 inches tall, usually branched above the middle; leaves ½ inch long or less, linear and entire or cleft into 2 or 3 linear lobes; corolla about ½ inch long or a little more, varying from white to purple.

LOUSEWORT or **WOOD BETONY** *(Pedicularis centranthera).* Stems 4 to 6 inches tall, smooth, clustered; leaves clustered near the base, 2 to 6 inches long, lobed part way to the midrib, the lobes doubly toothed; flowers in short, thick, terminal spikes; corolla 1 to 1½ inches long, purple or yellowish-purple.

NARROWLEAF BEARDTONGUE *(Penstemon angustifolius).* Stems 4 to 15 inches tall, mostly smooth, unbranched; leaves mostly 1 to 3 inches long, lanceolate, entire, sessile and more or less clasping; corolla ½ inch long or more, smooth or nearly so throughout; sterile stamen bearded about ½ its length.

BEARDLIP BEARDTONGUE *(Penstemon barbatus).* Stems 1 to 4 feet tall; basal leaves mostly oblong and petioled, those on the stem lanceolate to linear and sessile, 1 to 5 inches long, smooth; raceme long and loosely flowered; corolla red, strongly 2-lipped, usually densely hairy in the throat but smooth in one variety; sterile stamen not bearded.

BRIDGES BEARDTONGUE *(Penstemon bridgesii).* Stems 1 to 2 feet tall, usually several together, woody toward the base; leaves linear to narrowly elliptic, mostly 1 to 2½ inches long; raceme loose and rather few-flowered; corolla 1 inch long or less, red, strongly 2-lipped, glandular-hairy; sterile stamen not hairy.

MAT BEARDTONGUE *(Penstemon caespitosus).* Stems 1 to 6 inches long, often prostrate, woody below, arising from creeping stems and forming mats; leaves linear or nearly so, ½ inch long or less; racemes short and few-flowered; corolla blue or purple, about ½ inch long; strongly 2-lipped; sterile stamen hairy almost its entire length.

EATON BEARDTONGUE *(Penstemon eatoni).* Stems 1 to 2 feet tall, solitary or few, unbranched, smooth or nearly so; leaves lanceolate to elliptic toward the base of the stem but ovate or heart-shaped higher up and with clasping bases, smooth, entire; raceme narrow, the flowers rather crowded in clusters; corolla red, nearly 1 inch long, only slightly 2-lipped; sterile stamen slender, not hairy or only slightly so at the tip.

JAMES BEARDTONGUE *(Penstemon jamesii).* Stems 3 to 15 inches long, short-hairy below and glandular-hairy above; leaves lanceolate to linear, 1 to 4 inches long, entire or nearly so; raceme rather long and crowded; corolla ½ to ¾ inch long, glandular-hairy on the outside, conspicuously white-hairy within; sterile stamen longer than the corolla and conspicuously hairy.

TOADFLAX BEARDTONGUE *(Penstemon linarioides)*. Stems mostly 6 to 10 inches long, partly prostrate, somewhat woody; leaves linear, less than 1 inch long, numerous, evergreen, usually densely short-hairy but sometimes smooth; flowers rather numerous; corolla purple; sterile stamen usually bearded, especially at the tip.

THICKLEAF BEARDTONGUE *(Penstemon pachyphyllus)*. Stems 1 to 2 feet tall, smooth, unbranched; leaf blades oblong to ovate, 1 to 2½ inches long, the basal ones narrowed to a petiole, those on the stem sessile with wide, clasping bases; raceme 4 to 10 inches long, many-flowered; corolla blue, ½ to ¾ inch long; sterile stamen hairy nearly its entire length.

PALMER BEARDTONGUE *(Penstemon palmeri)*. Stems 1 to 3 feet tall, smooth, unbranched; leaves ovate, toothed, the bases clasping or grown together around the stem, 2 to 6 inches long; raceme 1-sided; flowers large, showy and fragrant; corolla white, tinged with pink, about 1 inch long with a short tube and a greatly inflated throat; sterile stamen longer than the corolla with shaggy yellow hairs at the top and glandular hairs at the base.

DESERT BEARDTONGUE *(Penstemon pseudospectabilis)*. Stem mostly 2 to 3 feet tall, several from the same base; leaves narrowly to broadly ovate, toothed, the upper ones with the bases grown together around the stem; corolla purple often with a yellowish tube, about ¾ inch long; sterile stamen not hairy.

RYDBERG BEARDTONGUE *(Penstemon rydbergii)*. Stems 6 to 24 inches tall, few to many, smooth except near the top; leaf blades elliptic to lanceolate, the basal ones narrowed to short petioles, those on the stem sessile and somewhat clasping at the base; raceme with several dense clusters of flowers; corolla ½ inch long or less, dark purple, smooth on the outside, hairy within; sterile stamen shorter than the corolla tube, densely golden-bearded at the tip.

THOMPSON BEARDTONGUE *(Penstemon thompsonae)*. Stems 2 inches long or less, partly prostrate, forming mats 4 to 10 inches across; leaves entire, less than 1 inch long, oblanceolate to oblong, densely white-hairy; racemes short, leafy, few-flowered; corolla about ½ inch long, blue-violet; sterile stamen golden-haired nearly its entire length.

UTAH BEARDTONGUE *(Penstemon utahensis)*. Stems several, smooth, 1 to 2 feet tall; leaf blades 1 to 3 inches long, smooth or nearly so, the basal ones oblanceolate, short-petioled, those on the stem lanceolate, sessile, clasping; raceme smooth; corolla red, about ¾ inch long, only slightly 2-lipped; sterile stamen smooth or nearly so.

WANDBLOOM BEARDTONGUE *(Penstemon virgatus)*. Stems 1 to 2 feet tall, varying from densely short-hairy to nearly smooth; leaves linear, 1 to 3 inches long, usually short-hairy; raceme usually densely flowered; corolla red, occasionally white, ½ to ¾ inch long, the lower lip usually hairy; sterile stamen smooth.

FLANNEL MULLEIN *(Verbascum thapsus).* Stems 1 to 6 feet tall, stout; leaves 4 to 16 inches long, very woolly; flowers yellow, sessile in a stout spike that may be as much as 20 inches long.

AMERICAN SPEEDWELL *(Veronica americana).* Stems 4 to 24 inches long, erect or partly prostrate and rooting at the lower nodes; leaf blades lanceolate to ovate, 1 to 3 inches long, short-petioled, all opposite; flowers in axillary racemes; corollas blue, about ¼ inch across.

PURSLANE SPEEDWELL *(Veronica peregrina).* Stems 3 to 14 inches tall, often branched; leaves 1 inch long or less, entire or the larger ones toothed, the lower ones opposite, the upper ones alternate; flowers very small, in the axils of the upper leaves; corolla white.

THYMELEAF SPEEDWELL *(Veronica serpyllifolia).* Stems 4 to 12 inches long, the lower portion creeping and rooting at the nodes, the flower-bearing portion upright; leaf blades ½ inch long or less, sessile or the lower ones short-petioled, entire or scalloped; corolla less than ¼ inch across, pale blue to white with violet lines on the upper lobes.

BIGNONIA FAMILY (BIGNONIACEAE)

Shrubs or small trees with alternate or opposite leaves and large, showy flowers; corolla irregular; stamens 5, usually only 4 of them with anthers; fruit a long, podlike capsule with many, fairly large, flat seeds.

DESERT-WILLOW *(Chilopsis linearis).* A large shrub or small tree up to 30 feet tall; leaves alternate or the lower ones opposite, linear, entire, mostly 3 to 5 inches long; flowers in terminal racemes; corolla about 1 inch long, white, usually streaked or spotted with purple; capsule slender, 5 to 10 inches long; wing of seed dissected into many hairs.

UNICORN PLANT FAMILY (MARTYNIACEAE)

Rather coarse, hairy, somewhat sticky plants with large leaves, showy flowers and peculiar, large, podlike fruits that end in a long, curved, hooked beak.

DEVILS-CLAWS *(Proboscidea arenaria).* This is a southern species which has been found in the park only in Havasu Canyon. It differs from the following species in having the corolla copper-colored on the outside and yellow within, and the leaves are usually wider than long and more distinctly lobed.

DEVILS-CLAWS *(Proboscidea parviflora).* Stems wide-branching, usually 10 to 20 inches high; lower leaves opposite, long-petioled, the blade entire or shallowly lobed, several inches long and nearly as wide, the upper ones smaller and usually alternate; flowers few, in terminal racemes; corolla reddish-purple to nearly white, often streaked with yellow, about 1 inch across; fruit, including the beak, about 5 to 8 inches long.

BROOMRAPE FAMILY (OROBANCHACEAE)

Plants without green color, parasitic on the roots of other plants; stems somewhat fleshy; leaves reduced to scales, alternate; corolla irregular, 2-lipped; stamens 4; fruit a capsule containing many very small seeds.

1. Flowers in a loose, terminal cluster on long, slender stalks.

Flowers in dense, terminal spikes or spikelike racemes, sessile or on very short stalks. 2.

2. Corolla lobes pointed; anthers hairy.

Corolla lobes rounded; anthers not hairy.

BROOMRAPE *(Orobanche fasciculata)*. Stems, leaves and corolla usually dull yellow but sometimes brownish-purple; stem 1 to 5 inches tall; corolla about ½ inch long, the lobes nearly round.

BROOMRAPE *(Orobanche ludoviciana)*. Stems 2 to 8 inches tall; flowers short-stalked; corolla usually purplish, ½ to ¾ inch long.

BROOMRAPE *(Orobanche multiflora)*. Stems 2 to 12 inches tall, sometimes branched; flowers sessile or nearly so; corolla dark purple-rose.

PLANTAIN FAMILY (PLANTAGINACEAE)

Herbaceous plants with the leaves all basal, the small flowers in long-stalked spikes. The fruit is a small, few-seeded capsule.

1. Leaf blades lanceolate or broader. 2.
   Leaf blades linear or nearly so. 4.

2. Spike usually more than 2 inches long, often ½ as long as the stem that bears it; leaf blades ovate, abruptly narrowed to a petiole.

Spike usually less than 2 inches long, usually much less than ½ as long as the stem that bears it; leaf blades lanceolate, gradually narrowed into a petiole. 3.

3. Leaves mostly more than 3 inches long, more or less woolly at the base of the petiole.

Leaves mostly less than 3 inches long, not woolly at the
base of the petiole.
TWEEDY PLANTAIN (*Plantago tweedyi*) 205
4. Bracts subtending the flowers of the lower part of the
spike much longer than the calyx, lanceolate or awl-shaped.
WOOLLY INDIANWHEAT (*Plantago purshii*) 205
Bracts subtending the flowers of the lower part of the
spike not longer than the calyx, ovate.
INLAND PLANTAIN (*Plantago insularis*) 205

INLAND PLANTAIN (*Plantago insularis*). Flowering stems 3 to 6 inches
tall; leaves linear, hairy, about ½ as long as the flowering stems or less; bracts
very similar to the calyx lobes; corolla lobes conspicuously brown at the base
and often striped with brown above.

BUCKHORN PLANTAIN (*Plantago lanceolata*). Flowering stems 4 to 24
inches tall; leaf blades 2 to 8 inches long, narrowed into somewhat shorter
petioles; bracts broad, about as long as the calyx; corolla lobes spreading and
remaining so.

RIPPLESEED PLANTAIN (*Plantago major*). Flowering stems 3 to 15 inches
tall; leaf blades 2 to 8 inches long on short petioles; bracts broadly ovate, mostly
shorter than the calyx; corolla lobes pointed.

WOOLLY INDIANWHEAT (*Plantago purshii*). Flowering stems 2 to 8 inches
tall, woolly or silky throughout; leaf blades linear, 1 to 4 inches long, sessile,
hairy; sepal lobes ovate, hairy.

TWEEDY PLANTAIN (*Plantago tweedyi*). Flowering stems 4 to 8 inches
tall; leaf blades 1 to 3 inches long; bracts about as long or somewhat shorter
than the calyx; corolla lobes spreading.

MADDER FAMILY (RUBIACEAE)
Our members of this family are all herbs though a few are slightly woody
at the base; flowers rather small, regular; calyx and corolla 4-lobed; stamens
4; style 1; ovary inferior. The flowers are mostly perfect but in some of the
bedstraws they are imperfect with the male and female flowers on separate
plants.

1. Leaves opposite. 2.
Leaves whorled. 3.
2. Fruits armed with hooked prickles.
KELLOGGIA (*Kelloggia galioides*) 207
Fruits not armed with hooked prickles.
HOUSTONIA (*Houstonia wrightii*) 207
3. Fruits smooth or nearly so, not hairy.

SMALL BEDSTRAW (*Galium trifidum* var. *pusillum*) 206
Fruits conspicuously hairy. 4.

4. Hairs of the fruit not hooked nor curved, soft, white;
stems more or less woody at the base. 5.
Hairs of the fruit hooked or curved; stems not at
all woody. 7.

5. Corolla purplish to dark purple-brown.
WRIGHT BEDSTRAW (*Galium wrightii*) 207
Corolla greenish, greenish-yellow or reddish. 6.

6. Leaves rigid and needlelike.
BEDSTRAW (*Galium stellatum* var. *eremicum*) 207
Leaves not rigid and not needlelike.
MUNZ BEDSTRAW (*Galium munzii*) 207

7. Leaves 5 or more in each whorl, stems weak. 8.
Leaves not more than 4 in each whorl. 9.

8. Stems very rough to the touch; plant without creeping
underground stems, annual.
CATCHWEED BEDSTRAW (*Galium aparine*) 206
Stems smooth or nearly so; plants with creeping
underground stems, perennial.
SWEET-SCENTED BEDSTRAW (*Galium triflorum*) 207

9. Leaves in each whorl equal in size; flowers sessile.
DESERT BEDSTRAW (*Galium proliferum*) 207
Leaves in each whorl unequal in size; flowers stalked.
TWINLEAF BEDSTRAW (*Galium bifolium*) 206

CATCHWEED BEDSTRAW (*Galium aparine*). Stems 4 to 60 inches long;
erect or scrambling over other plants, armed with prickly hairs on the 4 angles;
leaves 6 to 8 in each whorl, 1 to 2 inches long, linear to narrowly oblanceolate;
flowers 1 to 3 together in the upper leaf axils, very small; corolla white; fruit
covered with short, hooked prickles.

TWINLEAF BEDSTRAW (*Galium bifolium*). Stem erect, 2 to 6 inches tall,
smooth; upper leaves opposite, lower ones in whorls of 3 or 4, lanceolate, 2
inches long or less, usually of unequal length in each whorl; flowers solitary
on stalks in the leaf axils; corolla white; fruit armed with slender, hooked
prickles.

SMALL BEDSTRAW (*Galium trifidum* var. *pusillum* syn. *G. brandegei*). A
low, mat-forming plant with stems 2 to 5 inches tall, smooth or nearly so; leaves
4 in each whorl, smooth, narrowly oblanceolate, unequal in length, mostly ¼
inch long or less; flowers very small, 1 to 2 on short stalks in leaf axils; corolla
white; fruits smooth.

MUNZ BEDSTRAW *(Galium munzii).* Stems several from a somewhat woody base, 6 to 14 inches tall, slender; leaves in whorls of 4, usually broadly lanceolate, less than ½ inch long; flowers very small, in a many-flowered panicle; corolla greenish or sometimes reddish; fruit with spreading hairs.

DESERT BEDSTRAW *(Galium proliferum).* Stems 4 to 14 inches tall, erect or partly prostrate at the base, smooth or slightly rough on the angles; leaves in whorls of 4, oblong to narrowly ovate, 1-veined, about ¼ inch long; flowers nearly sessile between 2 leaflike bracts on short branches; corolla white or pale yellow; fruit covered with fine bristles.

BEDSTRAW *(Galium stellatum* var. *eremicum).* Stems 8 to 16 inches tall, somewhat woody toward the base, usually much-branched, the angles of the branches white; leaves in whorls of 4, rigid, ¼ inch long or less, lanceolate; flowers in crowded, much-branched, leafy panicles; corollas greenish-yellow; fruit densely white-hairy.

SWEET-SCENTED BEDSTRAW *(Galium triflorum).* Stems several, weak, mostly unbranched, 4 to 16 inches tall, erect or partly prostrate; leaves ½ to 2 inches long, 1-nerved, in whorls of 6; flowers 1 to 3 at the ends of axillary stalks; corolla greenish; fruits densely hairy with hooked hairs.

WRIGHT BEDSTRAW *(Galium wrightii).* Stems several or many, 6 to 24 inches tall, slender, hairy, somewhat woody at the base; leaves in whorls of 4, linear, less than ½ inch long; flowers in few-flowered, terminal panicles; corolla purplish-brown; fruit with white, straight bristles. Variety *rothrockii* syn. *G. rothrockii,* which also occurs in the park, differs in having the stem smooth or nearly so.

HOUSTONIA *(Houstonia wrightii).* Stems much-branched from the base, 2 to 6 inches tall; leaves linear or nearly so, ¼ to ¾ inch long, opposite; flowers clustered at the ends of the branches, white or pinkish.

KELLOGGIA *(Kelloggia galioides).* Stems several, smooth or nearly so, 4 to 10 inches tall; leaves opposite, lanceolate, ¼ to 1½ inches long; flowers in an open, branched cluster; corolla about 1 inch long, pink or lavender; fruit densely covered with short bristles.

HONEYSUCKLE FAMILY (CAPRIFOLIACEAE)

All but one of our members of this family are either erect or climbing shrubs with opposite leaves and perfect flowers; corolla regular or slightly irregular; petals united; ovary inferior; fruit berrylike in most cases.

1. Leaves pinnately compound; flowers small, numerous. 2.
   Leaves simple; flowers not very numerous. 3.
2. Corolla white; berries dark blue or black.
   BLUEBERRY ELDER *(Sambucus glauca* syn. *S. coerulea)* 208
   Corolla yellowish; berries red.

BUNCHBERRY ELDER *(Sambucus microbotrys)* 208

3. Corolla about 1 inch long or more, red on the outside, orange within; stems straggling over other plants.
   ARIZONA HONEYSUCKLE *(Lonicera arizonica)* 208
   Corolla not more than ¼ inch long, white or pinkish; stem not straggling over other plants.   4.

4. Plants low, nearly herbaceous; stems prostrate, creeping.
   TWINFLOWER *(Linnaea borealis)* 208
   Plants woody throughout; stems erect; berries white.   5.

5. Corolla with a long, narrow tube, the lobes spreading to form a flat top; anthers almost sessile.
   LONGFLOWER SNOWBERRY *(Symphoricarpos longiflorus)* 209
   Corolla bell-shaped or funnel-shaped, the lobes not spreading; anthers definitely stalked.   6.

6. Corolla bell-shaped, less than ¼ inch long.   7.
   Corolla funnel-shaped, more than ¼ inch long.   8.

7. A low, spreading shrub, not more than 5 feet high, some branches often bending over and rooting at the tip.
   SNOWBERRY *(Symphoricarpos parishii)* 209
   An upright shrub 3 to 6 feet tall.

   UTAH SNOWBERRY *(Symphoricarpos utahensis)* 209

8. Young twigs entirely smooth.
   MOUNTAIN SNOWBERRY *(Symphoricarpos oreophilus)* 209
   Young twigs densely hairy with short hairs.

   ROUNDLEAF SNOWBERRY *(Symphoricarpos rotundifolius)* 209

TWINFLOWER *(Linnaea borealis).* Stems slender, up to 3 feet long, forming loose mats; leaves evergreen, ovate to nearly round, ¼ to ¾ inch long, usually scalloped above the middle, short-petioled; flowers in pairs on upright stalks, hanging like bells; corolla white or pink, ¼ to ½ inch long; stamens 4; fruit dry.

ARIZONA HONEYSUCKLE *(Lonicera arizonica).* A straggling shrub; leaves ovate, 3 inches long or less, the uppermost pair with the bases united around the stem; flowers usually in a single, terminal cluster on each branch, very showy.

BLUEBERRY ELDER *(Sambucus glauca* syn. *S. coerulea).* A shrub or small tree, 6 to 20 feet tall; leaves with 5 to 9 leaflets, these oblong or lanceolate, 1½ to 6 inches long, finely toothed, often 1-sided at the base; flowers white, in a compound, flat-topped or umbrella-shaped cluster, 3 to 6 inches across; berries dark blue.

BUNCHBERRY ELDER *(Sambucus microbotrys* syn. *S. racemosa* var. *microbotrys).* A low shrub, 1½ to 5 feet tall; leaves with 5 to 7 leaflets, these ovate to lanceolate, 2 to 5 inches long, coarsely toothed; flower cluster 1½ to 3 inches across and about as high; flowers cream color; berries red.

MOUNTAIN SNOWBERRY *(Symphoricarpos oreophilus).* An erect much-branched shrub, 3 to 4½ feet tall, the young twigs smooth; leaves about 1 inch long or less, oval, entire or toothed, the petioles very short; flowers in axillary pairs or in few-flowered, terminal, spikelike clusters, corolla a little less than ½ inch long, rose color.

LONGFLOWER SNOWBERRY *(Symphoricarpos longiflorus).* A rather low, spreading shrub, 20 to 40 inches tall; leaves ½ inch long or less, narrowly lanceolate or oblanceolate, entire, the petioles very short; flowers solitary or in pairs in the upper leaf axils or in short, terminal racemes; corolla between ¼ and ½ inch long, pink.

SNOWBERRY *(Symphoricarpos parishii).* Stems 20 to 40 inches long; leaves less than 1 inch long, oval to elliptic; flowers in the axils of upper leaves or in short, terminal racemes; corolla ½ inch long or less, pink.

ROUNDLEAF SNOWBERRY *(Symphoricarpos rotundifolius).* An erect but straggling shrub, 3 feet high or less; leaves broadly oval to ovate or nearly round, about 1 inch long or less; flowers in the upper leaf axils; corolla light to deep pink.

UTAH SNOWBERRY *(Symphoricarpos utahensis).* A shrub, 3 to 6 feet tall; leaves ½ to 1½ inches long, oval or ovate, usually entire; flowers in small clusters or short spikes in the upper leaf axils; corolla pink.

VALERIAN FAMILY (VALERIANACEAE)

Herbaceous plants with opposite leaves and small, mostly perfect flowers but often with imperfect flowers mixed with them; corolla, in ours, nearly regular but the tube swollen on one side; stamens usually 3; ovary inferior. These plants are quite variable and the species are often difficult to distinguish.

1. Plants with a conical taproot; leaves rather thick, the lateral veins nearly parallel with the midrib.
    EDIBLE VALERIAN *(Valeriana edulis)* 210
    Plants with horizontal underground stems and fibrous roots; leaves thin, the lateral veins spreading. 2.
2. Fruits usually hairy.
    WESTERN VALERIAN *(Valeriana occidentalis)* 210
    Fruits usually smooth.
    VALERIAN *(Valeriana capitata* subsp. *acutiloba)* 209

VALERIAN *(Valeriana capitata* subsp. *acutiloba).* Stems 6 to 18 inches tall, smooth or somewhat hairy at the nodes; basal leaves petioled, the blades mostly oblanceolate and entire; stem leaves sessile or nearly so, often pinnately lobed with 2 to 4 entire lobes; corolla funnelform, white to pink.

EDIBLE VALERIAN *(Valeriana edulis).* Stems 4 to 24 inches tall, smooth or nearly so; basal leaves petioled, the blades entire or with a few lobes; stem leaves sessile or nearly so, usually 3- to 7-lobed; panicle large and open, especially in age; corolla yellowish or white.

WESTERN VALERIAN *(Valeriana occidentulis* syn. *V. micrantha).* Very similar to V. *acutiloba* but usually a larger plant, 12 to 32 inches tall, and some of the stem leaves may have as many as 9 lobes.

GOURD FAMILY (CUCURBITACEAE)

Herbaceous plants with tendrils, trailing or climbing, the leaves alternate, the flowers imperfect but the male and female flowers on the same plant. The ovary is inferior and the fruit is a large modified berry.

BUFFALO GOURD *(Cucurbita foetidissima).* Stems trailing or climbing, 5 to 15 feet long or more; leaves broadly ovate, somewhat heart-shaped at the base, 4 to 10 inches long; flowers large, yellow, scattered along the stem; corolla 3 to 4 inches long; fruit 3 to 4 inches in diameter, smooth.

BELLFLOWER FAMILY (CAMPANULACEAE)

Herbaceous plants with simple, alternate leaves and perfect flowers, the calyx and corolla lobes and stamens 5 each, the ovary inferior or partly so; fruit a capsule.

1. Corolla regular, purple; stamens simple.

PARRY BELLFLOWER *(Campanula parryi)* 210
Corolla irregular; stamens united to form a tube.   2.

2. Flowers very small; corolla white.

NEMACLADUS *(Nemacladus glanduliferus* var. *orientalis)* 210
Flowers medium-large, showy; corolla red.

CARDINAL FLOWER *(Lobelia cardinalis)* 210

PARRY BELLFLOWER *(Campanula parryi).* Stems 4 to 12 inches tall; lower leaves mostly oblanceolate, ½ to 2 inches long, entire or nearly so, the upper leaves linear and shorter; flower usually solitary at the end of the stem; corolla blue or purple, about ½ inch long.

CARDINAL FLOWER *(Lobelia cardinalis).* Stems 1 to 3 feet tall, unbranched; leaves 2 to 6 inches long, linear or oblong, usually toothed but sometimes entire; flowers in a terminal, spikelike raceme; corolla ½ to 1½ inches long, split down one side nearly to the base.

NEMACLADUS *(Nemacladus glanduliferus* var. *orientalis).* A low, much-branched plant, 2 to 8 inches high; basal leaves narrowly oblong, mostly less than 1 inch long, toothed; stem leaves reduced to small, linear bracts; flowers solitary on a slender stalk in the axil of nearly every bract; corolla white usually tipped with purple.

NEW MEXICO THISTLE
(Cirsium neomexicanum)

FLEABANE
(Erigeron formosissimus)

BLANKETFLOWER
(Gaillardia pinnatifida)

SUNFLOWER
(Helianthus petiolaris)

COMPOSITE FAMILY (COMPOSITAE)

This is the largest family of seed plants in the world. Nearly one-fifth of those in the park belong to it. It includes both woody and non-woody plants though the great majority are non-woody. The chief characteristic of the family is that in almost all cases the flowers are in heads subtended by an involucre of bracts so that what superficially looks like a single flower is really a bouquet of several or many flowers. The structural characters that are used to identify members of the family are shown in figure 2.

1. Corolla distinctly 2-lipped. 2.
   Corolla tubular or strap-shaped, not 2-lipped. 3.

2. Woody plants (shrubs); corollas yellow.
   TRIXIS *(Trixis californica)* 249
   Non-woody plants (herbs); corollas pink.
   PEREZIA *(Perezia wrightii)* 245

3. Woody plants (shrubs). 4.
   Non-woody plants (herbs). 42.

4. Corollas of ray flowers strap-shaped, those of disk
   flowers tubular. 5.
   None of the flowers with strap-shaped corollas. 13.

5. Ray flowers white, very small.
   MARIOLA *(Parthenium incanum)* 245
   Ray flowers yellow. 6.

6. Pappus of 1 or 2 awns. 7.
   Pappus of several scales. 8.
   Pappus of hairlike bristles. 11.

7. Flowers in a loose, few-flowered panicle; flower stalks
   not hairy.
   WHITE BRITTLEBUSH *(Encelia farinosa)* 237
   Flowers solitary at the ends of branches; flower stalks hairy.
   BUSH ENCELIA *(Encelia frutescens)* 237

8. Leaves and involucres bearing conspicuous oil glands. 9.
   Leaves and involucres not bearing conspicuous oil glands. 10.

9. Leaves pinnately lobed into 3 to 5 narrow lobes.
   DOGWEED *(Dyssodia porophylloides)* 237
   Leaves linear, entire, needlelike.
   PRICKLEAF DOGWEED *(Dyssodia acerosa)* 237

10. Ray flower 1; disk flowers 1 or 2.
    STICKY SNAKEWEED *(Gutierrezia lucida)* 240
    Ray and disk flowers 3 to 8 each.
    BROOM SNAKEWEED *(Gutierrezia sarothrae)* 240

11. Leaves and involucres not bearing conspicuous oil glands.
WATSON GOLDENWEED *(Haplopappus watsoni)*
Leaves and involucres bearing conspicuous oil glands. 12.

12. Leaves pinnately lobed into 3 to 5 narrow lobes.
DOGWEED *(Dyssodia porophylloides)*
Leaves linear, entire, needlelike.
PRICKLEAF DOGWEED *(Dyssodia acerosa)*

13. Pappus none. 14.
Pappus of awns. 21.
Pappus of hairlike bristles. 23.

14. Flowers all imperfect, the male and female flowers in separate heads. 15.
Flowers all perfect or some perfect and some imperfect in the same heads. 16.

15. Fruits densely hairy and armed with spines.
WOOLLY BURSAGE *(Franseria eriocentra)*
Fruit with several flat wings, not hairy.
WHITE BURROBRUSH *(Hymenoclea salsola)*

16. Akenes strongly flattened.
LAPHAMIA *(Laphamia congesta)*
Akenes not strongly flattened. 17.

17. Akenes densely long-hairy.
PRICKLY OXYTENIA *(Oxytenia acerosa)*
Akenes smooth or nearly so. 18.

18. Leaves 2 or 3 times pinnately lobed into narrow lobes.
FRINGED SAGEBRUSH *(Artemisia frigida)*
Leaves entire or 3-toothed at the tip. 19.

19. Involucre densely gray-hairy throughout.
BIGELOW SAGEBRUSH *(Artemisia bigelovii)*
At least the inner bracts of the involucre smooth. 20.

20. Heads very numerous, in dense panicles; outer bracts of involucres hairy; plants usually more than 1 foot high.
BIG SAGEBRUSH *(Artemisia tridentata)*
Heads less numerous, in narrow, more open panicles; bracts of involucre smooth or nearly so; plant 1 foot high or less.
BLACK SAGEBRUSH *(Artemisia arbuscula* subsp. *nova)*

21. Pappus of about 20 feathery awns.
BEBBIA *(Bebbia juncea)*

Pappus of 1 or 2 awns, these not feathery. 22.

22. Heads ½ to 1 inch across.
BUSH ENCELIA (*Encelia frutescens*) 237
Heads about ¼ inch across.
LAPHAMIA (*Laphamia congesta*) 243

23. Flowers imperfect, the male and female flowers on
separate plants. 24.
Flowers all perfect or some perfect and some imperfect
in the same heads. 26.

24. Branches not green; heads in dense, terminal panicles.
SEEP-WILLOW (*Baccharis glutinosa*) 233
Branches green, more or less angled. 25.

25. Heads solitary or in small clusters at the ends of the
branches; leaves evergreen, the larger ones toothed.
EMORY BACCHARIS (*Baccharis emoryi*) 233
Heads in large open panicles; leaves usually absent at
flowering time, usually entire if present.
SQUAW BACCHARIS (*Baccharis sergiloides*) 233

26. Bracts of involucre 5.
PORELEAF (*Porophyllum gracile*) 245
Bracts of involucre more than 5. 27.

27. Corolla purplish.
ARROWWEED (*Pluchea sericea*) 245
Corolla whitish. 28.
Corolla yellow. 33.

28. Heads 3- to 5-flowered. 29.
Heads more than 5-flowered. 30.

29. Leaves narrowly lanceolate or linear.
LONGLEAF BRICKELLIA (*Brickellia longifolia*) 234
Leaves ovate.
INYO BRICKELLIA (*Brickellia multiflora*) 235

30. Heads 40- to 50-flowered. 31.
Heads 8- to 26-flowered. 32.

31. Leaves spiny-toothed.
BRICKELLIA (*Brickellia atractyloides*) 234
Leaves mostly entire, never spiny-toothed.
BRICKELLIA (*Brickellia oblongifolia* var. *linifolia*) 235

32. Heads solitary at the ends of slender branches.
BRICKELLIA (*Brickellia scabra*) 235

Heads in a loose panicle.

BRICKELLIA *(Brickellia coulteri)*

Heads clustered in the leaf axils.

CALIFORNIA BRICKELLIA *(Brickellia californica)*

33. Bracts of involucre in quite distinct vertical rows. 34.
Bracts of involucre not in vertical rows. 38.

34. Twigs with a covering of soft, matted hairs. 35.
Twigs smooth or very short-hairy, not with matted hairs. 36.

35. Heads in leafy, terminal racemes; outer bracts of involucre with long, slender, green tips.

PARRY RABBITBRUSH *(Chrysothamnus parryi)*

Heads in paniclelike clusters; outer bracts of involucre without long, slender, green tips.

RUBBER RABBITBRUSH *(Chrysothamnus nauseosus)*

36. Bracts of involucre in sharply defined vertical rows; akenes smooth or nearly so; plant usually less than 1 foot high.

DWARF RABBITBRUSH *(Chrysothamnus depressus)*

Bracts of involucre obscurely in vertical rows; akenes hairy; plant usually more than 1 foot high. 37.

37. Bracts of involucre mostly with awl-shaped tips.

GREENES RABBITBRUSH *(Chrysothamnus greenei* var. *linifolius)*

Bracts of involucre without awl-shaped tips.

DOUGLAS RABBITBRUSH *(Chrysothamnus viscidiflorus)*

38. Leaves narrowly lanceolate, 3-nerved. 39.
Leaves linear or nearly so, 1-nerved. 40.

39. Leaves densely dotted with depressions.

GOLDENWEED *(Haplopappus salicinus)*

Leaves not dotted with depressions.

GOLDENWEED *(Haplopappus scopulorum)*

40. Bracts of involucre with a large, round gland at the tip.

PALELEAF GOLDENWEED *(Haplopappus acradenius)*

Bracts of involucre without a gland at the tip. 41.

41. Heads 7- to 15-flowered.

JIMMYWEED *(Haplopappus heterophyllus)*

Heads 18- to 30-flowered.

GOLDENWEED *(Haplopappus drummondii)*

42. Corollas all strap-shaped. 43.
Corollas all tubular. 62.

Corollas of ray flowers strap-shaped, those of disk
flowers tubular. 99.

43. Pappus of 5 scales each 2-lobed with a hairlike awn
between the lobes.
MICROSERIS *(Microseris linearifolia)* 244
Pappus of feathery bristles. 44.
Pappus of hairlike bristles, not feathery. 48.

44. Corollas yellow; leaves grasslike.
GOATSBEARD *(Tragopogon dubius)* 249
Corollas pink; leaves not grasslike. 45.

45. Heads 10- to 20-flowered; pappus bright white.
WIRE-LETTUCE *(Stephanomeria thurberi)* 248
Heads 3- to 9-flowered. 46.

46. Pappus bristles feathery their full length, bright white.
WIRE-LETTUCE *(Stephanomeria tenuifolia)* 248
Pappus bristles feathery on the upper 2/3 but naked or
only rough toward the base. 47.

47. Pappus brownish-tinged; plant perennial.
WIRE-LETTUCE *(Stephanomeria pauciflora)* 248
Pappus white; plant annual.
WIRE-LETTUCE *(Stephanomeria exigua)* 248

48. Akenes more or less flattened. 49.
Akenes not flattened. 51.

49. Akenes with a beak.
PRICKLY LETTUCE *(Lactuca serriola)* 243
Akenes without a beak. 50.

50. Akenes wrinkled crosswise, not 3-ribbed lengthwise or
indistinctly so.
COMMON SOW-THISTLE *(Sonchus oleraceus)* 248
Akenes strongly 3-ribbed on each face, not wrinkled crosswise.
PRICKLY SOW-THISTLE *(Sonchus asper)* 248

51. Akenes without a beak. 52.
Akenes with a beak; leaves all basal. 58.

52. Pappus, or most of it, falling off as the akenes mature;
corolla yellow. 53.
Pappus not falling off, remaining on the mature akenes. 55.

53. Corollas not much longer than the involucre, inconspicuous.
MALACOTHRIX *(Malacothrix clevelandi)* 244
Corollas much longer than the involucre, conspicuous. 54.

prickles or spines. 64.
Flowers perfect, or some imperfect but with the perfect
ones in the same heads; involucres not armed with
prickles or spines. 65.

64. Fruiting involucre armed with 6 to 30 straight,
spreading spines.
BURSAGE *(Franseria acanthicarpa)* 239
Fruiting involucre armed with stiff, hooked prickles.
COCKLEBUR *(Xanthium saccharatum)* 249

65. Leaves 2 or 3 times pinnately lobed. 66.
Leaves entire or once pinnately lobed. 67.

66. Plant densely gray-silky throughout, more or less woody
at the base.
FRINGED SAGEBRUSH *(Artemisia frigida)* 232
Plants more or less hairy but not gray-silky, not woody
at the base.
WORMWOOD *(Artemisia pacifica)* 232

67. Leaves smooth or somewhat hairy but not woolly, linear,
entire or some of the lower ones 3-lobed.
FALSE-TARRAGON *(Artemisia dracunculoides)* 231
Leaves always woolly, at least beneath. 68.

68. Leaves mostly entire or merely toothed.
LOUISIANA SAGEBRUSH *(Artemisia ludoviciana)* 232
Leaves all lobed nearly to the midrib into very narrow lobes.
CARRUTH SAGEBRUSH *(Artemisia carruthii)* 231

69. Pappus of 2 or 3 awns that readily fall off.
GUMWEED *(Grindelia aphanactis)* 240
Pappus not of awns that readily fall off. 70.

70. Pappus of 1 or 2 awns; plant woody toward the base.
LAPHAMIA *(Laphamia congesta)* 243
Pappus of several awns or scales. 71.

71. Flowers yellow.
HYMENOPAPPUS *(Hymenopappus lugens)* 243
Flowers white or pinkish. 72.

72. Leaves linear and entire or some of them pinnately lobed
with a few lobes; plant usually not woolly.
CHAENACTIS *(Chaenactis xantiana)* 235
Leaves, or some of them, twice pinnately lobed with
numerous lobes; plant more or less woolly. 73.

73. Pappus scales about 8 or 10.
CHAENACTIS *(Chaenactis douglasii)* 235
Pappus scales 4 or 5. 74.

74. Outer corollas not larger than the others.
CHAENACTIS *(Chaenactis macrantha)* 235
Outer corollas distinctly larger than the others.
CHAENACTIS *(Chaenactis stevioides)* 235

75. Leaves and involucres very spiny and prickly. 76.
Leaves and involucres not very spiny and prickly. 82.

76. Stems with spiny wings extending downward from the
leaf bases.
BULL THISTLE *(Cirsium vulgare)* 237
Stems without spiny wings or only very short ones. 77.

77. Bracts of involucre more or less densely woolly, the
outer ones turned downward.
NEW MEXICO THISTLE *(Cirsium neomexicanum)* 236
Bracts of involucre not or only slightly woolly, the
outer ones not turned downward. 78.

78. Inner bracts of involucre with long, narrow, usually red
or reddish tips. 79.
Inner bracts of involucre with more or less broadened,
twisted and ragged tips. 81.

79. Leaves smooth or nearly so on both sides.
THISTLE *(Cirsium rothrockii)* 236
Leaves more or less woolly, at least beneath. 80.

80. Spines of middle bracts of involucre ½ inch long or more,
stout; flowers purplish.
THISTLE *(Cirsium nidulum)* 236
Spines of middle bracts of involucre much shorter,
slender; flowers bright red.
THISTLE *(Cirsium arizonicum)* 236

81. Bracts of involucre with a broadly ovate body.
THISTLE *(Cirsium wheeleri)* 237
Bracts of involucre with a narrowly lanceolate or oblong body.
THISTLE *(Cirsium undulatum)* 236

82. Bracts of involucre white or whitish with no green color. 83.
Bracts of involucre green, at least in the center. 91.

83. Flowers imperfect, the male and female flowers in separate
heads on separate plants. 84.
All of the flowers either perfect or female; heads all alike. 88.

84. Plants usually at least 1 foot tall, with or without a basal rosette of leaves.

PEARLY EVERLASTING (*Anaphalis margaritacea*) 230
Plants much less than 1 foot tall; most of the leaves in a basal rosette. 85.

85. Heads sessile or nearly so among the leaves of the basal rosette.

PUSSYTOES (*Antennaria rosulata*) 231
Heads in clusters at the ends of upright stems. 86.

86. Leaves usually smooth and green on the upper surface.

PUSSYTOES (*Antennaria marginata*) 231
Leaves permanently woolly on the upper surface. 87.

87. Pistillate heads more than ¼ inch high; basal leaves often ¼ inch wide or more.

ROCKY MOUNTAIN PUSSYTOES (*Antennaria aprica*) 230
Pistillate heads less than ¼ inch high; basal leaves less than ¼ inch wide.

PUSSYTOES (*Antennaria arida*) 231

88. Heads very small, in clusters embedded in wool, the clusters subtended by leaflike bracts. 89.
Heads medium-sized, not embedded in wool, the clusters not subtended by leaflike bracts. 90.

89. Plant thinly but closely woolly; leaves linear or nearly so.

CUDWEED (*Gnaphalium grayi*) 239
Plant loosely woolly; leaves oblong or obovate.

CUDWEED (*Gnaphalium palustre*) 240

90. Leaves woolly on both sides.

CUDWEED (*Gnaphalium wrightii*) 240
Leaves woolly only on the lower side, green above.

CUDWEED (*Gnaphalium macounii*) 240

91. Leaves and involucres bearing conspicuous oil glands.

PORELEAF (*Porophyllum gracile*) 245
Leaves and involucres not bearing oil glands. 92.

92. Pappus of 2 to 8 bristles.

GUMWEED (*Grindelia aphanactis*) 240
Pappus bristles more than 8. 93.

93. Corolla white or whitish. 94.
Corolla yellow. 97.

94. Akenes 5-angled or 5-ribbed.

THOROUGHWORT *(Eupatorium herbaceum)*
Akenes 10-ribbed. 95.

95. Heads 40- to 50-flowered.

BRICKELLIA *(Brickellia oblongifolia* var. *linifolia)*
Heads less than 40-flowered. 96.

96. Heads solitary at the ends of slender branches.

BRICKELLIA *(Brickellia scabra)*
Heads in umbellike clusters at the ends of branches.

TASSELFLOWER *(Brickellia grandiflora)*
Heads clustered in the leaf axils.

CALIFORNIA BRICKELLIA *(Brickellia californica)*
Heads in a loose panicle.

BRICKELLIA *(Brickellia coulteri)*

97. Leaves closely toothed; plant not woody at the base.

NUTTALL GOLDENWEED *(Haplopappus nuttallii)*
Leaves entire; plant more or less woody at the base. 98.

98. Heads 7- to 15-flowered; bracts of involucre not, or only
slightly, green-tipped.

JIMMYWEED *(Haplopappus heterophyllus)*
Heads 18- to 30-flowered; bracts of involucre
definitely green-tipped.

GOLDENWEED *(Haplopappus drummondii)*

99. Pappus none. 100.
Pappus of hairlike bristles. 106.
Pappus of awns or scales, these sometimes united into
a low crown. 157.

100. Ray flowers white. 101.
Ray flowers yellow. 102.

101. Leaves alternate, finely dissected, with a pronounced odor.

WESTERN YARROW *(Achillea lanulosa)*
Leaves opposite, entire or nearly so, without odor.

SANVITALIA *(Sanvitalia aberti)*

102. Plants woolly; heads large.

DESERT-MARIGOLD *(Baileya multiradiata)*
Plants not woolly. 103.

103. Leaves entire. 104.
Leaves lobed or dissected. 105.

104. Leaves alternate; plant with strong odor.

TARWEED *(Madia glomerata)*

Families Of Plants 221

Leaves opposite; plant without strong odor.
SHOWY GOLDENEYE *(Viguiera multiflora)* 249

105. Receptacle flat.
RAGLEAF or **YELLOW-RAGWEED** *(Bahia dissecta)* 234
Receptacle cylindric, often more than 1 inch long.
PRAIRIE CONEFLOWER *(Ratibida columnaris)* 245

106. Ray flowers white, pink, purple or violet. 107.
Ray flowers yellow or orange. 136.

107. Ray corollas broad, 3-lobed at the tip; pappus bristles
densely feathery.
WHITE TIDYTIPS *(Layia glandulosa)* 244
Ray corollas narrow, not lobed at the tip; pappus
bristles not feathery. 108.

108. Bracts of involucre in several series of different lengths;
ray flowers not very narrow. 109.
Bracts of involucre in 1 series, all nearly equal in
length; ray flowers mostly very narrow and numerous. 124.

109. Pappus bristles stiff, awnlike, barbed. 110.
Pappus bristles soft, hairlike, not barbed. 111.

110. Stems practically none; heads rather large, showy, sessile
among the basal leaves.
TOWNSENDIA *(Townsendia exscapa)* 249
Leafy stems present but sometimes very short; heads
medium-sized.
TOWNSENDIA *(Townsendia arizonica)* 249

111. Stems mostly 4 inches tall or less; leaves linear, less
than ½ inch long.
ASTER *(Aster arenosus)* 232
Stems mostly more than 4 inches tall. 112.

112. Upper leaves much reduced, scalelike, entire.
DEVILWEED ASTER *(Aster spinosus)* 233
Upper leaves not scalelike. 113.

113. Leaves spiny-toothed; heads large, often 2 inches across.
MOHAVE ASTER *(Aster abatus)* 232
Leaves not spiny-toothed; heads smaller. 114.

114. Bracts of involucre smooth on the back. 115.
Bracts of involucre more or less densely glandular or
hairy on the back. 119.

115. Ray flowers white.

WHITE ASTER *(Aster commutatus)* 233
Ray flowers violet, purple or blue, sometimes very pale
but not pure white. 116.

116. Plants usually 2 feet tall or more. 117.
Plants 1 foot tall or less, not much-branched. 118.

117. Outer bracts of involucre thin, linear, conspicuously
green-tipped, more or less spreading; ray flowers blue
to nearly white.
SISKIYOU ASTER *(Aster hesperius)* 233
Outer bracts of involucre thick, oblong or ovate, not
green-tipped, not spreading; ray flowers violet.
ASTER *(Aster glaucodes)* 233

118. Outer bracts of involucre definitely shorter than the
inner ones, only partly green; stem leaves sessile but
usually not clasping.
ASTER *(Aster adscendens)* 232
Outer bracts of involucre nearly or quite as long as the
inner, often entirely green; stem leaves clasping.
LEAFYBRACT ASTER *(Aster foliaceus)* 233

119. Bracts of involucre not conspicuously many-ranked. 120.
Bracts of involucre conspicuously many-ranked. 121.

120. Involucre hairy on the backs of the bracts, not glandular.
ASTER *(Aster adscendens)* 232
Involucre and upper parts of stem with stalked glands.
ASTER *(Aster glaucodes)* 233

121. Bracts of involucre conspicuously glandular and sticky.
BIGELOW ASTER *(Aster bigelovii)* 232
Bracts of involucre conspicuously hairy but not glandular
nor sticky or only slightly so. 122.

122. Leaves regularly toothed, linear or nearly so.
ASTER *(Aster tephrodes)* 233
Leaves usually entire or with a few scattered teeth. 123.

123. Stems 16 inches tall or less; leaves linear or nearly so.
HOARY ASTER *(Aster canescens)* 232
Stems 24 inches tall or more; leaves mostly narrowly
lanceolate, narrowed to a petiole.
ASTER *(Aster aquifolius)* 232

124. Ray flowers very short and inconspicuous.
HORSEWEED FLEABANE *(Erigeron canadensis)* 238
Ray flowers conspicuous, much longer than the pappus. 125.

Families Of Plants 223

125. Stem leaves all or nearly all pinnately lobed. 126.
Stem leaves all entire or nearly so. 127.

126. Stems usually 1 foot tall or more; heads large, 1 inch
across or more; ray flowers white.
FLEABANE *(Erigeron oreophilus)* 239
Stems usually much less than 1 foot tall; heads
medium-sized, less than 1 inch across; ray flowers
usually purple.
FLEABANE *(Erigeron lobatus)* 238

127. Plants comparatively coarse, large-leaved and large-headed;
stems usually more than 1 foot tall. 128.
Plants comparatively slender, small-leaved and small-headed;
stems usually less than 1 foot tall. 129.

128. Stems very leafy throughout, the upper leaves not much
reduced; heads several, on short stalks.
ASPEN FLEABANE *(Erigeron macranthus)* 238
Stems more or less naked above, the upper leaves
greatly reduced; heads 1 to 3 on long, naked stalks.
FLEABANE *(Erigeron formosissimus)* 238

129. Stems hairy with wide-spreading hairs. 130.
Stems hairy with hairs pressed or curved against the
stem, not spreading. 132.

130. Flowering stems at first nearly leafless except near the
base, later producing long, leafy branches from the
lower leaf axils.
SPRAWLING FLEABANE *(Erigeron nudiflorus)* 239
Flowering stems leafy from the start. 131.

131. Plants definitely perennial, often slightly woody at the
base; stems and leaves rather coarsely hairy.
HAIRY FLEABANE *(Erigeron concinnus)* 238
Plants annual with no indication of parts more than
1 year old; stems and leaves softly hairy.
SPREADING FLEABANE *(Erigeron divergens)* 238

132. Flowering stems at first leafless except toward the base,
later producing leafy runners from the base or the
lower leaf axils.
TRAILING FLEABANE *(Erigeron flagellaris)* 238
Flowering stems leafy, at least above the middle, without
long, spreading runners. 133.

133. Akenes smooth.

HYMENOXYS
(Hymenoxys subintegra)

PHOTO MERKLE

PRICKLY LETTUCE
(Lactuca serriola)

PHOTO HAMILTON

GREENSTEM PAPERFLOWER
(Psilostrophe sparsiflora)

PHOTO MERKLE

THREADLEAF GROUNDSEL
(Senecio longilobus)

PHOTO MERKLE

with a few small bracts at the base.   145.
Bracts of the involucre unequal and in more than 1
series.   149.

145. Leaves mostly entire, narrowly linear; plant smooth.

BROOM GROUNDSEL *(Senecio spartioides)* 246
Leaves pinnately lobed, with narrow, linear lobes;
plant hairy.

THREADLEAF GROUNDSEL *(Senecio longilobus)* 246
Leaves neither entire and narrowly linear nor pinnately
lobed with narrowly linear lobes.   146.

146. Leaves entire, oblong, mostly basal.

GROUNDSEL *(Senecio werneriaefolius)* 246
Leaves more or less densely lobed, not mostly basal.   147.

147. Stems uniformly leafy up to the flower cluster.

GROUNDSEL *(Senecio macdougalii)* 246
Stems with the upper leaves much smaller than
the lower.   148.

148. Plants coarse, usually more than 2 feet tall; leaves with
few divisions, the terminal one 1 to 2 inches across.

GROUNDSEL *(Senecio quercetorum)* 246
Plants more slender, usually less than 2 feet tall; leaves
with numerous divisions, the terminal one less
than 1 inch across.

LOBELEAF GROUNDSEL *(Senecio multilobatus)* 246

149. Heads usually very small and very numerous; bracts of
involucres without green tips.   150.
Heads usually few and medium-large; bracts of involucre
often with green tips.   155.

150. Plant low; stems clustered from a branched base; heads
cylindric in a more or less flat-topped cluster.   151.
Plant taller, stems not clustered from a branched base;
heads in racemes or panicles, not cylindric.   152.

151. Leaves 3-nerved, the lower ones oblanceolate to nearly linear.

ROCK GOLDENROD *(Solidago petradoria)* 248
Leaves 1-nerved, the lower ones narrowly linear.

GOLDENROD *(Solidago graminea)* 246

152. Leaves very numerous, the upper ones not much smaller
than the lower ones.

TALL GOLDENROD *(Solidago altissima)* 246
Leaves not very numerous, the upper ones much smaller

than the lower ones. 153.

153. Stems smooth or nearly so.
MISSOURI GOLDENROD (*Solidago missouriensis*) 248
Stems densely short-hairy. 154.

154. Bracts of involucre oblong or ovate, rounded at the tip;
branches of panicle upright, not 1-sided.
BABY GOLDENROD (*Solidago nana*) 248
Bracts of involucre linear to lanceolate, pointed at the
tip; branches of panicle curved and usually 1-sided.
GOLDENROD (*Solidago sparsiflora*) 248

155. Leaves entire or toothed, not lobed, more than ½ inch wide.
GOLDENWEED (*Haplopappus parryi*) 242
Leaves much smaller, lobed, the lobes bristle-tipped. 156.

156. Leaves numerous, mostly less than 1 inch long; plant annual.
GOLDENWEED (*Haplopappus gracilis*) 242
Leaves fewer, scattered, the largest about 2 inches
long; plant perennial.
GOLDENWEED (*Haplopappus spinulosus*) 242

157. Receptacle with scales between the flowers. 158.
Receptacle without scales between the flowers. 163.

158. Ray flowers white. 159.
Ray flowers yellow. 160.

159. Heads large, showy; ray corollas 3-lobed at the tip.
WHITE TIDYTIPS (*Layia glandulosa*) 244
Heads small; ray corollas short, 2-lobed at the tip.
SANVITALIA (*Sanvitalia aberti*) 246

160. Akenes not very flat; pappus of 2 awns that readily fall off.
SUNFLOWER (*Helianthus petiolaris*) 242
Akenes very flat. 161.

161. Akenes with broad, white wings; pappus of 1 or 2 awns.
GOLDEN CROWNBEARD (*Verbesina encelioides*) 249
Akenes without wings; pappus of scales with 3
slender awns. 162.

162. Disk flowers purple.
HELIANTHELLA (*Helianthella microcephala*) 242
Disk flowers yellow.
HELIANTHELLA (*Helianthella quinquenervis*) 242

163. Ray flowers not yellow. 164.
Ray flowers yellow. 166.

164. Stems practically none; heads rather large, showy,
sessile among the basal leaves.

TOWNSENDIA *(Townsendia exscapa)* 249
Leafy stems present but sometimes very short; heads
medium to small.   165.

165. Leaves entire, linear to obovate.

TOWNSENDIA *(Townsendia arizonica)* 249
Leaves lobed and toothed, broadly ovate in outline.

PERITYLE *(Perityle emoryi* var. *nuda)* 245

166. Leaves and involucres bearing oil glands.   167.
Leaves and involucres not bearing oil glands.   171.

167. Leaves with a few stiff bristles at the base.

CHINCHWEED *(Pectis papposa)* 245
Leaves without bristles at the base.   168.

168. Stems woody toward the base; pappus scales dissected
into bristles.   169.
Stems not woody; pappus scales tipped with 1 or 2
bristles or none.   170.

169. Leaves pinnately lobed into 3 to 5 narrow lobes.

DOGWEED *(Dyssodia porophylloides)* 237
Leaves linear, entire, needlelike.

PRICKLEAF DOGWEED *(Dyssodia acerosa)* 237

170. Pappus scales each tipped with 1 to 3 bristles.

DOGWEED *(Dyssodia thurberi)* 237
Inner pappus scales tipped with bristles, the outer
ones without bristles.

DOGWEED *(Dyssodia pentachaeta)* 237

171. Leaves all basal.

HYMENOXYS *(Hymenoxys acaulis* var. *arizonica)* 243
Leaves alternate.   172.

172. Leaves mostly oblong, usually regularly and rather
bluntly toothed.

CURLYCUP GUMWEED *(Grindelia squarrosa)* 240
Leaves mostly obovate or oblanceolate, entire or lobed.   173.
Leaves linear and entire or with linear, entire lobes.   175.

173. Disk flowers reddish-purple.

BLANKETFLOWER *(Gaillardia pinnatifida)* 239
Disk flowers yellow.   174.

174. Stems and leaves densely woolly.

Families Of Plants   229

WESTERN YARROW (*Achillea lanulosa*). Stems 4 to 24 inches tall; leaves alternate, finely dissected into many small divisions; both stems and leaves hairy with soft hairs; heads small and numerous; both ray and disk flowers white, the ray flowers very short; pappus none; plant very aromatic.

ARIZONA MOUNTAIN-DANDELION (*Agoseris arizonica*). Flowering stems 4 to 10 inches tall; leaves all basal, linear or nearly so, entire, toothed or somewhat lobed; involucres ½ to 1 inch high, the midribs of the bracts often purplish; heads solitary, large and showy, the flowers yellow; beak of akene nearly as long as the body; pappus of numerous white bristles.

ORANGE MOUNTAIN-DANDELION (*Agoseris aurantiaca*). Very similar to the preceding except that the flowers are deep orange or sometimes brownish-red.

PALE MOUNTAIN-DANDELION (*Agoseris glauca*). Very similar to the Arizona mountain-dandelion except that the akene has a short, stout beak, usually less than ½ as long as the body.

PEARLY EVERLASTING (*Anaphalis margaritacea*). Stem 10 to 24 inches tall, more or less woolly; leaves linear or nearly so, 1 to 4 inches long, sessile, woolly beneath; heads rather small, white, in terminal clusters.

ROCKY MOUNTAIN PUSSYTOES (*Antennaria aprica*). Plants low, usually forming mats; stems 1 to 6 inches tall; basal leaves obovate or oblanceolate, ½ to 1 inch long, woolly on both sides; heads usually 3 to 8 in crowded, terminal clusters; bracts of involucre white or sometimes pink.

PUSSYTOES *(Antennaria arida).* Plant producing runners but usually not forming mats; stems 4 to 15 inches tall; leaves oblanceolate to linear, finely woolly on both sides; heads about 3 to 10 in a terminal cluster; bracts of involucre brownish at the base, white at the tip.

PUSSYTOES *(Antennaria marginata).* Plant producing runners but not forming mats; stems 3 to 12 inches tall; leaves ½ to 2½ inches long, obovate to oblanceolate, white-woolly below, smooth or nearly so above; heads 3 to 7 in a close, terminal cluster.

PUSSYTOES *(Antennaria rosulata).* Plants forming dense mats; leaves less than ½ inch long, in rosettes, silvery-woolly to almost smooth above; heads 1 to 3, sessile or nearly so; bracts of involucre white at the tip.

HEARTLEAF ARNICA *(Arnica cordifolia).* Stems 8 to 18 inches tall, usually unbranched, more or less hairy; leaves usually 2 or 3 pairs, the upper ones sessile, the lower petioled, the blades ovate to lanceolate, more or less heart-shaped at the base, 2 to 4 inches long and 1 to 3 inches wide; heads 1 to 3 or more, the rays about ½ inch long; pappus white.

LEAFY ARNICA *(Arnica foliosa).* Stems 10 to 40 inches tall, more or less hairy; leaves 5 to 10 pairs, the lower petioled, the upper sessile, the blades lanceolate to oblong; heads 5 to 15; rays about ½ inch long; pappus straw-colored. North Rim.

BLACK SAGEBRUSH *(Artemisia arbuscula* subsp. *nova).* A small shrub, usually 3 to 12 inches high, much-branched; leaves 1 inch long or less, silvery-hairy, 3-toothed at the tip; heads rather few in a racemelike panicle, very small, 2- to 6-flowered.

BIGELOW SAGEBRUSH *(Artemisia bigelovii).* Stems 8 to 12 inches tall, woody toward the base, the twigs silvery-hairy; leaves ¼ to ½ inch long, 3-toothed at the tip or entire, linear to wedge-shaped, silvery-hairy; heads very small and rather numerous in a spikelike panicle; flowers 2 to 5 in each head.

CARRUTH SAGEBRUSH *(Artemisia carruthii).* Stems 8 to 24 inches tall; leaves about 1 inch long or less, pinnately divided into very narrow segments, woolly on both sides or smooth and green on the upper side in one variety; heads in a narrow or spikelike panicle; flowers 20 to 30 in each head.

FALSE-TARRAGON *(Artemisia dracunculoides).* Stems several, 12 to 30 inches tall or more, unbranched up to the flowering portion; leaves linear to narrowly lanceolate, entire or some of them lobed, sessile, smooth or nearly so; heads very small and numerous in a leafy-bracted panicle, the heads nodding, 15-flowered or more.

FRINGED SAGEBRUSH *(Artemisia frigida)*. Stems 4 to 16 inches tall, branching from the often woody base, the twigs finely white-hairy; basal leaves crowded, finely dissected into very narrow divisions, silvery-hairy, the upper leaves somewhat less dissected; heads many, in a narrow, leafy panicle, each about 30- to 60-flowered.

LOUISIANA SAGEBRUSH *(Artemisia ludoviciana)*. Stems 10 to 40 inches tall; leaves numerous, 1 to 3 inches long, varying from narrow and entire to broader and lobed, usually woolly on the lower side and often on both sides; heads scattered or often clustered on the spikelike or racemelike branches of an open panicle, about 10- to 40-flowered.

WORMWOOD *(Artemisia pacifica)*. Stems several, 1 to 2 feet tall, not woody; basal leaves twice pinnately divided into linear lobes, more or less silky-hairy, petioled, 1½ to 3 inches long; upper leaves sessile and less dissected; heads many in a leafy panicle, 15- to 25-flowered.

BIG SAGEBRUSH *(Artemisia tridentata)*. This is the common shrub of sagebrush deserts. Stems 1 to 7 feet tall or more, much-branched; leaves 1½ inches long or less, 3-toothed or 3-lobed at the tip, silky-hairy, strong-scented; heads few or many on spikelike or racemelike branches of a panicle, 5- to 8-flowered.

MOHAVE ASTER *(Aster abatus)*. Stems several from a somewhat woody base, 1 to 2 feet tall, the bark whitish; leaves linear to lanceolate or oblong, sessile, mostly spiny-toothed, 1 to 3 inches long; heads solitary at the ends of long stalks, large and showy; ray flowers 40 to 60, blue-violet or lavender.

ASTER *(Aster adscendens)*. Stems 4 to 12 inches tall, more or less hairy; leaves entire, those on the stem linear to lanceolate, 1 to 4 inches long, those at the base elliptic to oblanceolate and petioled; heads solitary or few; ray flowers ¼ to ½ inch long, blue, violet or pink.

ASTER *(Aster aquifolius)*. Stems usually 2 feet tall or more, branched; leaves narrowly lanceolate or oblanceolate or linear, mostly narrowed to a slender petiole, entire or the lower ones somewhat toothed; heads medium-sized, terminal on most branches; ray flowers blue or purple.

ASTER *(Aster arenosus)*. Stems numerous, 2 to 5 inches tall, more or less hairy; leaves about ¼ inch long or less, linear or nearly so; heads solitary at the ends of slender branches; ray flowers short, white. South Rim.

BIGELOW ASTER *(Aster bigelovii* syn. *A. cichoriaceus)*. Stems 8 to 40 inches tall, glandular-hairy; leaves 2 to 4 inches long, oblong to lanceolate or oblanceolate, usually toothed; heads rather large and showy; ray flowers ¼ to ½ inch long, purple or violet.

HOARY ASTER *(Aster canescens* syn. *adenolepis)*. Stems 4 to 16 inches tall, varying from smooth to hairy; heads medium-small and quite numerous; ray flowers less than ½ inch long, deep blue to purple.

WHITE ASTER *(Aster commutatus)*. Stems 8 to 24 inches tall, hairy, with spreading branches; leaves 1½ inches long or less, densely hairy; heads 1 to few on the branches, the ray flowers short, white.

LEAFYBRACT ASTER *(Aster foliaceus)*. Stems usually several, 2 to 40 inches tall, often reddish, smooth to hairy; basal leaves obovate to oblanceolate, those on the stem ovate to lanceolate, 2 to 5 inches long, mostly entire; heads 1 to few, medium to large; ray flowers ½ inch long or less, rose to purple.

ASTER *(Aster glaucodes)*. Stems 12 to 20 inches tall, branched; leaves 1 to 3 inches long, mostly lanceolate or oblong, rather firm, veiny; heads few to many at the ends of branches; bracts of involucre often tinged purple at the tip; ray flowers ¼ to ½ inch long, white to violet. The typical plant with smooth stem and involucres apparently has been found only in Havasu Canyon but variety *pulcher* with glandular stem and involucres occurs on both Rims.

SISKIYOU ASTER *(Aster hesperius* syn. *A. coerulescens)*. Stems mostly 2 to 5 feet tall, very leafy; leaves linear to lanceolate, entire or sometimes with small teeth, 2 to 5 inches long; heads usually many in a long panicle; ray flowers ¼ to ½ inch long, blue to nearly white. In wet places.

DEVILWEED ASTER *(Aster spinosus)*. Stems 1 to 5 feet or more tall, usually spiny on the lower part with spines 1 inch long or less, branched and more or less broomlike above; leaves linear to lanceolate, the upper ones reduced to scales; heads small, solitary at the ends of short or long branches; ray flowers short, white.

ASTER *(Aster tephrodes)*. Stem single but often much-branched, 8 to 30 inches tall; leaves mostly linear or the lower lanceolate, shallowly toothed with spiny teeth, mostly sessile; heads solitary at the ends of branches, medium-large; ray flowers 1 inch long or less, violet or purple.

EMORY BACCHARIS *(Baccharis emoryi)*. An evergreen shrub, usually 2 to 8 feet tall or more; larger leaves wedge-shaped to oblong, the upper ones almost linear, 1 to 3 inches long including a short petiole, varying from entire to sharply few-toothed; heads 1 to 5 at the tips of branches; pistillate heads about 1 inch long; staminate heads less than ½ inch long. In the Canyon in moist places.

SEEP-WILLOW *(Baccharis glutinosa)*. A willowlike shrub with slender stems 3 to 9 feet tall; leaves linear or nearly so, 2 to 6 inches long, few-toothed or entire; heads many in compound clusters at the ends of branches. In the Canyon mostly along streams.

SQUAW BACCHARIS *(Baccharis sergiloides)*. A smooth shrub, 2 to 7 feet tall, the green, broomlike branches strongly angled, often almost leafless; larger leaves obovate, entire or nearly so, 1 inch long or less; heads rather small, numerous, in dense panicles. In Canyon.

RAGLEAF or **YELLOW-RAGWEED** *(Bahia dissecta).* Stems 1 to 3 feet tall, glandular in the flowering portion; leaves alternate, 2 or 3 times divided into oblong or linear segments, more or less short-hairy; involucres about ¼ inch high, glandular-hairy; ray flowers about ¼ inch long, yellow, wedge-shaped; disk flowers yellow; pappus none.

DESERT-MARIGOLD *(Baileya multiradiata).* Stems 1 or several from the same base, unbranched, each ending in a single, large, showy head, the entire plant woolly; leaves mostly in a basal rosette with only a few on the lower part of the stem, the basal ones 2 to 3 inches long, pinnately lobed into a few lobes, these again shallowly lobed; ray flowers bright yellow, about ½ inch long, 3- to 5-toothed at the tip.

BEBBIA *(Bebbia juncea).* A much-branched shrub, about 3 feet high or less, the branches slender, pale green becoming whitish with age; leaves rather far apart, linear or nearly so, about 1 inch long or less; heads solitary at the ends of rather long stalks; flowers yellow, the corollas all tubular. In Canyon.

BRICKELLIA *(Brickellia atractyloides).* A low much-branched shrub, 8 to 16 inches high; leaves alternate, short-petioled or almost sessile, ovate, spiny-toothed on the margins, bright green; heads solitary on naked stalks at the ends of branches, about 50-flowered, the corollas white or yellowish-white. In Canyon.

CALIFORNIA BRICKELLIA *(Brickellia californica).* A spreading shrub, 20 to 40 inches high with whitish bark; leaves mostly alternate, petioled, the blades triangular-ovate, 2 inches long or less, coarsely scalloped; heads small, 8- to 18-flowered, in axillary and terminal clusters; corollas yellowish-white.

BRICKELLIA *(Brickellia coulteri).* A low shrub, up to 1 foot high or more, white-barked, the younger branches short-hairy; leaves mostly opposite, about ½ inch long or less, triangular-ovate, the larger ones with 1 to 3 teeth on each side near the base; heads about 15- to 20-flowered, in a loose panicle. Havasu Canyon.

TASSELFLOWER *(Brickellia grandiflora).* Stems entirely herbaceous, branched or unbranched, 8 to 30 inches tall; leaves mostly alternate, petioled, triangular-ovate, varying from scalloped to sharply toothed; heads 20- to 40-flowered, clustered at the ends of stems and branches, often drooping; corollas whitish. Both Rims.

LONGLEAF BRICKELLIA *(Brickellia longifolia).* A much-branched shrub, 3 to 4½ feet high, with smooth, somewhat sticky, whitish bark; leaves alternate, short-petioled, the blades linear or nearly so, entire or nearly so, 1 to 5 inches long; heads small, 3- to 5-flowered, in small, short-stalked, axillary and terminal clusters; corollas whitish.

INYO BRICKELLIA *(Brickellia multiflora).* A branched shrub, 2 to 5 feet high with smooth, somewhat sticky, whitish stems; leaves alternate, ovate to lanceolate, 1½ to 3½ inches long, entire or nearly so; heads and flowers much as in the preceding species.

BRICKELLIA *(Brickellia oblongifolia* var. *linifolia).* Stems numerous, herbaceous or woody only at the base, 4 to 20 inches tall, usually unbranched below the flowering portion; leaves alternate, elliptic or oval, 1½ inches long or less, entire or nearly so; heads 1 to many, 4- to 50-flowered; corollas usually greenish-cream.

BRICKELLIA *(Brickellia scabra).* Stems somewhat woody, especially at the base, 15 to 30 inches tall with slender branches; leaves alternate, ovate, entire or somewhat toothed, less than ½ inch long; heads 1 or 2 on each branch, about 10- to 12-flowered; corollas yellowish-white or purple-tinged. In Canyon.

CHAENACTIS *(Chaenactis douglasii).* Stems 8 to 14 inches tall; leaves alternate, 2 or 3 times pinnate, rather thick, more or less woolly, 1 to 4 inches long; heads 2 to 6; flowers whitish to flesh-colored. North Rim.

CHAENACTIS *(Chaenactis macrantha).* Stems rather stout, 3 to 10 inches tall, branched, at first somewhat woolly but often becoming smooth; leaves ½ to 1½ inches long, 1 or 2 times pinnately lobed; heads solitary at the ends of branches, white-flowered, the flowers spreading at night, closely packed together in daytime. In Canyon.

CHAENACTIS *(Chaenactis stevioides).* Stems 4 to 12 inches tall, often branched throughout; leaves 1½ inches long or less, once or twice pinnately lobed into linear lobes; heads many terminating the branches; flowers creamy-white.

CHAENACTIS *(Chaenactis xantiana).* Stems about 6 to 14 inches tall, smooth or nearly so; leaves 1 to 2½ inches long, linear, entire or with 1 or 2 pairs of spreading, linear lobes; heads medium-large at the ends of the branches; flowers white or whitish. In Canyon.

GOLD-ASTER *(Chrysopsis fulcrata).* Stems 8 to 24 inches high, more or less hairy and glandular; leaves 1 to 2½ inches long, hairy, mostly oblong or elliptic, sessile, alternate; heads medium-sized and rather showy; ray flowers golden-yellow; bracts of involucre in several series.

ROUGH GOLD-ASTER *(Chrysopsis hispida).* Stems 4 to 20 inches tall, hairy and more or less glandular; leaves usually less than 1 inch long, oblanceolate or obovate to oblong, hairy, at least the lower ones petioled; heads 1 or more at the ends of branches; involucres quite glandular.

HAIRY GOLD-ASTER *(Chrysopsis villosa).* Very similar to the preceding but the involucre not glandular.

DWARF RABBITBRUSH (*Chrysothamnus depressus*). A low spreading shrub, usually 4 to 12 inches high, with upright, herbaceous twigs; leaves ¼ to ¾ inch long, narrowly oblanceolate, 1-nerved; heads small, about 5-flowered, in small, terminal clusters; bracts of involucre in 5 vertical rows; flowers pale yellow; pappus brownish white. South Rim.

GREENES RABBITBRUSH (*Chrysothamnus greenei* var. *linifolius*). A shrub, usually about 8 to 14 inches high, leaves very narrowly linear, less than 1 inch long; heads in compact, terminal clusters, 5-flowered; bracts of involucre in 5 vertical ranks.

RUBBER RABBITBRUSH (*Chrysothamnus nauseosus*). A shrub, usually between 1 and 7 feet high, the twigs covered with a dense white, gray or green felt which may look like the twig surface until it is scraped with a sharp knife; leaves linear, smooth or woolly, up to 2½ inches long; heads in terminal, more or less rounded clusters, these arranged in a panicle, mostly 5-flowered. This is a very variable species and numerous varieties have been proposed.

PARRY RABBITBRUSH (*Chrysothamnus parryi*). Quite similar to the preceding but usually less than 2½ feet high, the leaves sometimes up to 3 inches long, and the heads are in leafy racemes and mostly 10- to 20-flowered.

DOUGLAS RABBITBRUSH (*Chrysothamnus viscidiflorus*). The twigs of this species are not covered by a layer of felt but otherwise it closely resembles the rubber rabbitbrush and is often difficult to distinguish from it.

THISTLE (*Cirsium arizonicum*). Stems 1 to 4 feet tall; leaves 1 to 12 inches long, pinnately lobed, very prickly, woolly on the lower surface; heads 1 to several, often 2½ inches across, the involucre very prickly; flowers usually bright red.

NEW MEXICO THISTLE (*Cirsium neomexicanum*). Stems 1 to 4 feet tall; leaves 1 to 8 inches long, pinnately lobed, very prickly, more or less woolly on both sides; heads 1 to few at the ends of branches, 1 to 2 inches across; flowers usually lavender, occasionally white.

THISTLE (*Cirsium nidulum*). This species is believed to hybridize with both *C. arizonicum* and *C. rothrockii*. Therefore, intermediate forms are often found which are difficult to place in one species or another. Typical *C. nidulum,* however, differs from the others in having very long, stout, yellowish spines, often ½ inch long, on both involucre and leaves. The flowers are usually light red-purple.

THISTLE (*Cirsium rothrockii*). This species differs from its two close relatives, *C. arizonicum* and *C. nidulum,* in having the leaves smooth or nearly so on both sides. The flowers are usually rose-purple.

THISTLE (*Cirsium undulatum*). Stems 1 to 3 feet tall, more or less woolly;

leaves varying from pinnately lobed to nearly entire, more or less woolly on both sides, very prickly; heads rather few, 1 to 1½ inches across; flowers purple.

BULL THISTLE *(Cirsium vulgare)*. Stems 2 to 5 feet tall, with long prickly wings extending down from the bases of the leaves; basal leaves elliptic to oblanceolate and coarsely toothed, those on the stem lanceolate and pinnately lobed; the largest about 10 inches long, all armed with spines; heads 1 or few, 1 to 2 inches long; bracts of involucre numerous, in many series, mostly tipped with spines; flowers purple.

THISTLE *(Cirsium wheeleri)*. Usually our commonest thistle; stems 1 to 2 feet tall, comparatively slender; leaves all or nearly all pinnately lobed, very prickly, the largest about 5 inches long; heads few, 1½ inches across or less; flowers purple.

GRAY HAWKSBEARD *(Crepis intermedia)*. Stems 1 or 2, 12 to 28 inches tall, branching at or above the middle; basal leaves 6 to 16 inches long, pinnately lobed, the lanceolate lobes entire or toothed, the blade narrowed to a narrowly winged petiole, the stem leaves few, smaller, sessile; heads of medium size, the involucre nearly cylindrical.

WESTERN HAWKSBEARD *(Crepis occidentalis)*. Stems 1 to 3, 3 to 16 inches tall; basal leaves 3 to 14 inches long, varying from merely toothed to pinnately lobed with toothed lobes, the stem leaves smaller and sessile; heads somewhat larger than in the preceding species.

PRICKLEAF DOGWEED *(Dyssodia acerosa)*. A low, much-branched shrub, 3 to 6 inches high, leaves mostly opposite, less than ½ inch long, often much less, needlelike; heads rather few, terminal on the branches, about ¼ inch across; both ray and disk flowers yellow; plant ill-smelling.

DOGWEED *(Dyssodia pentachaeta)*. Stems woody only near the base, if at all; leaves and heads similar to those of the preceding species but most of the leaves with 2 or more needlelike lobes.

DOGWEED *(Dyssodia porophylloides)*. This shrub is readily distinguished from the other dogweeds by its size, 1 to 2 feet high, and by its leaves which are mostly alternate and have lanceolate or wedge-shaped lobes. In Canyon.

DOGWEED *(Dyssodia thurberi)*. This species differs from *D. pentachaeta* primarily in the characters given in the key. The 2 species are often difficult to distinguish. Both are likely to be found only within the Canyon.

WHITE BRITTLEBUSH *(Encelia farinosa)*. A much-branched, rounded bush, 1½ to 4½ feet high, woody below, herbaceous above; leaf blades ovate to lanceolate, densely white-hairy, 1 to 4 inches long, 1 to 2 inches across, entire or nearly so, with slender petioles 1½ inches long or less; heads usually about 1 inch across, rather showy; both ray and disk flowers yellow. In Canyon.

BUSH ENCELIA *(Encelia frutescens)*. A much-branched, white-barked shrub up to 4½ feet high; leaves short-petioled, the blades 1 inch long or less, oblong or ovate, entire or more or less toothed; heads solitary at the ends of branches, either with or without ray flowers, these yellow when present. In Canyon.

HORSEWEED FLEABANE *(Erigeron canadensis)*. Stem 1 to 4 feet tall, smooth or hairy; lower leaves petioled, the blades oblanceolate, entire or somewhat toothed, more or less hairy, the upper ones linear, entire, sessile; heads small, numerous, in a panicle; ray flowers white but very short and inconspicuous.

HOARY FLEABANE *(Erigeron canus)*. Stems usually several, 2 to 12 inches tall; basal leaves narrowly oblanceolate, 2½ inches long or less, usually surrounded by a cluster of old leaf bases; upper leaves linear and much shorter; heads usually solitary; ray flowers 25 to 40, blue or white.

HAIRY FLEABANE *(Erigeron concinnus)*. Stems several, 2 to 12 inches tall, hairy with spreading hairs, branched above; basal leaves narrowly oblanceolate, less than 2 inches long, those on the stem linear and much shorter, hairy like the stems; heads solitary on the branches; ray flowers 50 to 100, rose, violet or white.

SPREADING FLEABANE *(Erigeron divergens)*. A very variable species; stems 4 to 28 inches tall, freely branched, sometimes wide-spreading, the stems and leaves hairy with rather short, soft, spreading hairs; leaves oblanceolate to linear, entire to coarsely toothed; heads 1 to several on each branch; ray flowers 75 to 150, about ¼ inch long, very narrow, purple to white.

EATON FLEABANE *(Erigeron eatoni)*. Stems several, 2 to 12 inches tall; basal leaves conspicuous, the largest up to 6 inches long, linear or nearly so, the stem leaves few and much shorter; heads 1 or several on each stem, medium-large; ray flowers 20 to 50, white or pale blue.

TRAILING FLEABANE *(Erigeron flagellaris)*. Flowering stems 5 to 12 inches tall, few-leaved or almost leafless, trailing stems, often as long as the flowering stems or longer, frequently rooting at the tip; basal leaves in a prominent cluster, narrowly oblanceolate, 2 inches long or less, the stem leaves mostly linear; heads solitary; ray flowers 50 to 100, blue, pink or white.

FLEABANE *(Erigeron formosissimus)*. Stems 4 to 16 inches tall, more or less hairy and often glandular at the upper end; stem leaves lanceolate to oblong, sessile, 1 inch long or less, the basal ones longer and petioled; heads usually 1 or 2, large and showy; ray flowers 50 to 150, ¼ to ½ inch long, usually blue.

FLEABANE *(Erigeron lobatus)*. Except for the pinnately lobed leaves this species rather closely resembles some forms of *E. divergens* and perhaps it should be considered only a variety of that species. It is not likely to be found in the park except rather low in the Canyon.

ASPEN FLEABANE *(Erigeron macranthus)*. Stems 6 to 30 inches tall, smooth or nearly so; leaves mostly lanceolate, the upper ones sessile and somewhat clasping; heads usually several, large and showy; ray flowers about 75 to 150, mostly blue. Both Rims.

SPRAWLING FLEABANE *(Erigeron nudiflorus)*. This is another species that is evidently very closely related to *E. divergens* and possibly should be considered a variety of it. As indicated in the key, the early heads are borne on upright nearly naked stalks. Otherwise the plant very closely resembles some forms of *E. divergens*.

FLEABANE *(Erigeron oreophilus)*. Stems 1 foot high or more, usually widely branching; leaves 2 inches long or less, nearly all pinnately lobed into linear lobes; heads medium-large and showy; ray flowers very numerous and narrow, white.

BEAR RIVER FLEABANE *(Erigeron ursinus)*. Stems several, 2 to 10 inches tall, usually curved and reddish at the base; basal leaves oblanceolate, those on the stem linear or lanceolate, reduced upward both in size and number; heads solitary; ray flowers 30 to 100, blue to purple.

UTAH FLEABANE *(Erigeron utahensis)*. Stems several, 4 to 20 inches tall, more or less hairy; leaves mostly linear, 3 inches long or less, hairy; heads 1 to 10, rather large and showy; ray flowers 10 to 40, blue, pink or white. In Canyon.

THOROUGHWORT *(Eupatorium herbaceum)*. Stems 12 to 18 inches tall; leaves opposite, petioled, ovate to nearly triangular, the margins scalloped, the blades 2 inches long or less, the petioles much shorter; heads quite numerous in terminal clusters, 12- to 16-flowered, the corollas white.

BURSAGE *(Franseria acanthicarpa)*. A weedy, branched, annual herb, 8 to 28 inches tall, rough-hairy; leaves alternate, petioled, the blades ovate to triangular in outline, 2 or 3 times pinnately lobed; heads in racemes in the upper leaf axils, the staminate above, about 15-flowered, the pistillate below, 1-flowered; fruit varying from rough, glandular and hairy to nearly smooth, the body bearing 6 to 20 strongly flattened, short spines.

WOOLLY BURSAGE *(Franseria eriocentra)*. A branching, white-barked shrub, 1 to 3 feet high; leaves alternate, ovate, triangular or oblong, short-petioled or nearly sessile, toothed or lobed or both, the blades 1 to 2 inches long; heads in short racemes, the staminate heads above, about 30-flowered, the pistillate below, 1-flowered; fruit densely soft-hairy and bearing about 20 spines.

BLANKETFLOWER *(Gaillardia pinnatifida)*. Stems 6 to 30 inches tall, more or less hairy; leaves alternate but mostly on the lower part of the stem, oblanceolate in outline, at least some of them pinnately lobed; heads solitary on the branches, about 1 inch across, showy, the disk flowers reddish at the base and usually with reddish-purple veins.

CUDWEED *(Gnaphalium grayi)*. Stems 3 to 10 inches tall, closely woolly, varying from erect and unbranched to branched from the base and often wide-spreading; leaves 1½ inches long or less, linear or nearly so, woolly like the stem; heads very small, in headlike clusters, these on stalks in the axils of leaves.

CUDWEED *(Gnaphalium macounii).* Stems 15 to 30 inches tall, branched above, rather stout; leaves alternate, 2 to 4 inches long, sessile, white-woolly below, green and hairy above; heads in rounded clusters at the ends of stems, the bracts of the involucres straw-colored or whitish.

CUDWEED *(Gnaphalium palustre).* Stems 2 to 10 inches tall, usually becoming widely branched from the base, loosely woolly; leaves 1 inch long or less, oblong to obovate, loosely woolly on both sides; heads in small clusters terminating the stems and branches, the clusters subtended by leaflike bracts.

CUDWEED *(Gnaphalium wrightii).* Stems 1 to 2 feet tall, upright, usually much-branched, white-woolly; leaves 1 to 2 inches long, oblanceolate to linear, sessile, gray-woolly on both sides; heads many in an open panicle, often crowded at the ends of the branches; bracts of involucre pearly white.

GUMWEED *(Grindelia aphanactis).* Stems 1 or several, 10 to 16 inches tall, branching at least toward the top; leaves oblong to oblanceolate, 5 to 10 times as long as wide, entire or toothed or the lower ones lobed; heads medium-sized, scattered; bracts of involucre in 5 or 6 series; ray flowers none; disk flowers yellow; pappus of 2 or 3 awns.

CURLYCUP GUMWEED *(Grindelia squarrosa).* Stems 1 or several, 10 to 40 inches tall, branched near the top; leaves 1 to 3 inches long, 2 to 4 times longer than wide, usually regularly and closely toothed; heads 1 inch across or more; both ray and disk flowers yellow; pappus of 2 or 3 awns.

STICKY SNAKEWEED *(Gutierrezia lucida).* Stems 4 to 24 inches tall, much-branched, woody at least toward the base; leaves alternate, narrowly linear, 1 to 2 inches long or less; heads very small and numerous, usually with 1 ray flower and 1 or 2 disk flowers; corollas yellow.

BROOM SNAKEWEED *(Gutierrezia sarothrae).* Very similar to the preceding but the heads a little larger with 3 to 8 each of ray and disk flowers.

PALELEAF GOLDENWEED *(Haplopappus acradenius).* (Note: in "Flora of Arizona" by Kearney and Peebles, the genus *Haplopappus* is spelled *Aplopappus*). A low shrub with numerous, white-barked, smooth stems, 12 to 40 inches high; leaves alternate, linear to narrowly oblong, 1½ inches long or less; heads in small clusters, about 6- to 13-flowered; ray flowers none; disk flowers yellow. In Canyon.

GOLDENWEED *(Haplopappus drummondii).* Stems usually 12 to 20 inches tall, unbranched or branched near the top, more or less woody, whitish-barked; leaves linear or narrowly oblong, 2 inches long or less; heads clustered at the ends of stems or branches, 18- to 30-flowered; ray flowers none; disk flowers yellow.

BABY GOLDENROD
(Solidago nana)

PHOTO MERKLE

ROCK GOLDENROD
(Solidago petradoria)

PHOTO MERKLE

GOLDEN CROWNBEARD
(Verbesina encelioides)

PHOTO MERKLE

SHOWY GOLDENEYE
(Viguiera multiflora)

PHOTO MERKLE

GOLDENWEED *(Haplopappus gracilis)*. An annual herb, 2 to 15 inches tall, usually much-branched, hairy; leaves alternate, mostly 1 inch long or less, lobed with bristle-tipped lobes; heads medium-sized, usually quite numerous, resembling an aster but with both ray and disk flowers yellow.

JIMMYWEED *(Haplopappus heterophyllus)*. This species is very similar to *H. drummondii* but the heads are smaller and about 7- to 15-flowered.

NUTTALL GOLDENWEED *(Haplopappus nuttallii)*. A perennial herb with stems 4 to 12 inches tall; leaves 1 to 1½ inches long, oblong, sessile, spiny-toothed; heads 1 or several, medium-sized; bracts of involucre in about 3 series; ray flowers none; disk flowers yellow.

GOLDENWEED *(Haplopappus parryi)*. A perennial herb with stems usually 6 to 20 inches tall, finely hairy at least near the top; leaves 1 to 8 inches long, oblanceolate or the upper ones lanceolate, entire, petioled; heads 2 to many; ray flowers 12 to 20; both ray and disk flowers yellow. North Rim.

GOLDENWEED *(Haplopappus salicinus)*. This species is known only from the type locality on the Bright Angel Trail. It was collected in 1906 and again in 1913 but there have been no recent collections.

GOLDENWEED *(Haplopappus scopulorum)*. This is another species that is apparently very rare. It was collected on both Rims some years ago but we have not seen it.

GOLDENWEED *(Haplopappus spinulosus)*. This species resembles *H. gracilis* and has the same soft or white bristles on the teeth or lobes of the leaves, but it is a perennial herb, often somewhat woody at the base, and is usually a larger plant with larger heads. In Canyon.

WATSON GOLDENWEED *(Haplopappus watsoni)*. A low shrub with oblanceolate leaves less than 1 inch long and heads with both ray and disk flowers yellow. The entire plant is densely glandular with stalked glands. It has been collected in the park at about 7000 feet which might be on the South Rim or in the upper part of the Canyon. It is apparently rare for we have not found it.

HELIANTHELLA *(Helianthella microcephala)*. Stems 8 to 24 inches tall, leafy; basal leaves numerous, narrowly to broadly oblanceolate, tapering to long petioles, those on the stem smaller, narrow, nearly sessile, mostly opposite; heads relatively small, few to many in a more or less flat-topped panicle; ray flowers 8 to 10, less than ½ inch long; disk flowers purple or brown. In Canyon.

HELIANTHELLA *(Helianthella quinquenervis)*. Stems 1 to 5 feet tall, stout; usually a few basal leaves up to 20 inches long present; stem leaves about 4 pairs, lanceolate, tapering to a petiole; heads large, mostly solitary, long-stalked, nodding; ray flowers 1 inch long or more, pale yellow; disk flowers yellow.

SUNFLOWER *(Helianthus petiolaris)*. Stems 1 to 5 feet tall; leaves mostly alternate, petioled, the blades 1 to 6 inches long, ovate to lanceolate, entire or nearly so; heads solitary at the ends of stems and branches; disk about 1 inch broad or less, the flowers purple or brownish-red; ray flowers ½ to 1 inch long, yellow.

HAWKWEED *(Hieracium fendleri)*. Stems 8 to 12 inches tall, somewhat hairy; leaves mostly basal, oval to oblanceolate, petioled, 1 to 4 inches long, hairy, those on the stem few and small; heads few, ½ inch across or more; corollas all strap-shaped, light yellow.

WHITE BURROBRUSH *(Hymenoclea salsola)*. A low, much-branched shrub, usually 2 to 4 feet high, with white or straw-colored bark and green twigs; leaves alternate, very narrowly linear, entire or few-lobed, 1 to 2 inches long; heads small and numerous, the staminate and pistillate mixed in the same leaf axils or the staminate higher up on the branch than the pistillate; fruit with about 12 spirally arranged wings. In Canyon.

HYMENOPAPPUS *(Hymenopappus lugens)*. Stems 4 to 20 inches tall, more or less woolly; leaves mostly basal, twice pinnately lobed into linear lobes, 2 to 3½ inches long, those on the stem, if any, much smaller; heads solitary or few, less than ½ inch across; flowers yellow; akenes silky-hairy.

HYMENOXYS *(Hymenoxys acaulis* var. *arizonica)*. Flowering stems 4 to 12 inches tall, usually several from a much-branched base which is densely covered by hairy leaf bases; leaves all basal, 1 to 2 inches long, narrowly oblanceolate; heads solitary, about 1 inch across; ray flowers about 10, yellow.

HYMENOXYS *(Hymenoxys cooperi)*. Stems usually solitary, 8 to 30 inches tall, leafy; leaves ½ to 2 inches long, 3- to 5-lobed, the narrowly linear lobes often again lobed; heads 3 to 30 at the ends of branches, each about 1 inch across; both ray and disk flowers yellow.

PINGWING *(Hymenoxys richardsoni* var. *floribunda)*. Stems usually numerous, 5 to 18 inches tall, much-branched; leaves numerous both at the base and on the stem, 1 to 6 inches long, the smaller ones linear and entire, the larger ones divided into several linear lobes; heads usually numerous, ½ inch across or less.

HYMENOXYS *(Hymenoxys subintegra)*. Stems solitary or few, 8 to 20 inches tall, leafy; leaves 1 to 4 inches long, broadly linear and entire or divided into 3 broadly linear lobes; heads several or many, ½ to nearly 1 inch across; both ray and disk flowers yellow.

PRICKLY LETTUCE *(Lactuca serriola)*. Stem 20 to 80 inches tall, branched above; leaves alternate, oblong or oblanceolate, sessile and clasping at the base, more or less lobed, prickly on the midrib and margins; heads numerous in a panicle, each 6- to 12-flowered; corollas yellow. Plant with milky juice.

LAPHAMIA *(Laphamia congesta)*. Stems several from a woody base, 4 to 15 inches tall, branched; stems, leaves and involucres all short-hairy; leaves alternate, petioled, the blades narrowly oblong to ovate, less than ½ inch long, entire or few-toothed, the petiole about as long as the blade; heads solitary at the ends of numerous branches; flowers yellow.

WHITE TIDYTIPS (*Layia glandulosa*). Stems 4 to 20 inches tall, branched; leaves alternate, linear to lanceolate, sessile, 2 inches long or less, the basal ones usually toothed or lobed, the upper ones entire and much smaller; heads terminal on the branches, large and showy, often 1½ inches across; ray flowers white; disk flowers yellow. In Canyon.

SKELETON PLANT (*Lygodesmia exigua*). An annual herb, 2 to 8 inches tall, much-branched; lower leaves oblanceolate, less than 1 inch long, the upper ones much smaller and bractlike; heads solitary at the ends of branches, 3- to 6-flowered; flowers pink; akenes very small with abundant white pappus. In Canyon.

TARWEED (*Madia glomerata*). Stems 8 to 30 inches tall, unbranched or branched near the top, hairy and usually with stalked yellow glands near the top; leaves linear, entire, 1 to 2½ inches long; heads very small, in dense, terminal clusters of 5 to 30 or more in open panicles; ray flowers very short and inconspicuous; disk flowers 1 to 10, yellowish.

MALACOTHRIX (*Malacothrix clevelandi*). Stems usually several, 4 to 16 inches tall, branched like a panicle, smooth, often reddish; leaves mostly basal, pinnately lobed or toothed, 1 to 4 inches long; heads solitary at the ends of the branches of the panicle; bracts of involucre green but often purple-tinged and with a narrow, whitish border. In Canyon.

MALACOTHRIX (*Malacothrix sonchoides*). Stems 2 to 20 inches tall, smooth or nearly so; leaves much as in the preceding species; heads similar to those in the preceding species but the flowers about ¼ inch long, bright yellow and showy.

MALACOTHRIX (*Malacothrix torreyi*). With the exception of the character given in the key this species is very similar to the preceding one and may be difficult to distinguish from it.

MICROSERIS (*Microseris linearifolia*). Flowering stems 4 to 28 inches tall; leaves all basal or nearly so, 1 foot long or less, linear, entire or pinnately lobed; heads solitary at the ends of the stems, ¼ to ½ inch long, smooth, 5- to 150-flowered; flowers yellow but scarcely longer than the involucre and thus inconspicuous; akenes black, ¼ to ½ inch long; pappus about as long as the akenes. In Canyon.

PRICKLY OXYTENIA (*Oxytenia acerosa*). A much-branched shrub, 3 to 6 feet tall, the stems rather slender and conspicuously marked with longitudinal ridges and furrows; leaves 1 to 6 inches long, very narrowly linear and entire or with 5 to 7 very narrowly linear lobes; stems and leaves short-hairy; heads small and very numerous, in rather dense panicles; flowers whitish; akenes very small but densely long-hairy with white hairs which are about as long as the corollas and often make the heads look woolly. In Canyon.

MARIOLA *(Parthenium incanum).* A low, much-branched shrub, 1 to 3 feet tall; leaves mostly obovate in outline, with 3 to 7 roundish lobes, about 1 inch long or less, densely white-woolly beneath, less so above; heads small, numerous, in small panicles; both ray and disk flowers whitish. In Canyon.

CHINCHWEED *(Pectis papposa).* A low, much-branched herb, 4 to 10 inches tall; leaves narrowly linear, 2 inches long or less, with 2 to 5 bristles near the base; heads solitary in the axils of the upper leaves; bracts of involucre 7 to 9, dotted with glands; both ray and disk flowers yellow; pappus of disk flowers of 12 to 20 short, feathery bristles. In Canyon.

PEREZIA *(Perezia wrightii).* A stout herb, 1 to 3 feet tall, smooth; leaves numerous, alternate, oblong to ovate, sessile and somewhat clasping at the broad base, irregularly many-toothed; heads numerous, medium-sized, 8- to 12-flowered, the flowers pink. In Canyon.

PERITYLE *(Perityle emoryi* var. *nuda).* A much-branched, widely spreading herb; leaves mostly alternate, 1 to 3 inches long, the petiole about as long as the ovate, irregularly lobed and toothed blade; heads medium-small, scattered; pappus of very small scales forming a short crown. In Havasu Canyon.

ARROWWEED *(Pluchea sericea).* A slender, very leafy, willowlike shrub, 15 feet tall or less, silvery-silky throughout; leaves lanceolate to almost linear, sessile, leathery, ¼ to 2 inches long; heads about ¼ inch across, in small, terminal clusters, the flowers purplish. In Canyon.

PORELEAF *(Porophyllum gracile).* A bushy, perennial herb with a somewhat woody base, 8 to 28 inches tall, with a strong, disagreeable odor; leaves few, alternate, very narrowly linear, 2 inches long or less; heads solitary on the branches; involucre about ½ inch long, the 5 bracts often purple-tinged; corollas purplish-white with purple lines. In Canyon.

GREENSTEM PAPERFLOWER *(Psilostrophe sparsiflora).* Stems 6 to 14 inches tall, branched, usually several from a branched base; leaves narrowly oblanceolate to linear, ½ to 2 inches long, entire, alternate; heads clustered at the ends of the stems and branches, the disk small but the rays about ¼ inch long, these remaining on the akenes and becoming papery.

WOOLLY PAPERFLOWER *(Psilostrophe tagetina).* Very similar to the preceding except that the stems and leaves are more or less woolly. Apparently rare in the park.

PRAIRIE CONEFLOWER *(Ratibida columnaris* syn. *R. columnifera).* Stems 10 to 32 inches tall, more or less branched above; leaves alternate, deeply lobed into 5 to 13 linear or oblong divisions; heads large and showy, solitary at the ends of stem and branches; scales between the disk flowers woolly at the tip; ray flowers about 1 inch long or less, yellow, drooping.

SANVITALIA *(Sanvitalia aberti).* Stems 4 to 14 inches tall, branched; leaves opposite, narrowly lanceolate to almost linear, ½ to 2 inches long, short-petioled; heads medium-small, terminal on the branches; ray flowers short, white, green-striped on the back.

THREADLEAF GROUNDSEL *(Senecio longilobus).* Stems 1 to 3 feet tall, often several together forming a clump, more or less woolly when young, leafy to the top; leaves pinnately divided into narrowly linear lobes or the upper ones entire and very narrowly linear; heads several to many, about ½ inch long and about as wide; both ray and disk flowers yellow.

GROUNDSEL *(Senecio macdougalii).* Stems 1 to several, 8 to 36 inches tall, not woolly; leaves 1½ to 5 inches long, rather sharply pinnately lobed, the lobes often toothed; heads several or many in a more or less flat-topped cluster, relatively small, about ¼ inch high; rays about ¼ inch long.

LOBELEAF GROUNDSEL *(Senecio multilobatus* syn. *S. lynceus, S. stygius* and *S. uintahensis).* Stems 4 to 20 inches tall, 1 or several in a cluster, varying from quite woolly to nearly smooth; leaves 4 inches long or less and 1 inch wide or less, the lower part of each leaf deeply pinnately lobed with toothed lobes, the upper part shallowly lobed or merely toothed; heads ¼ to ½ inch long, the involucre usually woolly at least at the base; rays about ¼ inch long.

GROUNDSEL *(Senecio quercetorum).* Stems stout, 2 to 3½ feet tall, smooth or nearly so; leaves pinnately lobed or toothed, those near the base up to 10 inches long, those on the upper part of the stem smaller; heads medium-sized; rays about ¼ inch long. In Canyon.

BROOM GROUNDSEL *(Senecio spartioides).* Stems 8 to 24 inches tall, usual-ly several or many in a fairly large clump, more or less woody at the base, smooth or nearly so; leaves narrowly linear and entire or sometimes with 1 or 2 pairs of short lobes near the base, smooth or nearly so; heads usually many in a panicle, the involucre nearly cylindrical, the rays rather few.

GROUNDSEL *(Senecio werneriaefolius).* Stems 2 to 8 inches tall, more or less woolly; leaves all basal or near the base, linear to oblanceolate, 2 inches long or less, woolly or smooth when old; heads 1 or several, between ¼ and ½ inch long; rays 5 to 12, less than ¼ inch long. North Rim.

TALL GOLDENROD *(Solidago altissima).* Stems 2 to 3½ feet tall, more or less hairy; leaves lanceolate to elliptic, sharply toothed, especially above the middle, hairy on the underside; heads on 1-sided branches of a panicle, small; rays usually fewer than the disk flowers.

GOLDENROD *(Solidago graminea).* Stems 3 to 8 inches tall, usually several from a branched base, very leafy; leaves linear, grasslike, 1-nerved, ½ to 3 inches

DATIL YUCCA
(Yucca baccata)
PHOTO MERKLE

ARIZONA ROSE
(Rosa arizonica)
PHOTO MERKLE

FLANNEL MULLEIN
(Verbascum thapsus)
PHOTO MERKLE

Families Of Plants 247

long; heads very small and numerous; involucres straw-colored.

MISSOURI GOLDENROD *(Solidago missouriensis).* Stems 8 to 24 inches tall, smooth; basal leaves oblanceolate, those on the stem lanceolate to linear, 3-nerved; heads numerous on more or less 1-sided branches of a round or somewhat flat-topped panicle; ray flowers usually fewer than the disk flowers, both yellow.

BABY GOLDENROD *(Solidago nana).* Stems 2 to 30 inches tall, both stems and leaves white-hairy; leaves mostly oblanceolate, petioled, ½ to 2 inches long; heads rather large for a goldenrod, in a compact panicle.

ROCK GOLDENROD *(Solidago petradoria).* This species is very similar to *S. graminea* but the leaves are broader and 3-nerved.

GOLDENROD *(Solidago sparsiflora).* This species is very similar to *S. missouriensis* but the stems are definitely hairy.

PRICKLY SOW-THISTLE *(Sonchus asper).* Stems rather stout, 1 to 5 feet tall; leaves more or less lobed and spiny-toothed, sessile and clasping the stem by rounded lobes; head medium-sized, the corollas all strap-shaped and yellow.

COMMON SOW-THISTLE *(Sonchus oleraceus).* Very similar to the preceding species and often difficult to distinguish from it. In addition to the characters given in the key the lobes at the bases of the leaves are usually pointed instead of rounded.

WIRE-LETTUCE *(Stephanomeria exigua).* Stems 4 to 20 inches tall, rather slender, more or less branched, smooth or nearly so; lower and basal leaves narrowly oblong, coarsely toothed or pinnately lobed, the upper ones very small and bractlike; heads small, at the tips of branches; flowers 3 to 7 in each head, bright pink.

WIRE-LETTUCE *(Stephanomeria pauciflora).* Stems 12 to 20 inches tall, smooth, much-branched, forming rounded bushes, somewhat woody at the base; lower leaves narrow, 1 to 3 inches long, pinnately lobed with short, narrow lobes, sometimes little more than teeth, the upper leaves entire and bractlike; heads solitary on the branches, short-stalked, 3- to 5-flowered.

WIRE-LETTUCE *(Stephanomeria tenuifolia).* Stems 8 to 20 inches tall with several slender branches, not woody at the base and not forming rounded bushes; leaves and heads much as in the preceding species.

WIRE-LETTUCE *(Stephanomeria thurberi).* Stems 8 to 20 inches tall, branched mostly near the top; leaves mostly crowded near the base, 1 to 2 inches long, pinnately lobed, those higher up very small, linear, entire; heads larger than in any of our other species of wire-lettuce, 10- to 20-flowered, in a naked panicle.

COMMON DANDELION *(Taraxacum officinale).* Flowering stems 2 to 16 inches tall; leaves all basal, 2 to 6 inches long, usually pinnately lobed; heads solitary, 1 to 2 inches across with many yellow flowers.

SMOOTH DANDELION *(Taraxacum laevigatum).* Very similar to the preceding except for the differences given in the key.

TOWNSENDIA *(Townsendia arizonica).* Stems 1 to 8 inches tall, hairy, several from the same base; leaves 1½ inches long or less, hairy, linear to oblanceolate; heads 1 to 3 on each stem; rays about ¼ inch long, white to lilac.

TOWNSENDIA *(Townsendia exscapa).* Stems practically none; leaves 2 inches long or less, narrowly oblanceolate or linear, rather sparsely hairy; heads moderately large, sessile among the leaves; rays ¼ to ½ inch long, white or purple-tinged.

GOATSBEARD *(Tragopogon dubius).* Stems 1 to 3 feet tall; leaves alternate, linear and grasslike, mostly 5 or 6 inches long, rather numerous, sessile and clasping at the base; heads large; bracts of involucre 10 to 13, about 1 to 2 inches long, much longer than the flowers; flowers numerous, lemon-yellow.

TRIXIS *(Trixis californica).* A much-branched shrub, 1 to 3 feet high, the lower stems gray, the upper branches tan, leafy on the upper branches to the heads; leaves alternate, lanceolate, sessile or nearly so, entire or with very small teeth; heads between ½ and 1 inch long, 9- to 14-flowered; corollas yellow, all 2-lipped, the outer lip 3-lobed, the inner 2-lobed.

GOLDEN CROWNBEARD *(Verbesina encelioides).* Stems 1 to 3 feet tall, usually branched at least above; lower leaves opposite, the others alternate, petioled, the blades ovate to lanceolate, 1 to 4 inches long, sharply toothed, densely white-hairy beneath; heads several, 1 to 1½ inches across; rays 10 to 15, yellow.

SHOWY GOLDENEYE *(Viguiera multiflora).* Stems several, slender, 10 to 36 inches tall; leaves mostly opposite, the blades linear, 1 to 2 inches long with very short petioles; heads 1 or several on each stem or branch, rather long-stalked; rays about 8 to 10, ½ to 1 inch long, yellow; akenes smooth, without a pappus.

COCKLEBUR *(Xanthium saccharatum).* Stems 8 to 36 inches tall; leaf blades 2 to 5 inches long and nearly as wide, ovate to heart-shaped, the petiole about as long as the blade; burs 1 to 3 in the leaf axils, about 1 inch long, very prickly with hooked prickles.

INDEX TO FAMILY, GENERIC, AND COMMON NAMES

PRINTED BY

NORTHLAND PRESS

FLAGSTAFF, ARIZONA